REVISE FOR SCIENCE GCSE

SALTERS

GILL ALDERTON
DAVID BERRINGTON
MICHAEL BRIMICOMBE

HIGHER

Heinemann Educational Publishers
Halley Court, Jordan Hill, Oxford, OX2 8EJ
a division of Reed Educational & Professional Publishing Ltd
Heinemann is a registered trademark of Reed Educational & Professional Publishing Ltd

OXFORD MELBOURNE AUCKLAND
JOHANNESBURG BLANTYRE GABARONE
IBADAN PORTSMOUTH NH (USA) CHICAGO

First published 1999

ISBN 0 435 63117 9

03 02 01 00 99
10 9 8 7 6 5 4 3 2 1

Edited by June Thompson

Designed and typeset by Ken Vail Graphic Design

Illustrated by Ken Vail Graphic Design,
Graham-Cameron Illustration (Virginia Gray), Barry Atkinson and John Plumb

Cover artwork by Stephen May

Printed and bound in Great Britain by The Bath Press

Contents

How to use this book

This book is divided into three sections:
• AT2 biology, • AT3 chemistry, and • AT4 physics.

Each of the three sections is further divided into topics.

If you are studying for Single Award you can leave out the sections and questions marked with a vertical black line in the margin of the text because these are for Double Award.

If you are studying for Double Award you should do all these sections.

Helping you revise

1 The words in **bold** are all key words you need to know. A useful revision idea would be to build up your own glossary of these as you work through the book. For quick reference to a word or topic use the *Index* at the back of the book.

2 There are lots of questions in the book and they are an important part of your revision. There are:

   - Now Do This questions to help you stop and think about the subject as you read.
   - Exam questions at the end of each topic to help you practise for the exam.

   The answers to all these are at the back of the book so you will never get stuck.

3 In the *Exam Revision* section at the back of the book there is a *Concept map* for each AT. These will help you check that you remember everything you need to know and will help you see the connections between topics more clearly.

   The best plan is to make your own personal map of the subject which makes your own connections between topics.

Good luck with your exams!

Life processes and cell activity

This section looks at living things and asks the question, how do we know that they are living?

You will have met this in *Staying alive* when you beamed down to the surface of another planet to look for signs of life.

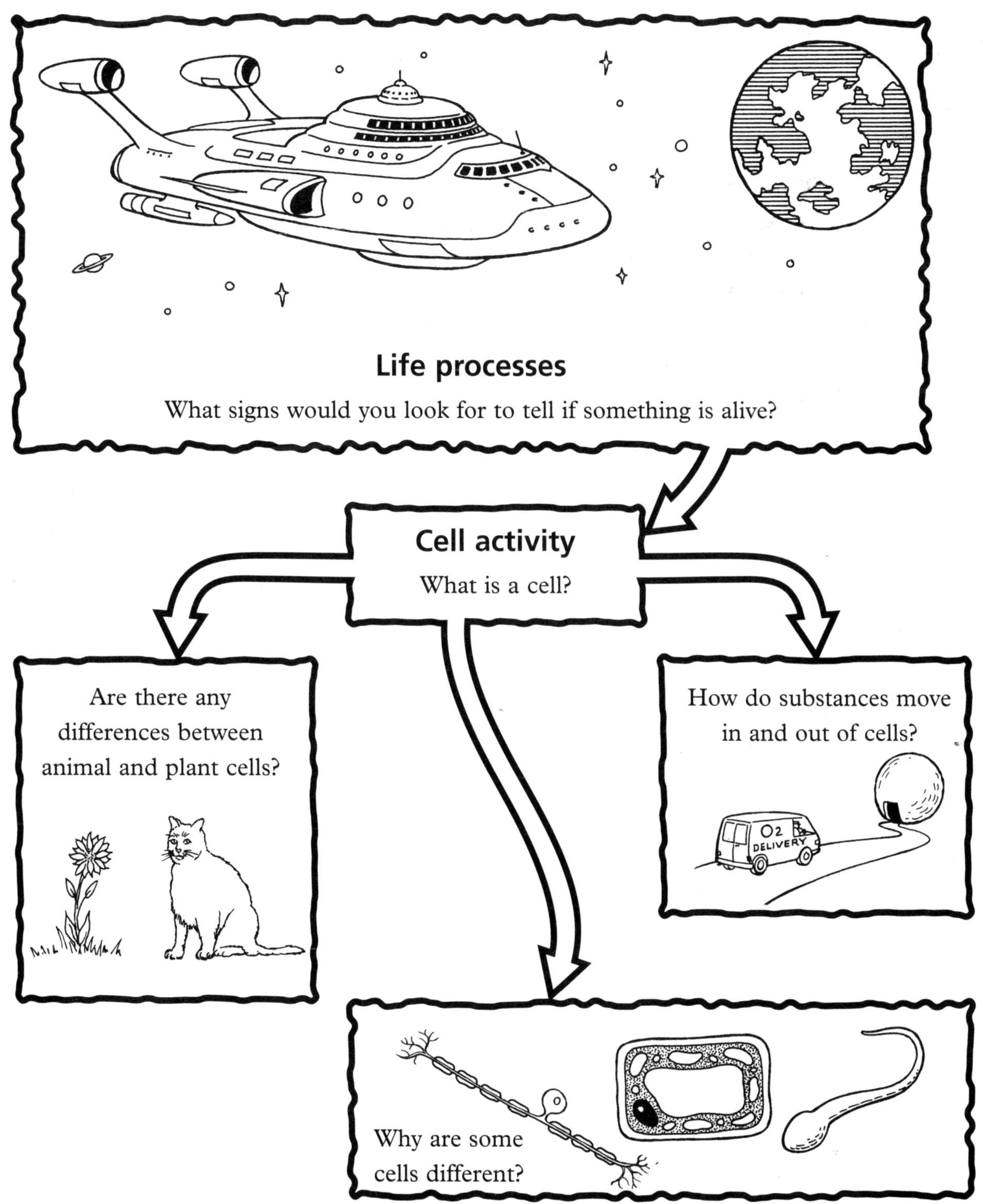

The basics of life

Seven life processes

All living things carry out the following seven activities.
This makes them different from non-living things.

1 **M**ovement – animals move their whole bodies, plants move as they grow
2 **R**eproduction – they make new individuals like themselves
3 **S**ensitivity – they are aware of, and can respond to changes in their surroundings
4 **G**rowth – they all get bigger
5 **R**espiration – they release energy from their food
6 **E**xcretion – they get rid of waste products they have made
7 **F**eeding – animals eat, plants make their own food by photosynthesis in their leaves.

These activities form the name Mrs Gref which might help you to remember them.

Cells

All living things are made of cells. These are so tiny that you can only see them using a microscope.

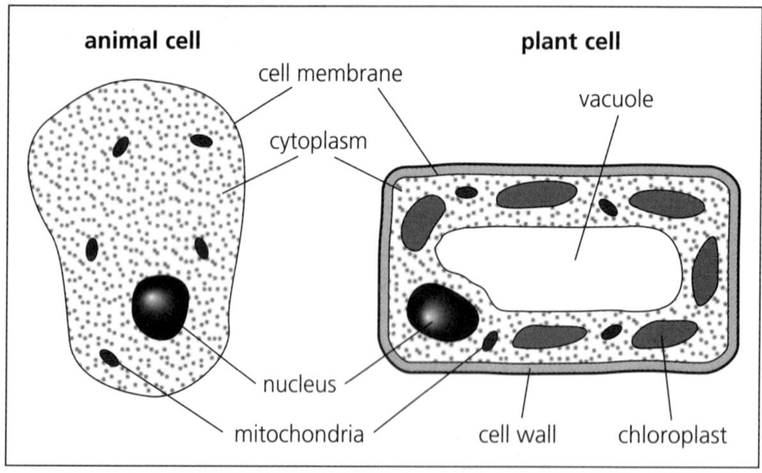

Now do this

1 What do the initials Mrs Gref stand for?
2 Which part of a plant cell
a is needed for photosynthesis
b controls what moves in and out of the cell
c supports the plant?

Most cells contain:
- a **nucleus** which controls everything a cell does
- **cytoplasm** – a watery jelly where most of the cell's reactions occur
- a **cell membrane**, which controls what goes in and out of the cell
- **mitochondria**, which release energy from food (respiration).

Plant cells also have a few extras:
- A **cellulose cell wall** to help support the plant. Think of the size of tall trees, and remember they have no bones to hold them up.
- **Chloroplasts** for making their own food by photosynthesis.
- A large **cell vacuole**, a space filled with a fluid called cell sap.

On the move

Cell membranes allow certain chemicals to pass through them but not others. They are called **selectively permeable**. There are three different ways in which chemicals move through cell membranes: **diffusion**, **osmosis** and **active transport**.

- **Diffusion** is the movement of particles from an area of high concentration to an area of low concentration. It does not require energy and occurs in solids, liquids and gases. Oxygen diffuses through cell membranes when it leaves the lungs (high concentration) to move into the blood (low concentration).
- **Osmosis** is only the movement of water. It does not require energy.
- **Active transport** is the movement of particles from an area of low concentration to an area of higher concentration. It requires energy and occurs in the uptake of minerals from soil water for example.

The right cell for the job

Cells contain the same basic parts, but they also have important differences. They are specialised to do different jobs. These are examples:

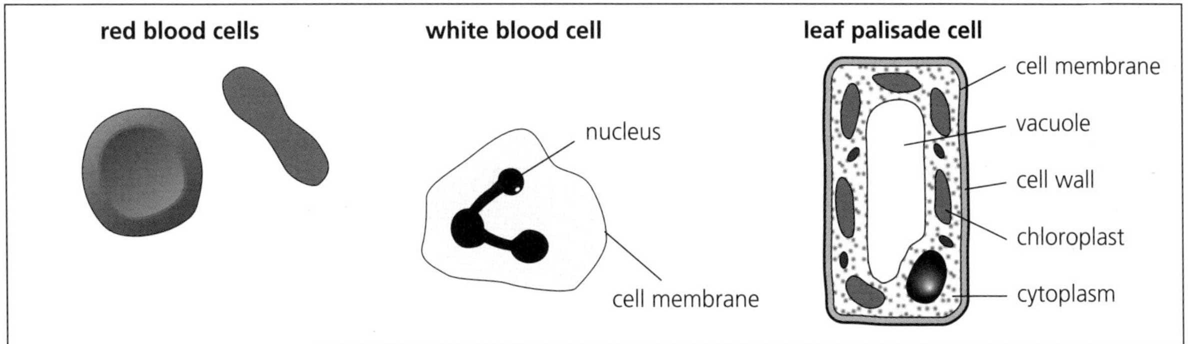

Red blood cells carry oxygen. They have no nucleus to make more space for oxygen.

White blood cells fight infection, so they can change their shape to 'eat' microbes.

Palisade leaf cells near the surface of leaves are long and thin with lots of chloroplasts to trap as much light as possible for photosynthesis.

Cells, tissues and organs

Tissues are groups of cells which do the same job, for example, muscle cells make up muscle tissue.

Organs are different types of tissues grouped together to do one job, for example, muscle and gland tissues make up the stomach.

Organs working together form an **organ system**, for example, the stomach and several other organs are part of the digestive system.

Now do this

3 Why do red blood cells have no nucleus?

4 What does selectively permeable mean?

5 Explain how minerals are taken up into a plant from the soil.

6 Name the process involved when oxygen passes from the lungs to a blood capillary.

Exam questions

1 Look at the drawing of a newly discovered organism which was found in a tropical swamp.

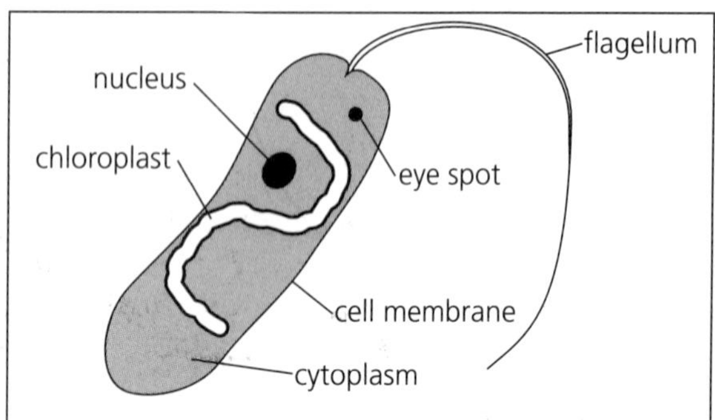

a List **two** things you can see from the drawing that tells you that the organism is likely to be an animal. [2]

b Explain one reason why the organism might be thought of as a plant. [1]

[3 marks]

2 The drawing shows three different types of cell.

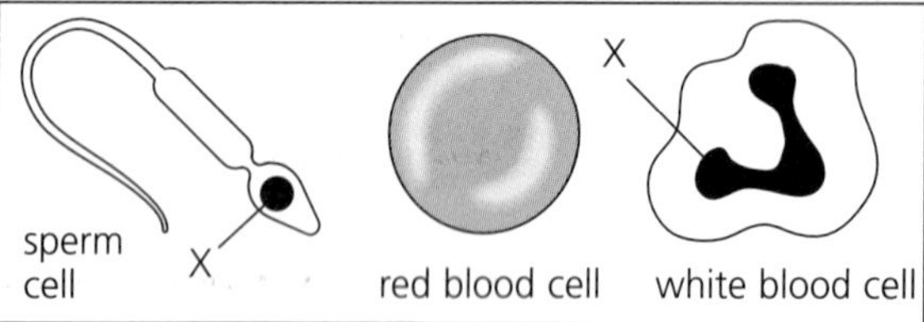

a Name the structure labelled **X** in the cells. [1]

b What is the function of **X**? [1]

c Suggest **two** ways in which the red blood cell is specialised to carry oxygen. [2]

d Explain why the sperm cell contains a large number of mitochondria. [2]

[6 marks]

3 Cell membranes are selectively permeable.

a What does selectively permeable mean? [1]

b List the **three** different processes by which chemicals can enter cells. [3]

c Explain which one of these processes is responsible for the movement of glucose from the small intestine into the blood capillaries of the villi. [2]

d In the kidneys all the glucose which has been filtered into the kidney tubule has to be reabsorbed back into the blood. Suggest which process enables this to occur and give a reason for your answer. [3]

[9 marks]

4 The drawing shows a cell.

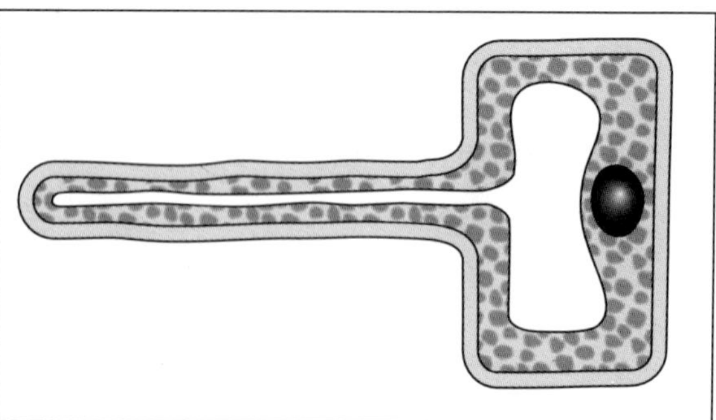

a Look at the cell. Decide whether it is an animal or plant cell and give a reason for your answer. [1]

b Where would you expect to find this type of cell? [1]

c How is this cell specialised to do its job? [2]

[4 marks]

Humans as organisms

You will have met the ideas covered in this section when you worked on the units *Staying alive*, *Keeping healthy*, *Sports science*, *Controlling change* and *Communicating information*. This section is divided into nine spreads.

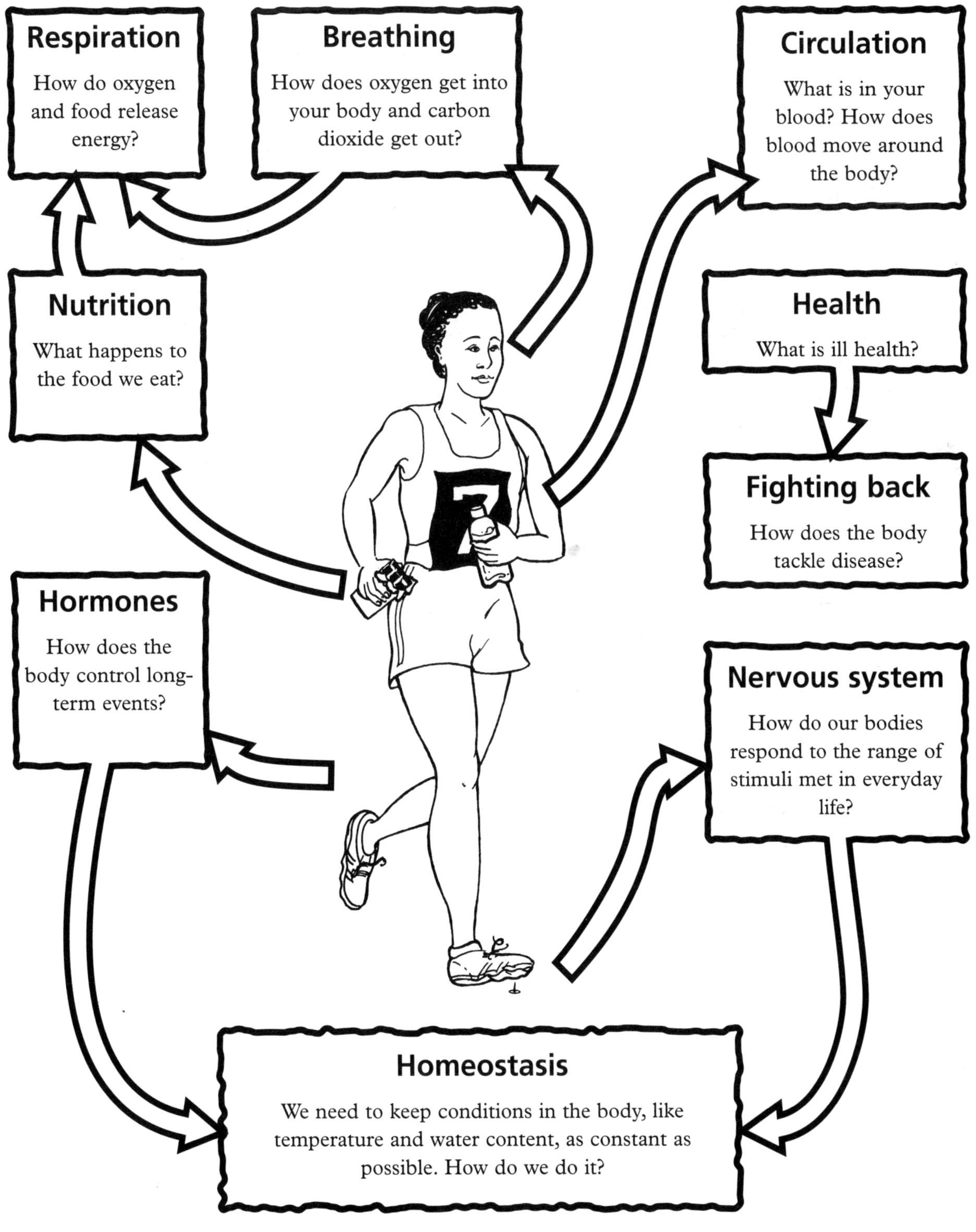

Nutrition

The food you eat gives all your cells the energy they need. Food contains large insoluble molecules which need to be broken down into small soluble molecules. This breakdown is called **digestion**. It occurs in the **digestive system**. The small soluble molecules can then move into the blood to be transported to the body cells.

The digestive system

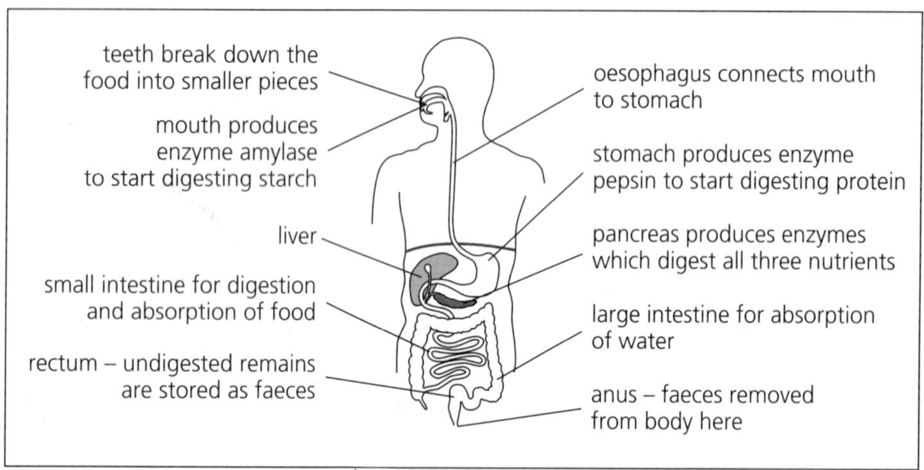

Digestion in action

There are two types of digestion;

1 **Mechanical** digestion which physically breaks down the food, starting with the grinding and tearing actions of the teeth, and continuing with the squashing and squeezing actions of muscles throughout the digestive system.

2 **Chemical** digestion uses **enzymes** to speed up the break down of the food molecules throughout the digestive system.

There are three main types of large molecules in food which have to be broken down: **proteins, carbohydrates** and **fats**.

In chemical digestion, enzymes break down the large molecules:

Proteins are digested to amino acids.

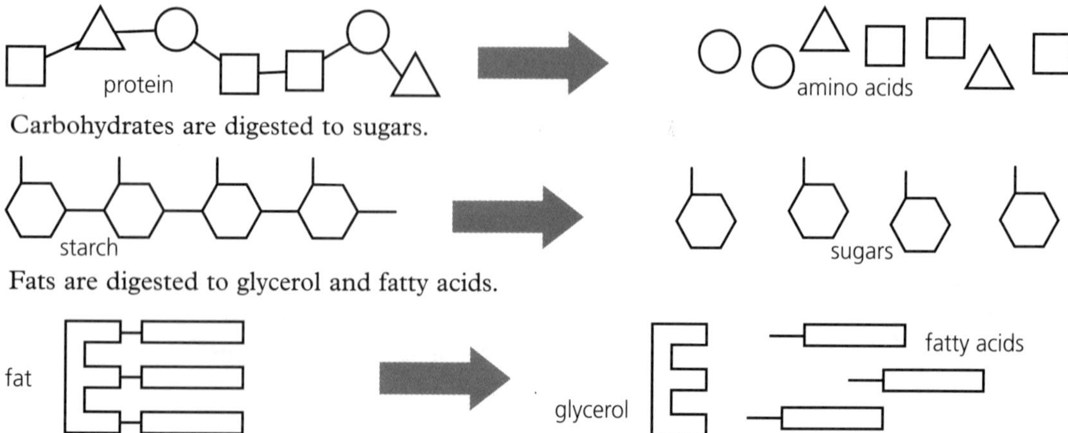

Carbohydrates are digested to sugars.

Fats are digested to glycerol and fatty acids.

Protein digestion starts in the stomach with the enzyme pepsin. The stomach makes an acid to provide pepsin with the right acid conditions. The acid also kills germs on the food. The food passes into the small intestine where enzymes from the pancreas carry on digesting it. These enzymes do not work well in acid conditions. So the liver adds juices which neutralise the acid left over from the stomach.

Fat digestion takes place in the small intestine where the liver adds **bile** which breaks downs fats into smaller droplets (**emulsifies** fats). This gives the enzymes a larger surface area to attack and therefore speeds up fat digestion.

Examiner's tip

Bile does not contain enzymes. Therefore emulsifying physically breaks down the fat. It is not chemical break down.

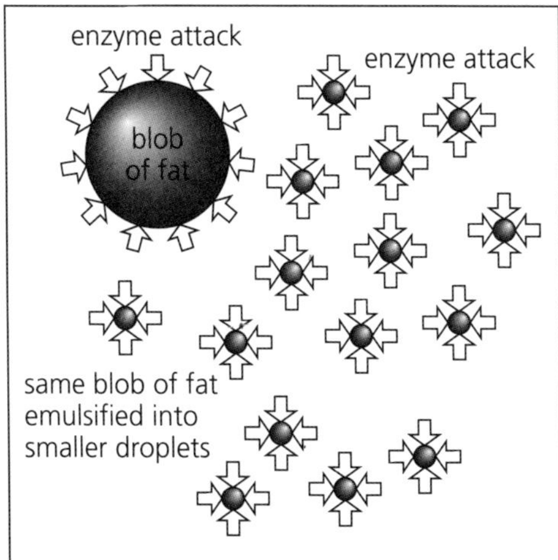

Now do this

1 What do you understand by the term digestion?

2 Carbohydrates are made of sugars joined together. What are fats and proteins made of?

3 How do enzymes help with digestion?

4 Explain how bile helps speed up the digestion of fats.

5 Name **two** parts of the digestive system that produce enzymes.

6 Give **two** uses of stomach acid.

Absorbing food

In the small intestine the small, soluble food molecules pass into the blood. They are **absorbed**. The small intestine has lots of finger like projections called **villi** to increase the surface area for absorbing the digested food.

The small intestine is good at absorbing food as:

- it is very long
- villi give it a huge surface area
- the walls are very thin and permeable
- it has a good blood supply to transport digested food.

food enters the digestive system (mouth)

food is digested

digested food is absorbed into the blood by diffusion

undigested food passes out of the body as faeces

Examiner's tip

Healthy living also requires a balanced diet to provide the correct nutrients for your body. You need a range of carbohydrates, proteins, fats, vitamins and minerals in the correct proportions.

Now do this

7 Where in the digestive system is water absorbed?

8 What are villi and how do they help with absorption?

9 Describe what happens to a cheese sandwich between it entering the mouth and it arriving in the blood.

Circulation

Your body has a **transport system** to carry materials such as oxygen and food to all the body cells. The transport system has three main parts.

1 A fluid called **blood** to carry the materials.
2 A network of tubes called **blood vessels**.
3 A pump, called the **heart**.

Blood

Blood is made up of:

- **plasma** – a watery fluid which transports foods, water, hormones and waste products such as urea
- **platelets** – tiny cell fragments without nuclei which help blood to clot if the skin is torn
- **white blood cells** – defend the body against disease
- **red blood cells** – transport oxygen around the body. They are adapted to do this well because they do not contain a nucleus so they have more space to carry oxygen; they have a large surface area to pick up more oxygen; they contain haemoglobin which carries the oxygen.

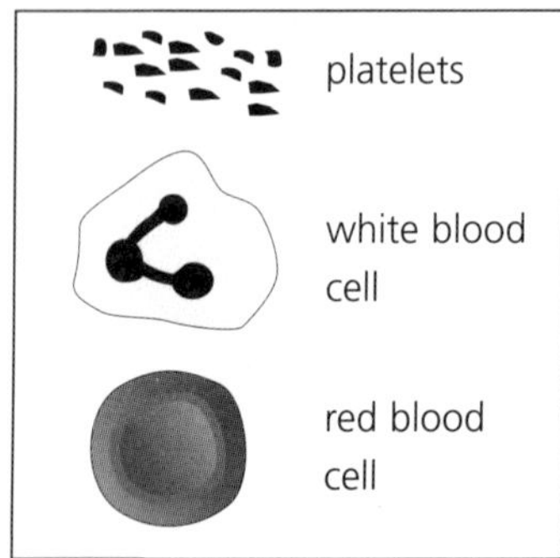

oxygen + haemoglobin $\rightleftharpoons$ oxyhaemoglobin

Scab formation

Clotting is important because it stops us bleeding to death. It also helps scabs to form which plug cuts and other holes in the skin to prevent microbes (infection) getting in.

1 Cut skin causes a soluble protein in the blood to become insoluble and form strands called fibrin.

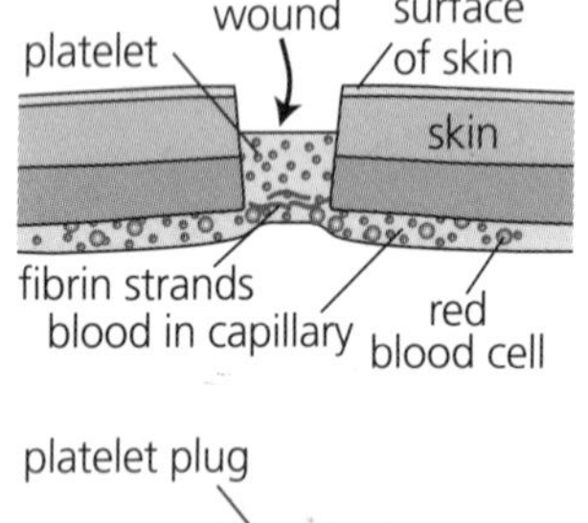

2 Platelets try to plug the wound and the strands of fibrin get tangled up with the platelets.

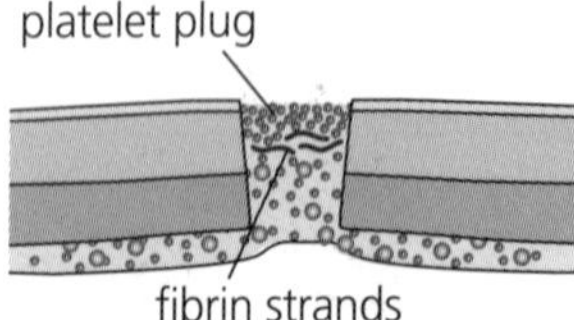

3 Red blood cells also get trapped in the strands, effectively sealing the wound.

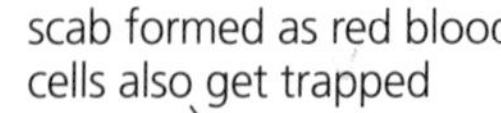

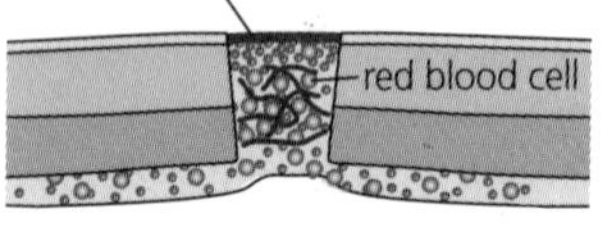

4 The plug dries out and hardens to form a scab which protects the underlying skin until it has had time to be repaired.

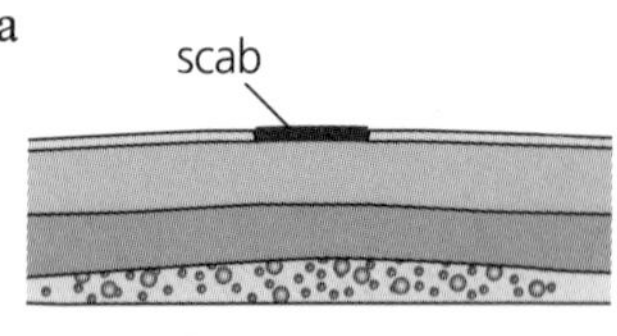

Now do this

1 Draw up a table with the following headings, and complete it using the main components of blood (parts that blood is made up of).

Component	What it looks like	What it does

2 Give **two** reasons why it is important that blood can form clots.

3 What does fibrin do if you cut yourself?

Blood vessels

The blood is carried around the body in blood vessels. There are **three** different types of blood vessel.

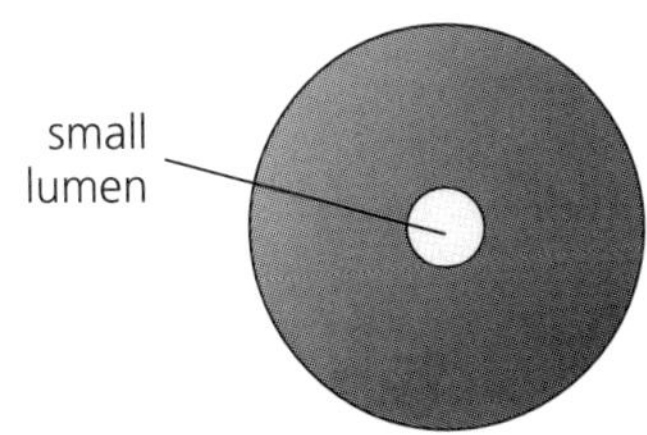

Arteries carry blood away from the heart and have thick elastic muscular walls to withstand high blood pressure.

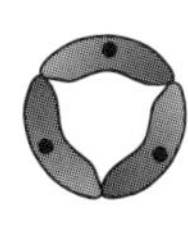

Capillaries link arteries and veins and have walls only one cell thick to allow materials to diffuse in and out of surrounding body cells.

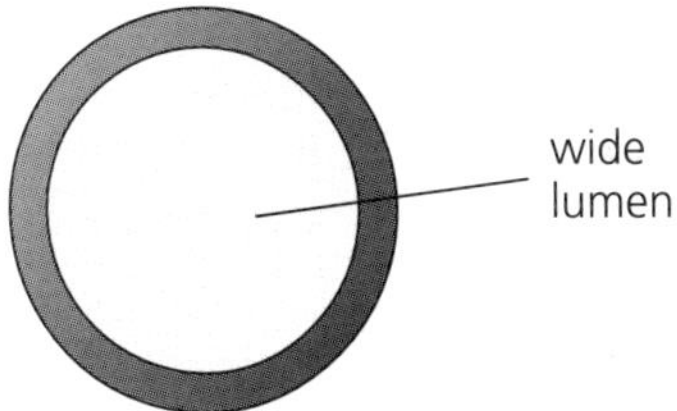

Veins carry blood at a lower pressure back to the heart and have thin muscular walls because the blood is no longer at high pressure. Valves help to keep the blood moving in the right direction.

How does blood move around the blood vessels?

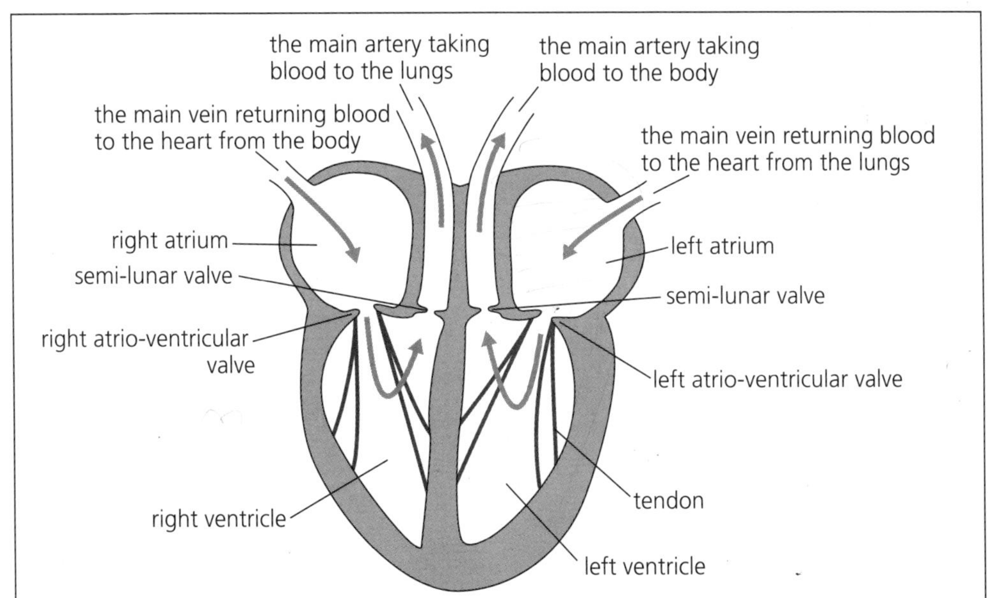

Blood has to be pumped around the body, and this is the job of the **heart**.

The heart is made of muscle. It contains **four** chambers and **four** valves.

The right and left atria collect blood coming in from the veins, and the right and left ventricles contract to squirt blood out into the arteries at high pressure. It needs the pressure because some of the blood has a long way to go through the body!

The arrows show the direction of blood flow. The valves stop the blood flowing backwards.

Now do this

4 Why do arteries need thick, muscular walls?

5 Explain why the ventricles have thicker, more muscular walls than the atria.

6 What type of tissue is the heart made of?

7 Why does the heart have valves?

Breathing

You breathe in air to take oxygen into your body to be used in respiration (to release energy from your food). This produces carbon dioxide which needs to be removed from the body. This is **gas exchange**. Gas exchange occurs in the **lungs**, which are in the chest and are protected by the **ribs**. The air enters your lungs through the **trachea** (windpipe). At the end of the bronchioles are lots of little air sacs called **alveoli** where gas exchange takes place.

Your lungs

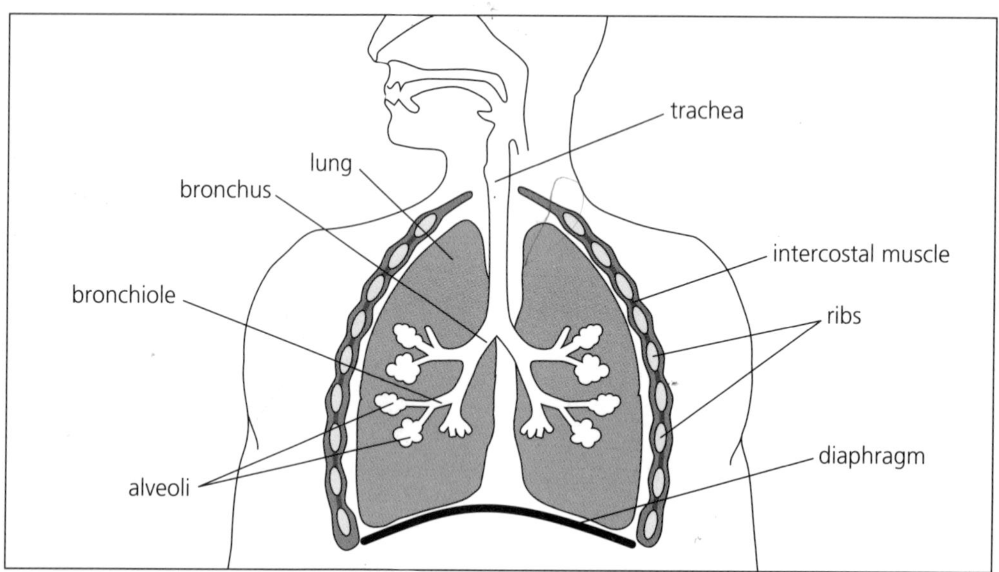

Breathing in and breathing out

Movements of the ribcage and diaphragm result in the ventilation of the lungs. These movements help us to breathe.

When we inhale (breath in), the lung volume increases and therefore the air pressure decreases. When we exhale (breath out) the lung volume decreases and the air pressure increases. The air pressure in the lungs is continuously changing. The bronchi and larger bronchioles have pieces of cartilage in their walls to support them and prevent them from collapsing as the air pressure changes.

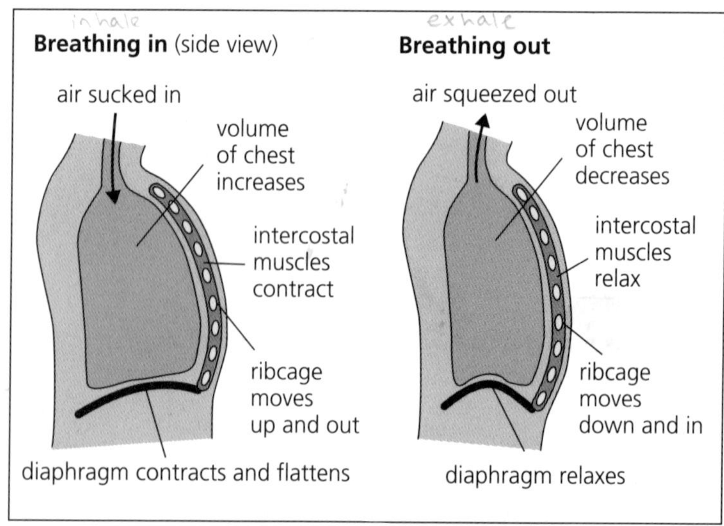

Now do this

1. Describe the changes in the position of the ribs and diaphragm that occur when we inhale and exhale.
2. Explain why the bronchi and larger bronchioles contain pieces of cartilage.

Getting oxygen into the blood

When you breathe in, there is a lot of oxygen (a high **concentration**) in the alveoli. There is very little oxygen (a low concentration) in the blood in the capillaries. So oxygen moves from the alveoli into the blood. Movement like this from a high to a low concentration is called **diffusion**.

One air sac is called an alveolus, lots are called alveoli.

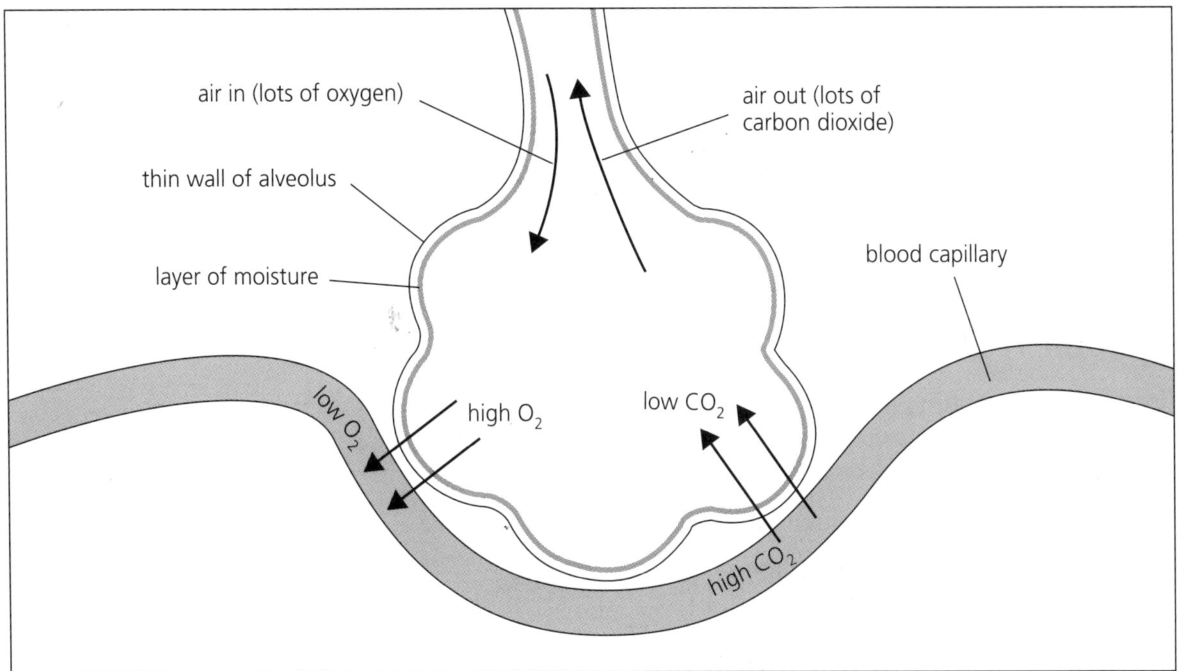

The lungs are good at diffusion because they have:

- a large surface area (thousands of alveoli) which means that a large amount of oxygen can move across
- moist surfaces which make diffusion faster
- thin walled alveoli which make diffusion faster
- lots of blood capillaries for oxygen to diffuse into.

Gas exchange

Blood coming back to the lungs has a high concentration of carbon dioxide. This diffuses into the lungs and is breathed out. Blood from the lungs has a high concentration of oxygen in it. The oxygen breathed in to the lungs has diffused into the blood. Oxygen moves into the blood at the same time as carbon dioxide moves into the lungs. In gas exchange the lungs **exchange** (swap) oxygen for carbon dioxide. The blood exchanges carbon dioxide for oxygen.

Now do this

3 Why do we need oxygen?

4 Explain why oxygen diffuses from the alveoli into the blood.

5 Give **three** ways in which alveoli are adapted for gas exchange.

6 Blood coming back to the lungs has a higher concentration of carbon dioxide than the air in the alveoli. How does carbon dioxide pass from the blood into the alveoli?

7 Your lungs look pink because they have such a lot of blood capillaries in them. Why do lungs need so much blood?

Respiration

Cells need energy to keep them working. To release energy they require a supply of food and oxygen. Food comes from the digestive system and is carried to the cells dissolved in the blood. Oxygen comes from the lungs and is carried round the body by the red blood cells. The food, in particular glucose, and oxygen pass easily through the thin capillary walls to enter the body cells.

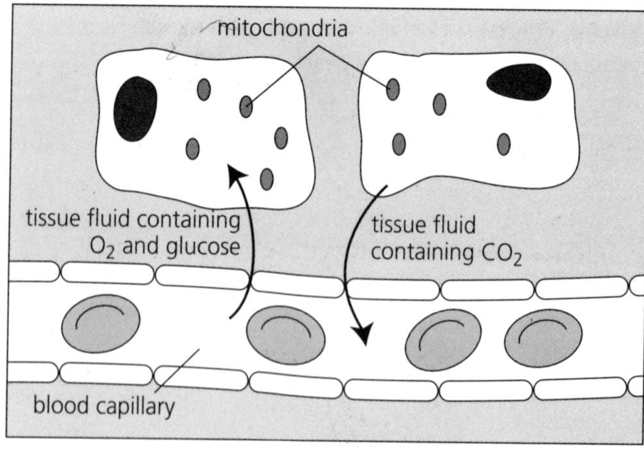

Aerobic respiration

Energy is released from glucose when it reacts with oxygen in our cells. This is called **aerobic respiration**. The glucose and oxygen react to make water and carbon dioxide. This is the oxidation of glucose.

Aerobic respiration can be written as a word equation:

glucose + oxygen → water + carbon dioxide + energy

The chemical equation is:

$C_6H_{12}O_6$	+ $6O_2$	→ $6H_2O$	+ $6CO_2$	+ energy
glucose	+ oxygen	→ water	+ carbon dioxide	

Respiration happens in *all* of our cells *all* of the time, so it is sometimes also called **cellular** respiration. It happens in parts of the cell called **mitochondria**, which are sometimes called the power houses of the cell.

Running out of oxygen

If you exercise vigorously, the dissolved oxygen in your blood and tissues is used up faster than you can replace it. Cells then begin to use **anaerobic respiration**.

glucose → lactic acid + some energy

The amount of energy released is much less than in aerobic respiration. Also, lactic acid is poisonous and causes pain and cramp in the muscles, so you soon slow down. Afterwards, you go on breathing heavily until the oxygen levels in your tissues have been restored. This is called repaying the **oxygen debt**.

Now do this

1. What is the chemical equation for aerobic respiration?
2. Draw up a table to show the differences and similarities between aerobic and anaerobic respiration.
3. Where in the cell does aerobic respiration take place?
4. What does the term 'oxygen debt' mean?

Making the most of exercise

Working your muscles needs energy. So the more we exercise the more energy we need. This is how the body copes:

- you breathe faster and deeper to bring more oxygen into the body (your **breathing volume** increases)
- your heart pumps faster to speed up blood flow around the body and get more oxygen and glucose to the respiring cells (your **pulse rate** increases)
- aerobic respiration in the muscle cells increases.

A fit person will have a strong heart muscle, which when exercising, can easily beat faster and increase the volume of blood flowing through it. The lungs will also expand easily to take in more oxygen. When exercise is over, the pulse rate and breathing rate soon return to normal. An unfit person will take longer to recover from exercise.

Now do this

5 Imagine you have just run up four flights of stairs to the top of a block of flats. Explain two ways your body will change while running from the ground floor to the top.

Examiner's tip

Do not confuse respiration and breathing.

All living things need energy therefore all living things respire – even plants!

Breathing describes special methods which have been developed for gas exchange. Therefore breathing usually applies to active organisms which have lungs or a special area for gas exchange like the gills of a fish.

Plants are not very active therefore they do not have special breathing methods. Gas exchange occurs by diffusion through holes in their leaves.

The nervous system

We are aware of and can respond to changes in our surroundings. These changes are called **stimuli** and they are detected by parts of our bodies called **receptors**.

Receptors are part of **sense organs**. We have five sense organs which detect stimuli:

- ears detect sound
- eyes detect light
- noses detect chemicals (odour)
- tongues detect chemicals (flavour)
- skin detects texture, pressure and temperature change (hot and cold).

Passing the message

When receptors detect a stimulus, they send a message to the brain. Messages are carried by specialised nerve cells called **neurones**. There are two types of nerve cells or **neurones**:

- nerve cells carrying messages towards the central nervous system from the sense organs are called **sensory neurones**
- nerve cells carrying messages away from the central nervous system are called **motor neurones**.

Information

The brain and spinal cord is called the **central nervous system**.

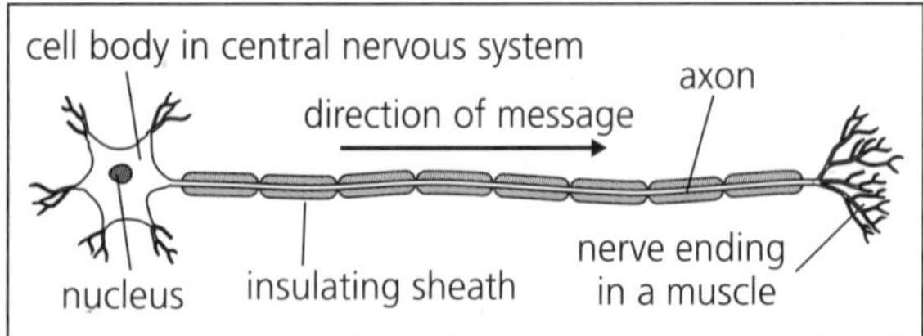
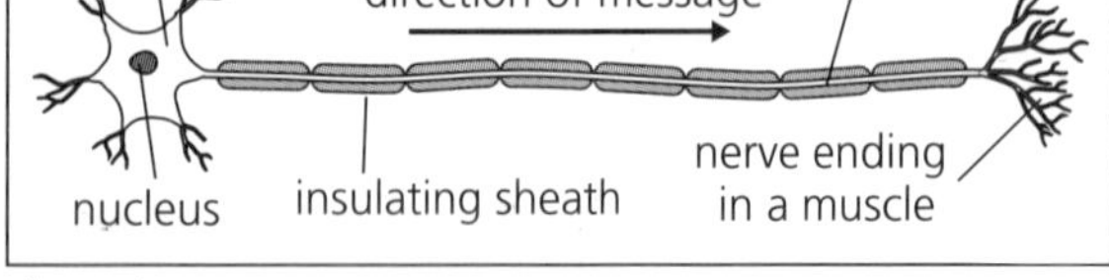

A motor neurone

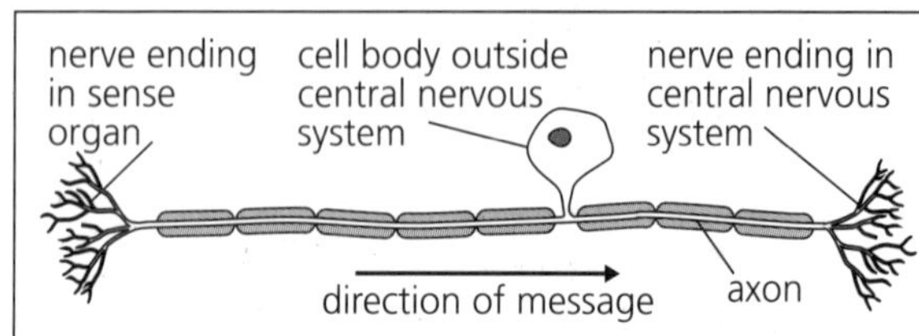

A sensory neurone

Within the spinal cord there are small connecting neurones which enable a message to go to different destinations. A message coming in may be passed on to a motor neurone to produce a response to the stimulus, but it may also be passed on to the brain to allow a more co-ordinated response. In most nervous responses, a receptor responds to a stimulus and the sensory neurone passes the message on to the central nervous system (brain) for analysis. The brain then responds by sending messages down the appropriate motor neurones to cause a response.

Fast response – the reflex action

We often need to react very quickly to stimuli. For example, if you pick up a hot plate which burns you, you quickly drop it. For this we need our body to act on information from receptors automatically and quickly. There is no time to consult the brain to think about it.

What actually happens when you touch something hot?

1 Temperature receptors in your skin detect the hot stimulus.
2 They send the message along a sensory neurone to the central nervous system.
3 The central nervous system sends the message along a motor neurone to a muscle (an **effector**).
4 The muscle contracts and moves your hand away from the hot object.

??? *Now do this*

1 You are walking in the park when a ball comes flying towards your eyes. It doesn't hit you but you blink. Write a nerve pathway to show how this happens and add the names of the parts involved (e.g. the receptor is the retina).

This is called a **reflex action**. Reflex actions are often protective. For example, suckling, swallowing and coughing. The pathways taken by nerve messages can be shown like this:

Now do this

2 Write down three examples of reflex actions.

stimulus → receptor → sensory neurone → central nervous system → motor neurone → effector (muscle) → response

A sense organ up close – the eye

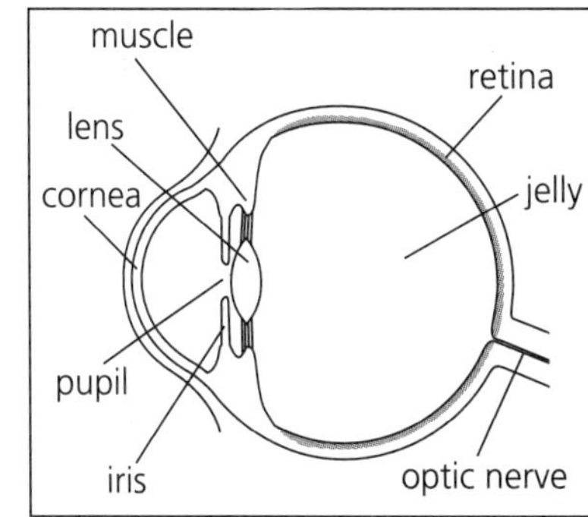

This is how you see:

1 Light enters the eye through the cornea.
2 The cornea starts to bend the light.
3 The lens can be adjusted so that it bends the light enough to make it focus on the retina.
4 The retina contains receptors which respond to the light.
5 The receptors send messages along the optic nerve to the brain.
6 The brain interprets the messages.

This shows how you get a clear image of what you are looking at. The apparent size of an object depends on its actual size and its distance from the eye.

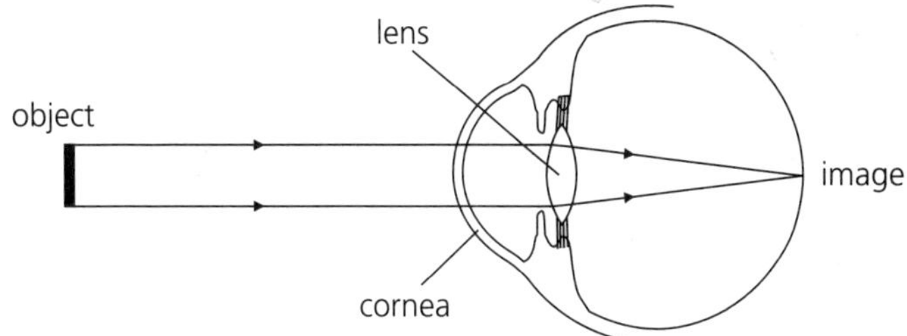

The two most common defects of vision are long sightedness and short sightedness. In both cases the light does not focus on the retina. In a short sighted person the eyeball is too long, or the lens bends the light too much, so that the light is focused in front of the retina. In a long sighted person the light would naturally focus behind the retina.

A concave lens will spread the light out a little more before it reaches the eye thereby enabling the eye to focus the light on the retina. A convex lens will bend the light in a little more, again so that the eye can focus it on the retina rather than behind it.

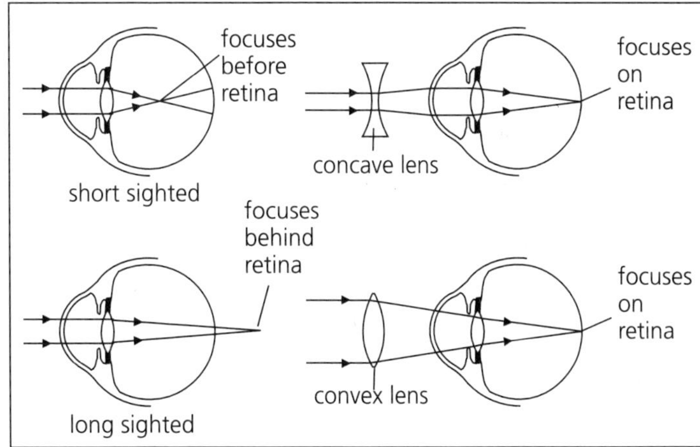

Now do this

3 Complete the table opposite.

4 Explain what sort of glasses you would require if you were short sighted.

Name	Function
retina	detects the light stimulus
iris	controls amount of light entering the eye
lens	changes shape to bend the light
optic nerve	carries messages to the brain

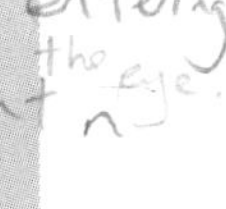

Hormones

Your body is controlled by **hormones** as well as the nervous system. Hormones are chemical messengers produced by groups of cells called **glands**. They travel in the blood plasma and work on groups of cells in the body. Each hormone acts in a particular way on a particular group of **target cells**.

Hormones are usually slower acting than nervous responses. They control the more general and longer lasting changes in your body, for example all the many changes which happen during puberty.

The two control systems

Nervous control	Hormonal control
nervous messages are electrical signals	hormones are chemicals
nervous messages travel through neurons	hormones travel through the blood
messages travel quickly	hormones travel more slowly
responses are very quick	responses tend to be slower
response is very specific, it can only travel along a neurone	response can be very widespread because the blood travels through all of the body

Hormones in action

Two hormones control a woman's menstrual cycle, **oestrogen** and **progesterone**:

- oestrogen repairs the uterus wall
- progesterone keeps the uterus wall thick and in position
- oestrogen and progesterone together control **ovulation** (ovaries releasing eggs).

Now do this

1 What is the definition of a hormone?

2 Explain why nervous responses are more specific than hormonal responses.

Preventing pregnancy . . .

Hormones can be used in **contraceptive pills** to prevent ovulation and make the body think it is pregnant. This means that a woman will not release eggs and therefore cannot get pregnant.

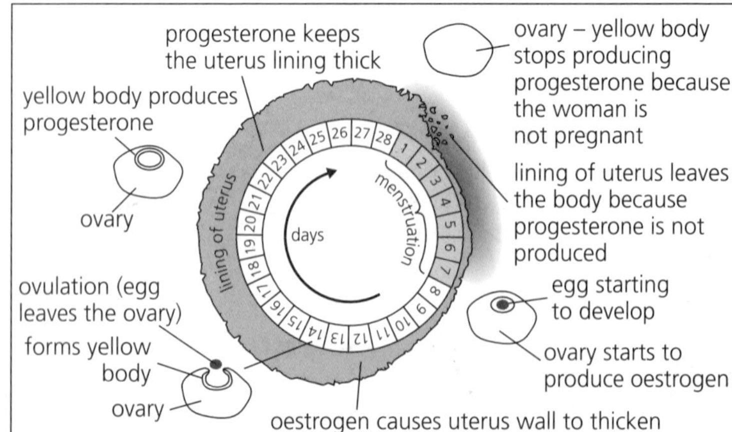

. . . and helping pregnancy

Some women have difficulty in getting pregnant. Hormones can be used to help them produce more eggs which will increase their chances of getting pregnant.

Now do this

3 Explain why a pregnant woman will not normally menstruate.

4 How does a contraceptive pill work?

5 What part does oestrogen play in the menstrual cycle?

Controlling sugar (glucose) levels

Glucose is needed by all your cells for energy. But it is very important to have the right amount available for them in your blood. Too much or too little can be fatal.

The amount of glucose is controlled by two hormones called **insulin** and **glucagon**. These are produced by the pancreas.

When there is *too much* glucose in the blood, the pancreas releases insulin. Insulin lowers the level of glucose by:

- making cells take up more glucose
- making **liver** cells change glucose to **glycogen** where it can be stored.

Once the blood glucose level is back to normal, the pancreas stops releasing insulin.

When there is *too little* glucose in the blood, the pancreas releases glucagon. Glucagon increases the level of glucose by:

- making liver and muscle cells change glycogen back to glucose
- glucose passes back into the blood.

Once the blood glucose level is back up to normal, the pancreas stops releasing glucagon. This is an example of a **feedback mechanism** because the change in blood glucose levels brought about a response in the body which resulted in the glucose levels returning to normal and the response being stopped.

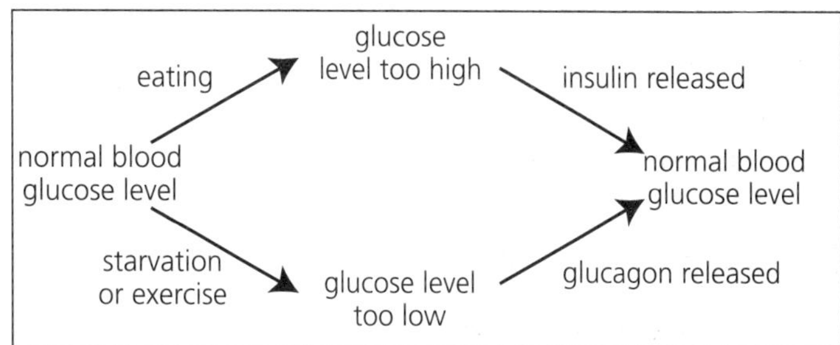

Some people do not make any insulin, or do not make enough. This means they suffer from **diabetes**. In these cases the level of glucose in the blood can go up and down wildly. Many diabetics control their blood glucose by injecting themselves with insulin. Insulin needs to be injected because it is a protein and would be digested if taken by mouth.

Examiner's tip

Glucagon is released when all the glucose has gone, glu from glucose and gon from gone.

Fight or flight

The hormone **adrenaline** prepares the body for action. It is produced by the two **adrenal glands**. It makes the heart beat faster and increases the breathing rate. This forces blood around the body more rapidly, delivering more oxygen and glucose to the muscles to release more energy. It also shuts down blood flow to the skin and stomach so there is more blood available to go to the brain and muscles.

Now do this

6 Which organ produces the hormones concerned with glucose control?

7 What might cause the blood glucose level to suddenly increase?

8 Explain why the blood insulin concentration of someone running a half marathon would be expected to be low.

9 Explain why you might go very pale if faced by a charging bull.

Homeostasis

It is important to keep conditions inside your body constant to enable your cells to work most efficiently. Maintaining these conditions is a process called **homeostasis**.

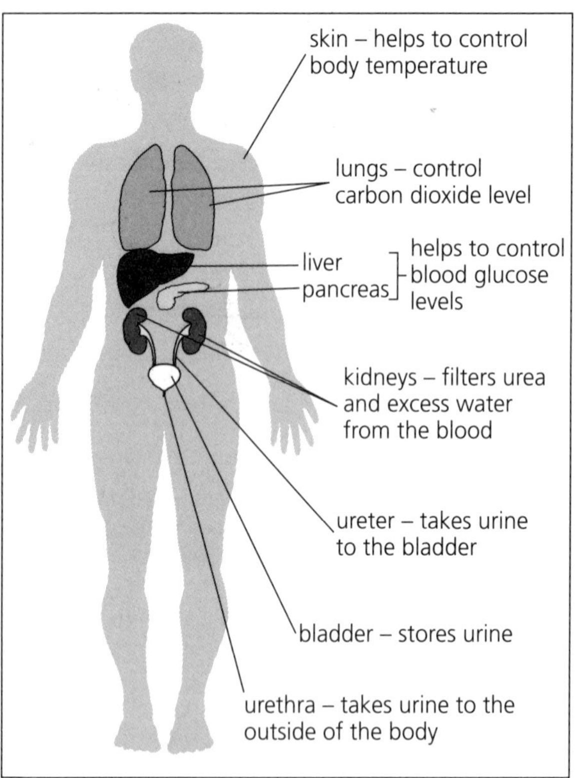

What needs controlling in your blood?

- glucose levels
- water and salt levels
- carbon dioxide level
- temperature
- waste products such as urea.

Now do this

1. What does homeostasis mean?
2. Which **two** body organs control blood glucose level?
3. What is passed out of the bladder down the urethra?

The water balance

If the balance of water in the body is upset we either dry out or swell up with excess fluid. We cannot survive either extreme for long. We rely on the kidney to help.

food and drink (water in) **urine, sweat and breath (water out)**

The role of the kidney

We have two kidneys whose role is to filter urea and water out of the blood to produce **urine**. Urine contains a variable amount of water. If it is a hot day and you have lost a lot of water through sweating, your blood will contain very little water. The kidneys will produce concentrated urine (urine with very little water in it). If it is a cold day, or if you have had a lot to drink, your blood will contain more water and the kidneys produce watery urine so that the water level of the blood returns to normal.

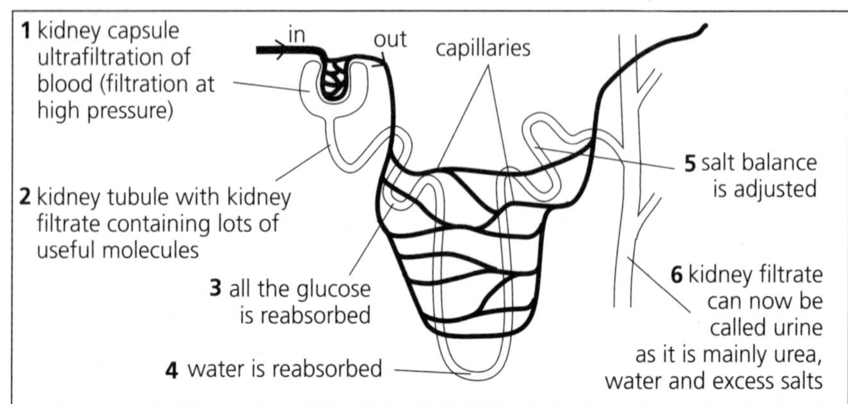

During stage 1 in the diagram, small molecules are filtered out of the blood into the kidney tubule. These include urea, water, salt and glucose, some of which are useful to the body and need to be taken back into the blood. Returning these to the blood is called **selective reabsorption**. All the glucose is reabsorbed. The amount of salt and water reabsorbed is controlled by hormones and depends on their relative levels in the blood. Red and white blood cells and platelets are too big to be filtered and stay in the blood.

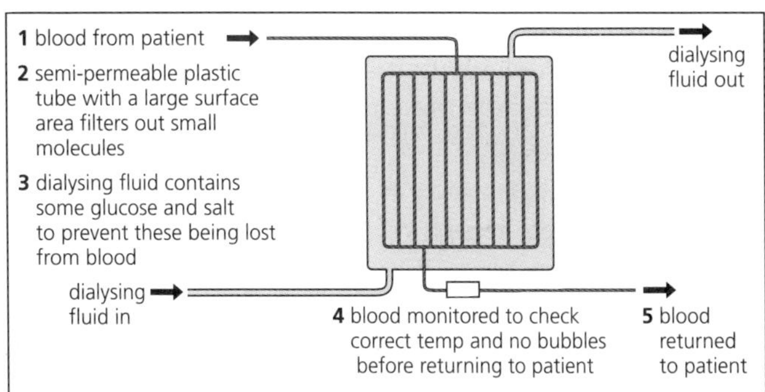

If your kidneys stop working you need to be attached to a kidney machine several times a week for 3 to 4 hours to prevent a build up of urea in your blood and to maintain the correct water and salt balance. This process is called **dialysis**.

Now do this

4 Explain why you produce more urine on a cold winter day than on a hot summer day.

5 Which molecule is filtered out of the blood in the kidney capsule but is not found in urine?

6 Give **two** ways in which a dialysis machine is adapted to be like a kidney.

Controlling body temperature

When our cells respire, some of the energy released is **heat** energy. We use this to keep us warm. The **liver** has a lot of reactions going on all the time, therefore it releases a lot of heat energy – it is like the boiler in a central heating system!

It is very important to keep your body temperature at around 37°C as this is the best temperature for your enzymes to work.

If you are in a hot climate or room and your temperature rises above 37°C the brain switches on cooling mechanisms, e.g. sweating. If you are in cold surroundings the brain switches on warming mechanisms, e.g. shivering.

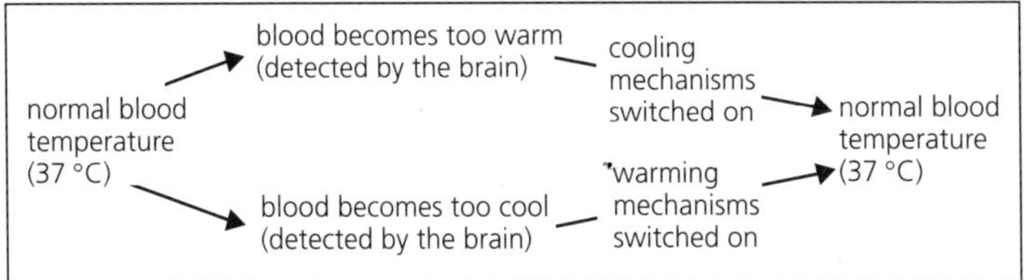

Now do this

7 Which part of the body checks the temperature of the blood?

8 Explain how sweating helps cool us down.

9 Explain why it is so important for us to control our body temperature.

Cooling mechanisms	Warming mechanisms
sweating – heat from the body used to evaporate sweat from the skin surface	shivering – muscles move so their cells respire faster to release the energy for movement and heat energy at the same time
vasodilation – blood vessels near skin surface open to allow blood to flow near to the surface of the body and lose heat by radiation to the air	vasoconstriction – blood vessels running near skin surface close, diverting the blood back to the warmer parts of the body
take some clothes off!	put some extra clothes on!

Health

You can recognise ill-health by the symptoms it causes. For example, lots of itchy, boil like spots are the symptoms of chicken pox.

Ill-health can be divided into four main groups according to the cause.

- **Inherited** diseases such as haemophilia, which are passed from parents to children in their genes.
- Diseases of **ageing** such as dementia. These are caused by the body gradually wearing out.
- Diseases caused by **environmental conditions**. For example food poisoning, caused by poor hygiene.
- **Infections** such as tetanus, caused by **microbes** which get into the body. Many can be passed on from one person to another.

Infections caused by microbes

Microbes which cause infection come from four different groups of living things.

Viruses

Viruses are the smallest microbes. They can only grow and breed in living cells so they always damage other organisms. They take over cells causing them to make millions of copies of the virus. They cause AIDS, measles, polio, flu.

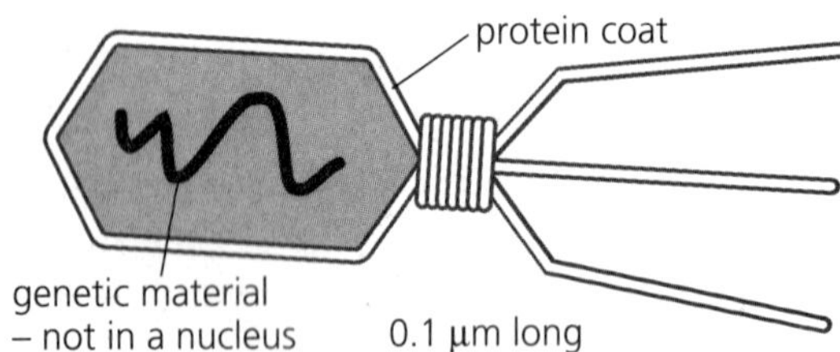

Bacteria

Most bacteria are harmless and many are valuable and useful to us. A few cause nasty diseases such as tetanus, food poisoning, whooping cough.

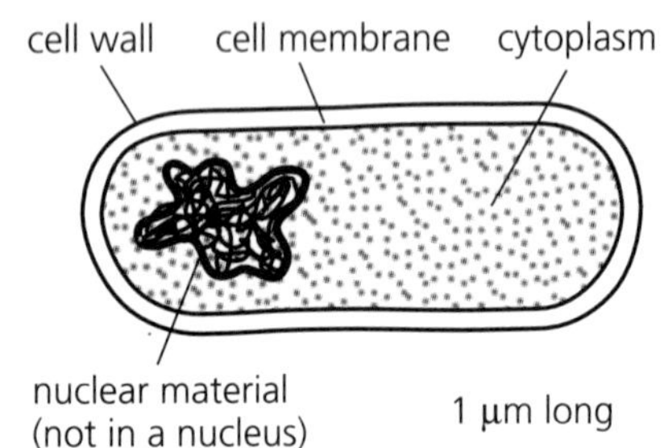

Protozoa

Protozoa are very simple single-celled animals and most are harmless. Some cause malaria, amoebic dysentery.

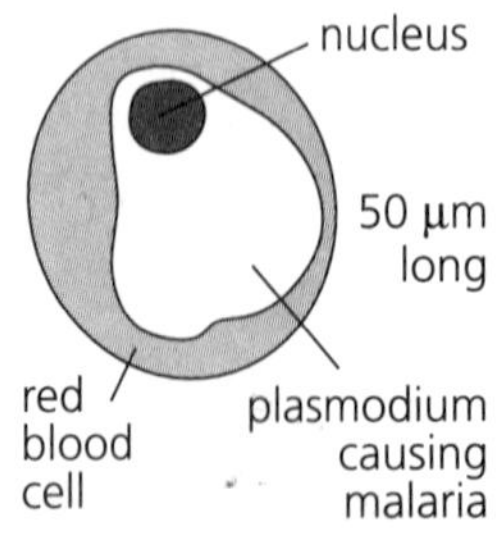

Fungi

Some fungi are useful such as yeast; some cause ringworm, thrush, athlete's foot.

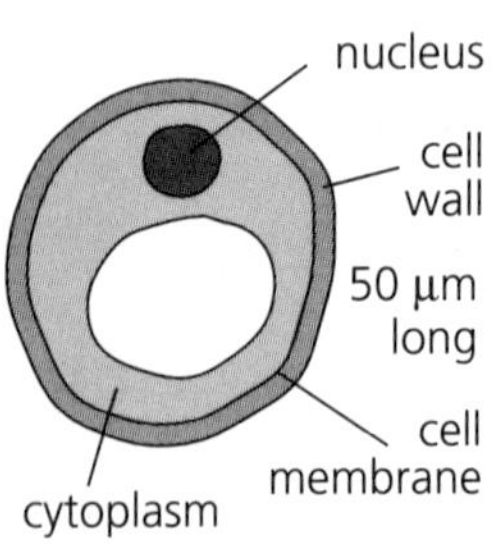

Just think
Malaria is caused by a protozoan which hitches a lift in mosquito saliva. This is how it gets into us when mosquitoes suck our blood!

Defence against disease

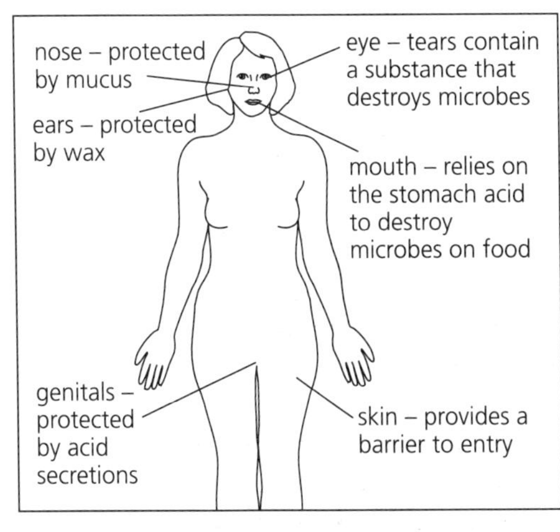

Your body is ideal for microbes because they need warm, moist places with plenty of food in order to grow. So your body has to defend itself against them.

Your first line of defence is your skin which keeps microbes out of most parts of the body.

Breaching the defences

Some microbes may get past the first line of defence.

Some cells in the trachea also produce mucus. The mucus traps dirt and microbes on their way to the lungs. The trachea is lined by millions of cilia (microscopic hairs). The cilia beat continuously to move the mucus and trapped bits back up the trachea to the throat. Once here they can be swallowed and are no longer a threat to the lungs. If the cilia are stopped, the mucus moves down into the lungs trapping the microbes in an ideal growing environment.

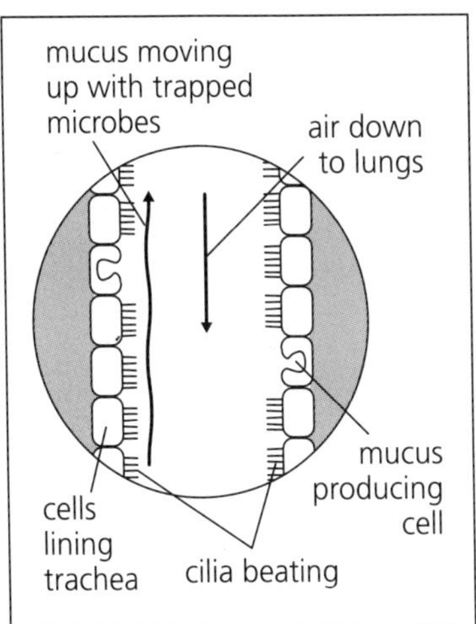

Now do this

1 Write down the **four** different causes of ill-health and for each, give one example of such an illness.

2 Name the **four** different types of organism which make up the group called microbes.

3 Which group does the organism causing malaria belong to?

4 How are the eyes protected from microbe invasion?

We have some chemicals to help with our hygiene. **Germicide** is the name given to chemicals which kill germs (microbes). There are two important types of germicide in everyday use. **Disinfectants** are powerful but too corrosive to use on our skin – they are ideal for toilets and drains! The milder form is **antiseptic**, which can be used on the skin.

Safe working procedures when using bacteria

When using bacteria it is very important to keep the whole working area sterile. Germicides are used to achieve this.

Always examine growing bacteria without removing the lid of their container. Sterilise materials thoroughly at the end of the procedure.

You must maintain aseptic conditions at all times or you may find the bacteria making a home on you!

Fighting back

If your skin is damaged, your blood forms a second line of defence by clotting and forming a scab over the wound. This blocks entry to microbes. If microbes still manage to invade the body, the white blood cells swing into action.

There are two types of white blood cell. One type 'eats' the microbes.

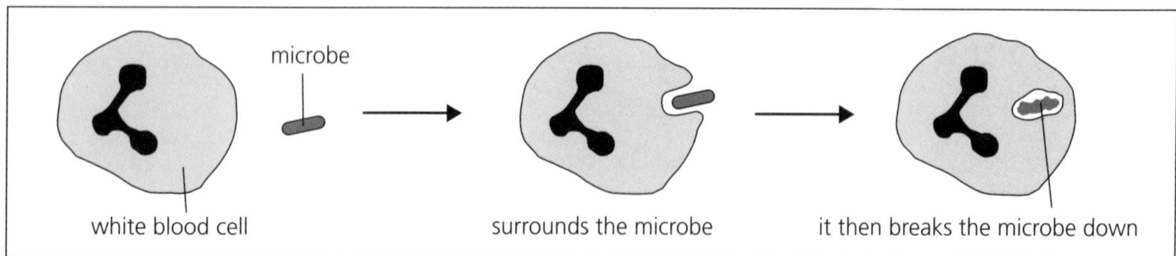

The other type produces chemicals called **antibodies** which attack the microbes and destroy them. It has to 'recognise' the microbe first to make the right antibody quickly.

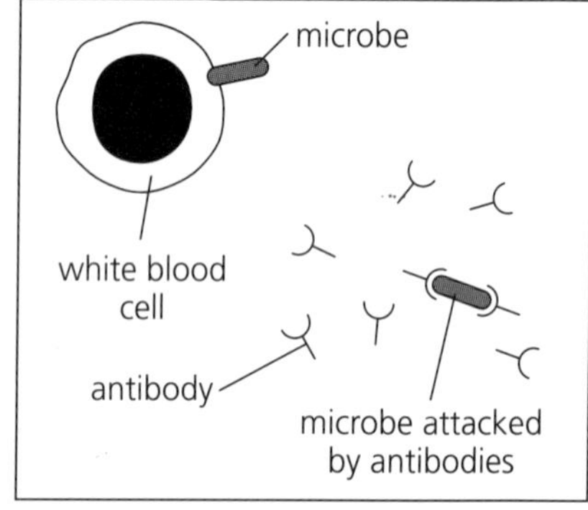

Now do this

1. If the skin is damaged, how does the body continue to protect itself?
2. What is an antibody?

Immunity

If you get a new infection you have never met before, it takes time for new antibodies to be made. During this time the microbes multiply and may cause illness or even death.

The good news is, if you survive the first time, the second time round is never so bad, because the body is ready and waiting to make the antibodies. These often kill the microbes before they cause damage.

Immunisation

We can **immunise** ourselves against some illnesses by injecting weakened or dead microbes of an illness into the body. These microbes cannot multiply and make us ill, but they cause the body to make antibodies against them. Later, if the active microbes of the same illness invade, your body can make the antibodies again quickly and stop them causing illness.

Now do this

3. You are going abroad for a holiday. Before you go, you have to have several injections. One is for tetanus.

   Explain how the injection will prevent you getting tetanus while you are on holiday.

Replacing body parts

Sometimes we have illnesses which lead to organs not working properly, for example kidney or heart failure. Sometimes it is possible to remove such an organ and replace it with a healthy one from another person. These operations are called **transplants**. Unfortunately the body sees the new organs as antigens, and produces antibodies against them. The new organ is rejected.

Another word for microbes and other foreign materials in your body is **antigen**.

To prevent this, organs are very closely matched before being transplanted, and the patient is treated with drugs which 'turn down' their body's defence system. If it is turned down too far, the patient is in danger of being unable to fight any infections they might meet.

Alcohol and drugs

A healthy person is more than someone who is free from disease. Other things apart from disease can affect your health and ability to cope with life. Tiredness can make your reaction times slower which is a problem when you are driving and need to react quickly to events on the road. Alcohol and some other drugs have the same effect, even if you only take them in very small quantities.

Too much alcohol can also damage you in other ways:
- alcohol slows down brain activity and too much can slow it down so much that you pass out
- too much alcohol over a long period can permanently damage your brain and poison your liver.

Solvents such as glue and aerosol propellant also slow down brain activity, sometimes so much that the user dies.

Smoking

Smoking tobacco can be very harmful to your health in several ways:
- the nicotine in tobacco makes the cilia in the trachea stop moving so that they no longer push dirt and mucus out of the lungs. This can lead to lung infections and smoker's cough.
- nicotine can make arteries narrow which puts more pressure on the heart and can lead to heart attacks.

Now do this

4 State **two** things which can be done to help prevent a transplanted organ being rejected.

5 Explain why smoking makes someone more likely to get lung infections.

6 Explain why alcohol, drugs or tiredness may affect your reaction time.

Exam questions

1 Look at the diagram. It shows the digestive system.

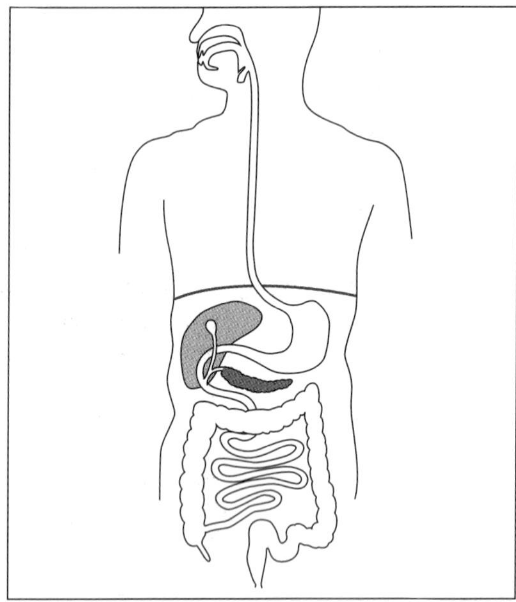

a On the diagram label the liver, pancreas and stomach. [3]

b The absorption of food into the blood occurs in the villi. Draw an X on the diagram to show where the villi are found. [1]

c Give **two** ways in which villi are specialised for absorption. [2]

d Kim had fish and chips to eat. Fill in the table to show the main changes to this food in his digestive system. The first one is done for you.

Food	Nutrient	Broken down to
fish	protein	*amino acids*
chips	starch	
chips	fat	

[3]

e Explain how bile helps in the digestion of one of these nutrients. [3]

f Name the group of chemicals which cause foods to be broken down. [1]

[13 marks]

2 The blood provides a transport system for the body.

a List **three** things that the blood transports around the body. [3]

b Describe the main events which occur when you cut yourself. [4]

c Look at the diagrams. They show a blood cell attacking bacteria at the site of a cut.

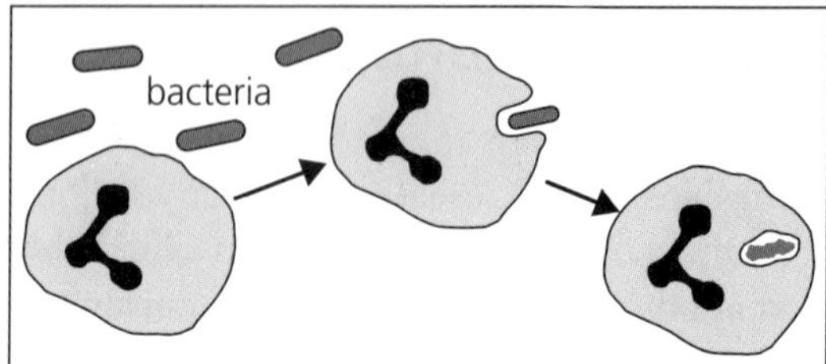

Which type of blood cell is shown in the diagram? [1]

d Use the diagram to help you explain how the blood cell gets rid of bacteria. [2]

Jenny is just recovering from the flu. A close look at her blood shows it contains lots of flu antibodies.

e What is an antibody? [1]

f Explain how Jenny's antibodies have been produced. [2]

[13 marks]

3 Max has just passed his driving test and decided to celebrate with a few friends. The table shows the concentration of alcohol in Max's blood during the celebrations.

Time	Alcohol (mg per 100 cm^3 blood)
5 pm	70
6 pm	100
7 pm	210
8 pm	180
9 pm	140
10 pm	90
11 pm	50

a Use the information in the table to draw a line graph.

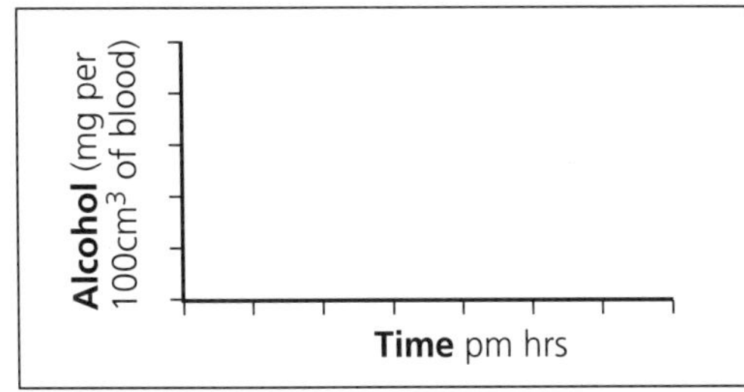

[3]

b Give **one** reason why it is unsafe to drive with alcohol in your blood. [1]

c Long term alcohol abuse can seriously damage your health.

Explain **one** way in which alcohol may do this. [2]

[6 marks]

4 Julia has been feeling very tired and generally unwell. Her doctor tested her urine and found it contained glucose which suggested that she had diabetes. Eventually she learnt to control the diabetes with injections of insulin.

a What is insulin? [1]

b Suggest why insulin needs to be injected rather than taken by mouth? [1]

c Where in the body is insulin normally produced? [1]

d Insulin and glucagon are both concerned with homeostasis. Explain what homeostasis is using the actions of insulin and glucagon as an example. [5]

[8 marks]

5 Look at the drawing of a section through the eye.

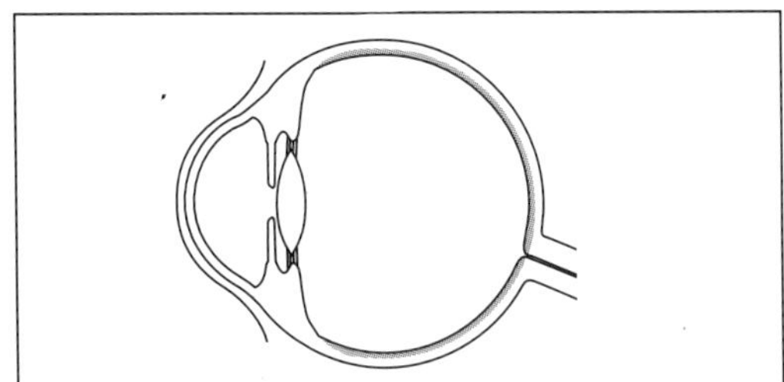

a Lee has to wear contact lenses. Show on the drawing where abouts the contact lens would be worn. [1]

b Which part of the eye is sensitive to light? [1]

c Describe how the eye works. [4]

Sometimes Lee has to wear his glasses which have the same frames as his brother Joe. Lee is short sighted but his brother is long sighted.

d Explain how Lee's glasses differ from those of his brother. [2]

e Explain what is meant by short sighted, and suggest one reason why it might occur. [2]

[10 marks]

6 Brenda accidentally touches a hot pot from the oven. She moves her hand away, very quickly. The diagram shows the pathway involved.

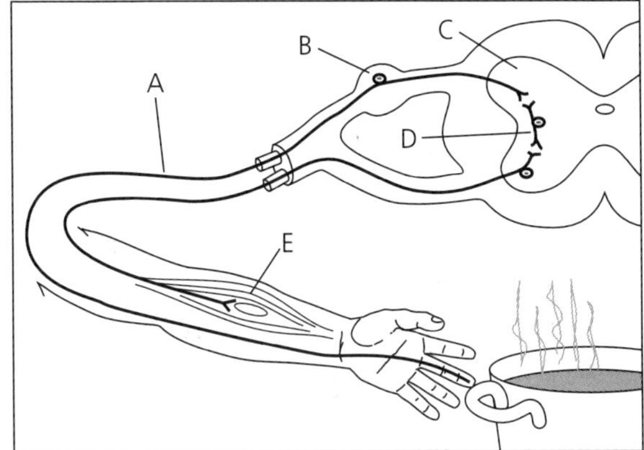

a Which label shows the sensory neuron? [1]

b Which label shows the effector? [1]

c Describe the nerve pathway which allows her to react so quickly. [3]

Brenda's reaction was a reflex action.

d Give **two** other examples of reflex actions. [2]

[7 marks]

7 Look at the table. It shows the composition of the gases which a person breathes in and out.

Gas	Air in	Air out
	21 %	16 %
carbon dioxide	0.04 %	4 %
nitrogen	78 %	78 %
water vapour	variable	saturated

a One of the boxes in the table has been left empty.

Suggest what should be written in the box. [1]

b Which gas does not change during breathing? [1]

c Describe fully how movements of the ribcage and diaphragm result in ventilation of the lungs. [5]

[7 marks]

8 Look at the table. It shows the energy value of certain foods.

Food	Energy (kJ in 100 g food)
bacon	940
baked beans	270
mashed potatoes	340
pasta	1400
sausages	1200

a Which **two** foods have the most energy? [2]

b Simon had sausage (200 g), bacon (100 g) and baked beans (150 g) for his breakfast.

Calculate how much energy his breakfast contained. [2]

c Our bodies release the stored energy in food.

i Name the process that releases this energy. [1]

ii Name **two** substances in addition to energy, which are produced by this process. [2]

[7 marks]

9 Sarah was doing a sponsored run around the school field. By the time she reached the fifth lap she was aware of certain changes in her body.

a List **three** changes in her body you would expect her to notice. [3]

b For each change explain how the exercise might have caused it. [3]

c Sarah had to start walking on the sixth lap because she developed cramp in her leg muscles. Suggest what might be causing the cramp? [1]

d When Sarah finally stopped she had developed an oxygen debt. What do you understand by the term 'oxygen debt'? [3]

[10 marks]

10 Look at the diagram of a section through a human heart.

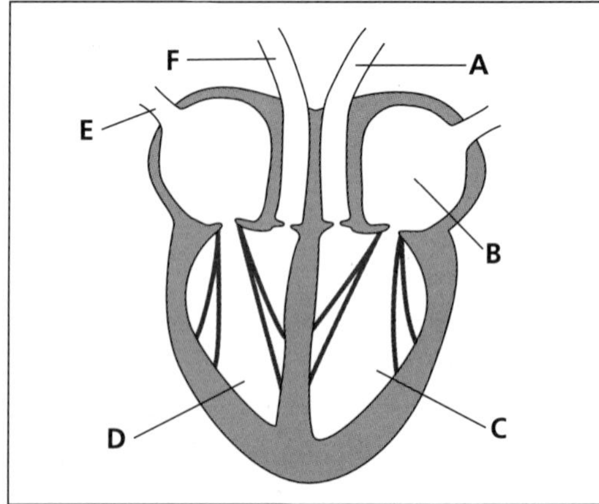

a Name the chamber labelled D. [1]

b Which labelled blood vessel contains oxygenated blood? [1]

c State whether the blood in each of the vessels E and F is flowing towards the heart or away from the heart. [2]

d What is the function of the valve between chambers B and C? [2]

[6 marks]

11 The figure shows how we control our body temperature.

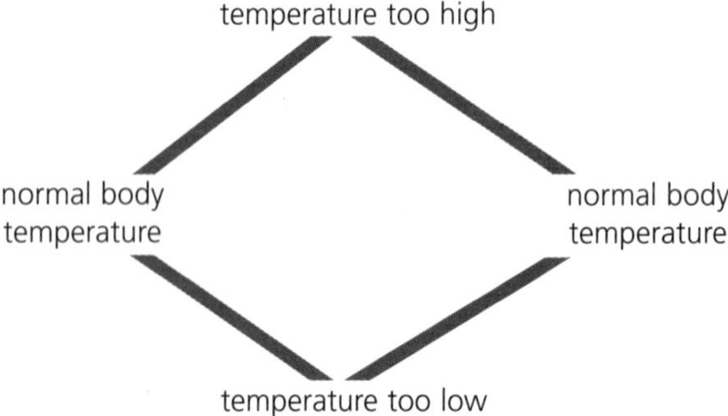

a Draw an arrow head on the end of each line to show how temperature control is achieved. [2]

b Which part of the body detects changes in the body temperature? [1]

Sonil went for a swim, leaving his friends sunbathing on the beach. Later he came back to sit with them, but he soon started to shiver and feel cold.

c Suggest why the wet Sonil feels cold although his friends feel warm. [2]

[5 marks]

Green plants as organisms

You will have met most of these ideas in the units *Controlling change*, *Staying alive*, *Balancing acts* and *Energy for today and tomorrow*. This section is divided into three topics.

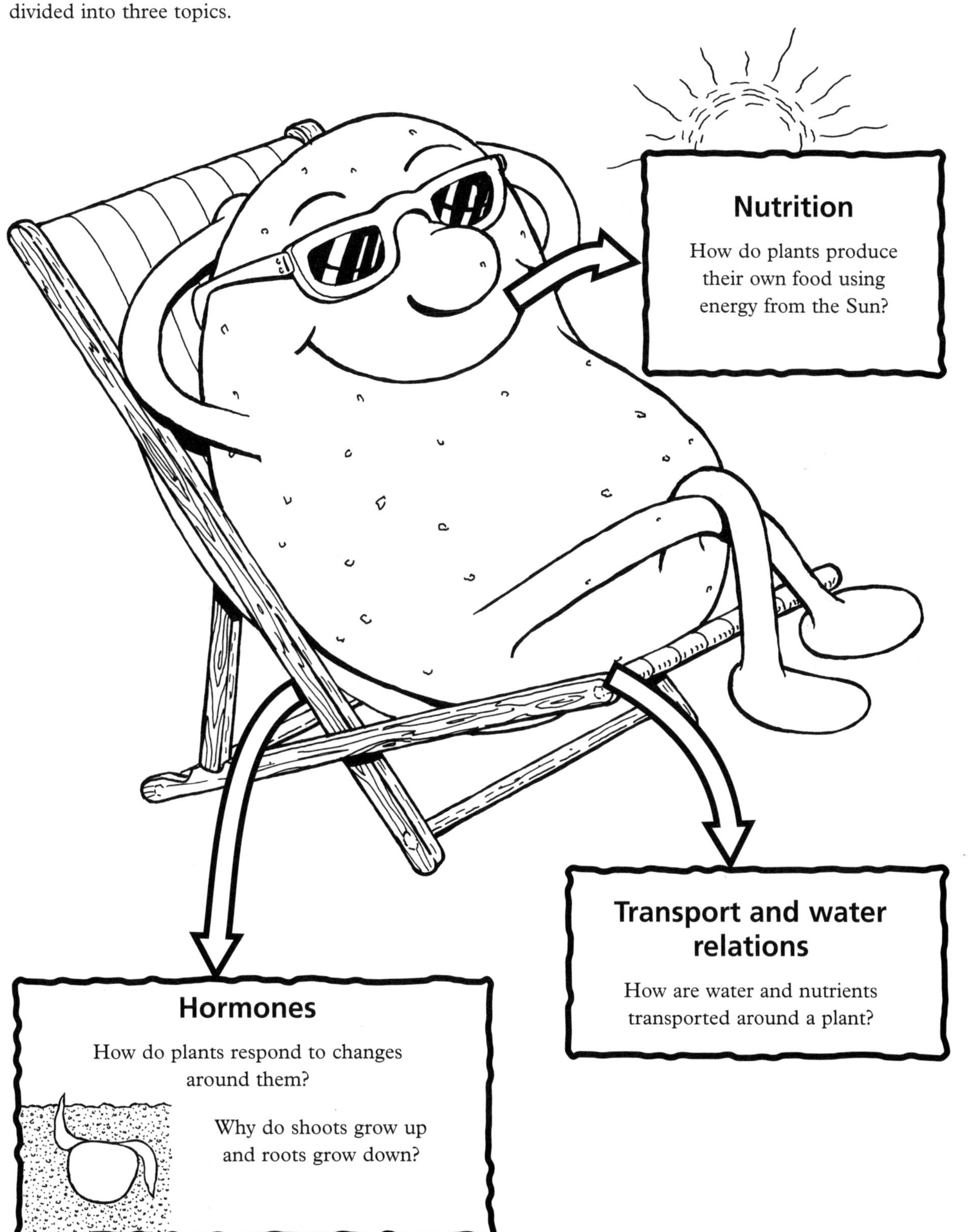

Nutrition

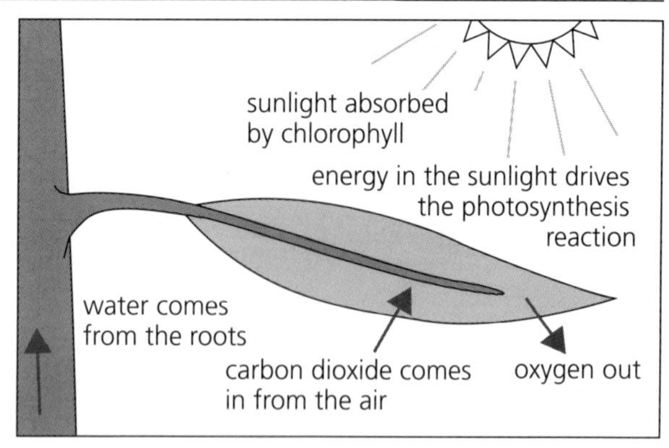

Plants make their own food by **photosynthesis**. In photosynthesis, carbon dioxide and water react together to form sugar (glucose) and oxygen. This reaction needs a supply of energy. Sunlight supplies the energy.

The green **chlorophyll** in plant leaves absorbs some of the energy from sunlight and uses it to 'drive' photosynthesis. Photosynthesis can be summed up in the equations:

REACTANTS			**PRODUCTS**	
carbon dioxide	**+ water**	→	**glucose**	**+ oxygen**
$6CO_2$	$+ 6H_2O$	→	$C_6H_{12}O_6$	$+ 6O_2$

If all the glucose is not needed immediately by the plant, it forms starch which can be stored. Starch is a polymer made of small glucose molecules joined together to make a large molecule. If glucose is needed in another part of the plant, it can be transported there.

glucose soluble + glucose soluble + glucose soluble → starch insoluble

Animals cannot make their own food and so they must eat plants or other animals. Therefore sunlight is the ultimate source of energy for *all* living things.

Now do this

1. Lions depend on sunlight for their food. Explain why.
2. Explain why we test leaves for starch to see if photosynthesis has taken place.

Speeding up photosynthesis

- The more carbon dioxide there is the faster photosynthesis happens because carbon dioxide is one of the reactants.
- The more light there is the faster photosynthesis happens because the energy of the light is used to drive the photosynthesis reaction. The colour of the light is also important. Most plants appear green because they reflect green light. This means green light is not absorbed or used to drive photosynthesis. Red and blue light are absorbed, therefore these colours are the most important ones for photosynthesis.
- The higher the temperature is, the faster photosynthesis occurs.
- Supplies of mineral elements such as nitrogen, potassium and phosphorus help plants to use the products of photosynthesis more efficiently.

In short supply?

If carbon dioxide, light or warmth are in short supply they limit the rate at which photosynthesis can happen. They are called **limiting factors**.

On a hot, sunny day the temperature is usually high enough and there is plenty of light for photosynthesis to take place. In these conditions, the rate of photosynthesis will depend on how much carbon dioxide there is. Carbon dioxide is the limiting factor.

On a hot, sunny day a plant will photosynthesise more quickly than on a cold, dull day. Plants grow faster in the summer because they can photosynthesise more food.

Where do proteins come from?

Photosynthesis makes glucose and starch. These are called **carbohydrates**. However, all living things need proteins, and plants need nitrogen to make these.

Plants are surrounded by nitrogen gas in the air, but it is so unreactive that most plants cannot use it. Instead they absorb **nitrates** dissolved in water from the soil. They then use the nitrogen from the nitrates to make proteins.

carbohydrates from photosynthesis + nitrogen from soil nitrates → protein

Healthy plants must have a supply of nitrates in their soil. To make sure the soil contains enough nitrates for crops we can use a fertiliser.

Fertilisers

Fertilisers contain three main chemicals, nitrates, phosphates and potassium compounds.

Plants need these chemicals for healthy growth. They are often called plant **nutrients**.

Nutrient	Job in the plant
nitrate	growth of leaves and stems
phosphate	healthy root growth
potassium	healthy leaves and flowers

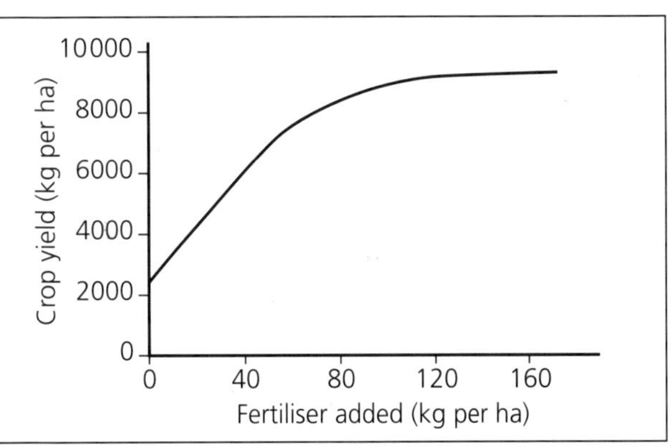

Farmers use fertilisers to help their plants to grow big and healthy. So fertilisers increase the amount of crop produced (crop yield).

A good fertiliser must be:

- cheap and easy to transport
- soluble enough for the plant to absorb it, but not too soluble that it will wash away with the first heavy rains
- easy to apply
- not too smelly.

Plants also require very small amounts of minerals such as magnesium which they need to produce chlorophyll. Tiny amounts of these may also be included in fertilisers.

??? Now do this

3 Do plants photosynthesise at night? Explain your answer.

4 Name **four** substances a plant must absorb from the soil.

5 Explain why a farmer is likely to need to fertilise a field used for growing wheat.

On the move

Water

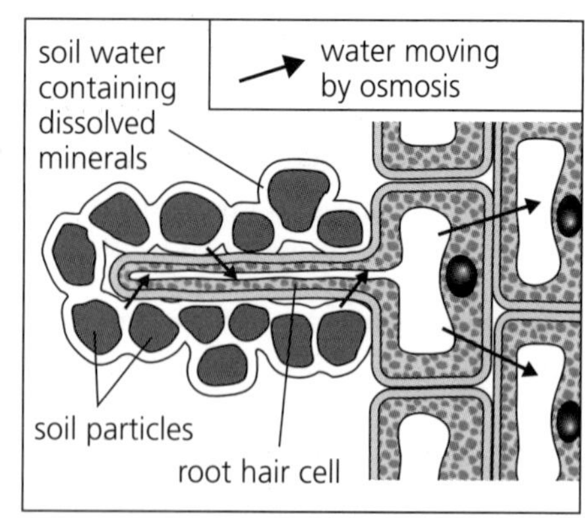

Plants need water for photosynthesis. They also need it for transporting things like auxins and minerals around the plant.

Water enters the plant through specialised cells in its roots called **root hair cells**.

Root hair cells are good at taking up water and nutrients from the soil because they are:

- long and thin and have a large surface area
- have thin walls to help water to pass through.

Water moves into the root hair cells by **osmosis** which is a special type of diffusion in which water moves from an area of high water concentration to an area of low water concentration through a **partially permeable membrane**. Cell membranes are partially permeable and allow water to pass through them during osmosis.

Inside the plant, the water moves across the root by osmosis and is then transported by the **xylem vessels**. These are long tubes which take water to all parts of the plant. They are made up of dead cells with strengthened walls. They also help to support the plant.

Another part of the plant's transport system is the **phloem**. It transports soluble substances such as sucrose and amino acids from the leaves where they are made to where they are needed for growth.

The effect of osmosis can be demonstrated using two identical potato chips. Osmosis depends on differences in concentration. A potato chip left in water will swell as water passes into its cells by osmosis. The other piece of potato left in concentrated sugar solution shrinks as water passes out of the cells by osmosis.

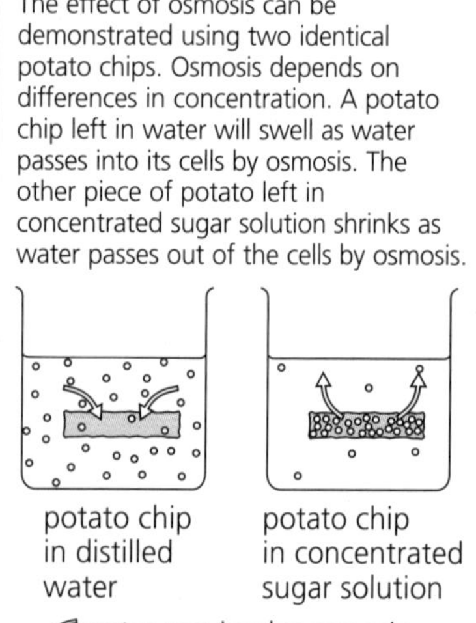

Going up!

Plants do not have a pump to keep water moving up through their xylem vessels. Water is 'sucked' up the xylem by **transpiration**.

This is what happens in transpiration:

- water evaporates from the leaf into the surrounding air
- water sucked up through the xylem replaces the water lost from the leaf by evaporation
- water from the roots replaces water lost from the xylem.

Water constantly moves through the plant.

The amount of water leaving the leaf is controlled by small holes called **stomata**. Stomata can open or close by changing the shape of their **guard cells**.

top surface of leaf
waterproof cuticle
upper epidermis
palisade layer has lots of chloroplasts, full of chlorophyll
air space
spongy layer
vein
lower epidermis
underside of leaf
stoma – mainly on the underside to reduce water loss
waterproof cuticle
movement of water

Stomata allow carbon dioxide for photosynthesis to enter the plant. Photosynthesis increases on a hot sunny day and so the stomata will be open. But this lets water out, so to prevent excessive water loss, most stomata are on the underside of a leaf.

Now do this

1 Explain why raw potato chips increase in mass when they are left in distilled water but decrease in mass when they are left in a concentrated salt solution.

2 Why does a plant need more water on a sunny day?

Hormones

Plants can detect changes in their surroundings. They respond to these changes by growing in different ways. This growth is controlled by chemicals called **auxins**. Auxins are produced in shoot and root tips. Then they are transported through the plant dissolved in water. Auxins are plant **hormones** because they act as chemical messengers.

Auxins affect cell growth and development to control:
- growth of shoots and roots
- flowering
- ripening of fruit.

How do plants grow?

The shoots of a plant always grow towards the light. This is called **phototropism**. To make a plant grow towards the light, auxins are made at the tip of the shoot. They diffuse down the shaded side causing it to grow faster, resulting in the tip bending over towards the light.

'Photo' means light and 'tropism' means growth.

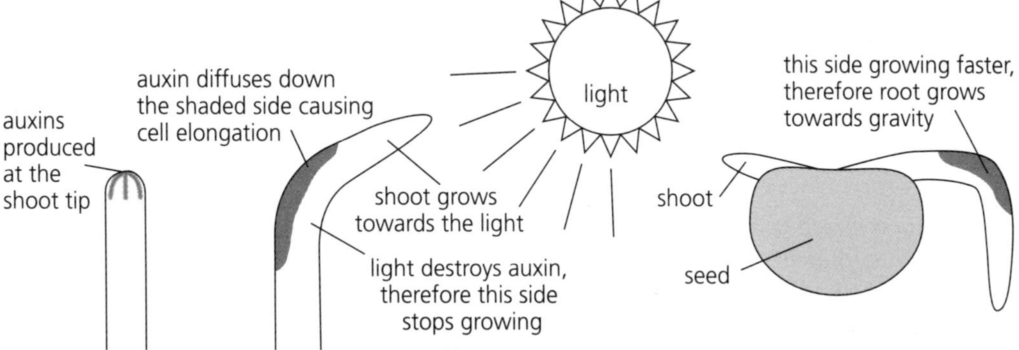

Plant roots always grow downwards in the direction of gravity. They need to do this to find the water the plant needs and to anchor the plant in the ground.

Roots are **geotropic** because they grow towards gravity.

Now do this

3 Give **two** uses of auxins in plants.

4 Name **two** stimuli plants respond to. Explain why it is important that plants can respond to these stimuli.

5 Why do bulbs planted upside down still grow into normal plants.

Using plant hormones

We use synthetic auxins to trick plants and make them behave in ways which are more convenient for us. For example, it can take plants a long time to produce young new plants naturally. So, we cut the shoots off plants and dip the cut end in auxins to make them grow roots. Gardeners use auxins, known as rooting powder, to make new plants. Because they are cuttings of the original plant they are also genetically identical and will have exactly the same characteristics as the parent plant.

Exam questions

1 Sonny cut five cylinders from a piece of raw rhubarb. Each cylinder was 50 mm long and 5 mm in diameter. Each cylinder was placed in a sugar solution of different concentration. After 12 hours the length of each cylinder was measured again. Sonny's results are shown below.

Concentration of sugar solution (mol per dm³)	0	0.2	0.4	0.6	0.8
Length of cylinder after 12 hrs (mm)	53.3	52.0	48.2	46.1	44.9
Change in length (mm)	+3.3	+2.0	−1.8		−5.1

a Calculate the change in length for the cylinder in the 0.6 mol sugar solution and complete the table. [1]

b Plot a graph to show the changes in length of the rhubarb cylinders in the different concentrations of sugar solution. [4]

c Use the graph to work out the concentration of sugar solution which would cause **no** change in the length of the cylinders. [1]

d Explain the process which causes the change in size of the rhubarb cylinders. [4]

[10 marks]

2 a The following equation for photosynthesis is not complete. Fill in the blanks.

$? + H_2O \rightarrow C_6H_{12}O_6 + ?$ [2]

b Name the **two** other requirements for photosynthesis to occur. [2]

c Name the transport system which moves the products of photosynthesis around the plant. [1]

d Describe an experiment to show that the rate of photosynthesis in a water plant is affected by the wavelength of light. You may include a diagram in your answer. [5]

Look at the following graph. It shows the rate of photosynthesis of the same plant at different temperatures and carbon dioxide concentrations.

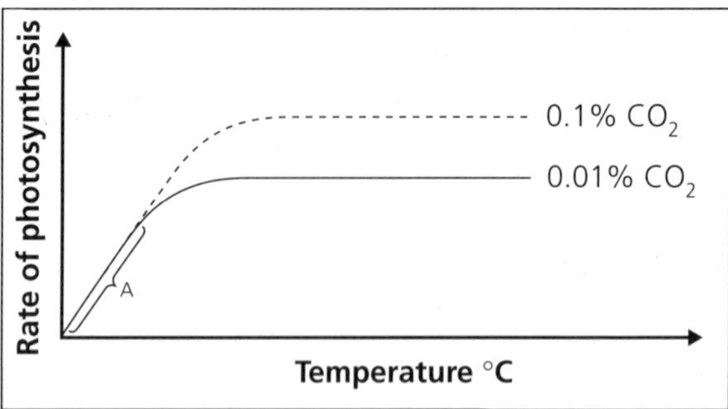

e What do you understand by the term limiting factor? [1]

f Explain what is acting as a limiting factor at point A on the graph. [1]

[12 marks]

3 a Explain how plants respond to changes in their environment. [3]

Gerry helped his sister plant lots of bulbs for the spring. Gerry was not sure which was the top and the bottom of the bulb and he was worried that many of them were planted upside down. His sister explained that it would not matter, the bulbs would still grow.

b Explain how a bulb is able to grow when it is planted upside down. [2]

Look at the diagrams. They show some seedlings growing.

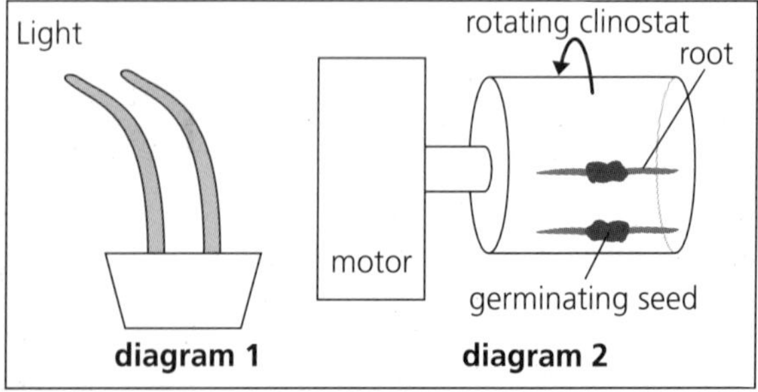

c Describe the role of auxin in the growth shown in diagram 1. [3]

d Suggest how the rotating clinostat is causing the response shown in diagram 2. [2]

Auxins are now used commercially for a number of different jobs.

e Describe one commercial use of auxins. [2]

[12 marks]

Variation, inheritance and evolution

You will have met these ideas in the units *Evolution* and *Balancing acts*. This section is divided into four spreads.

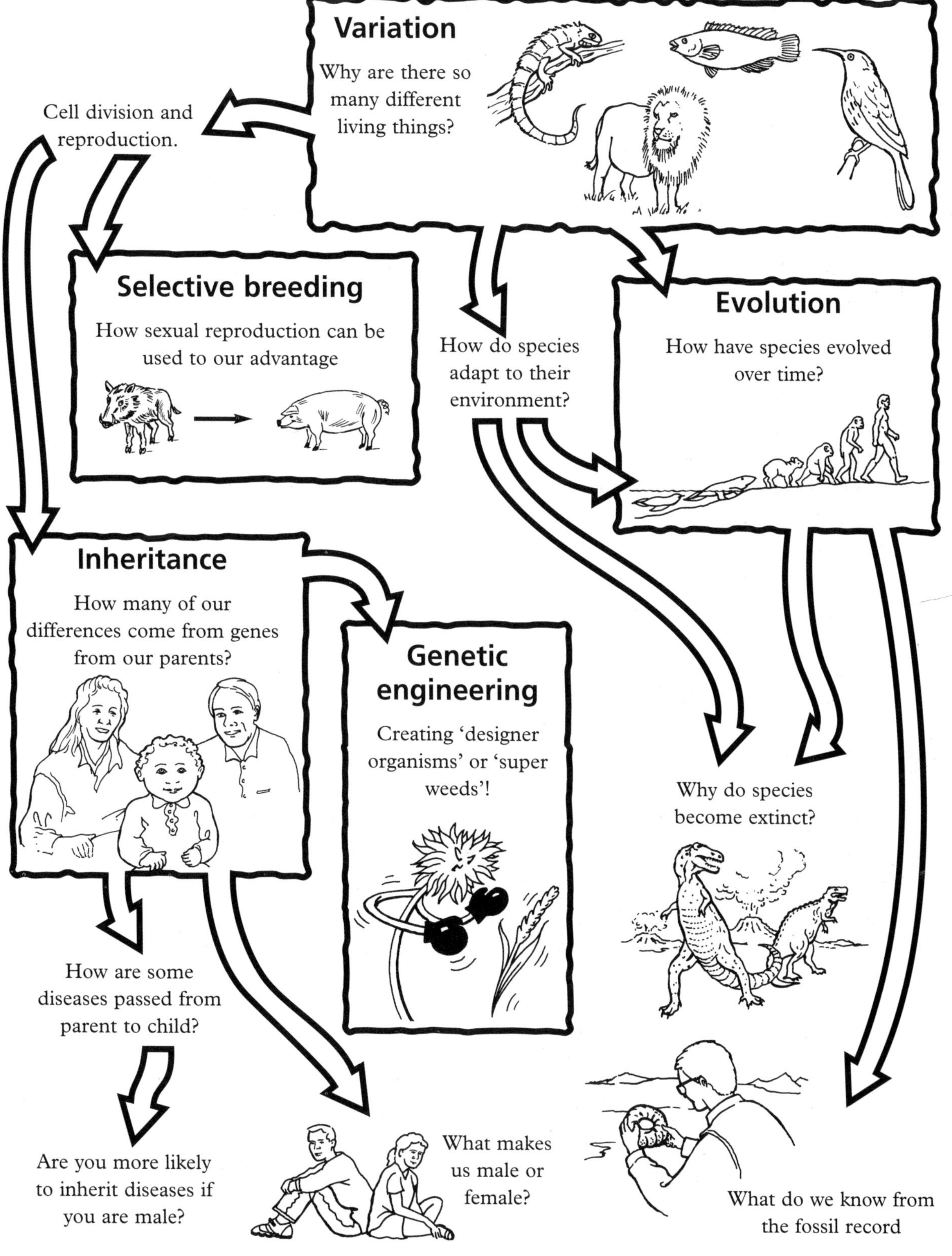

Variation

Variety, the spice of life

Living things can be divided into groups called **species**. A species is a group of organisms which can mate to produce fertile offspring. Members of a species all look fairly similar, but there can be a lot of differences between them. Look at these different members of the dog species.

The difference is called **variation**.

There are **two** main causes of variation:

- **hereditary** – differences caused by the information we inherit from our parents, this controls things like eye colour, sex, blood group
- **environmental** – differences caused by the conditions in which we grow up, this controls things like hair style, tattoos, pierced ears.

Inherited differences

Inherited differences are found in species which **reproduce** sexually. (When plants and animals reproduce they make new plant and animals – offspring – like themselves.)

In **asexual reproduction** one parent produces offspring which are identical to the parent. For example, spider plants and strawberries both grow runners with new plants on them.

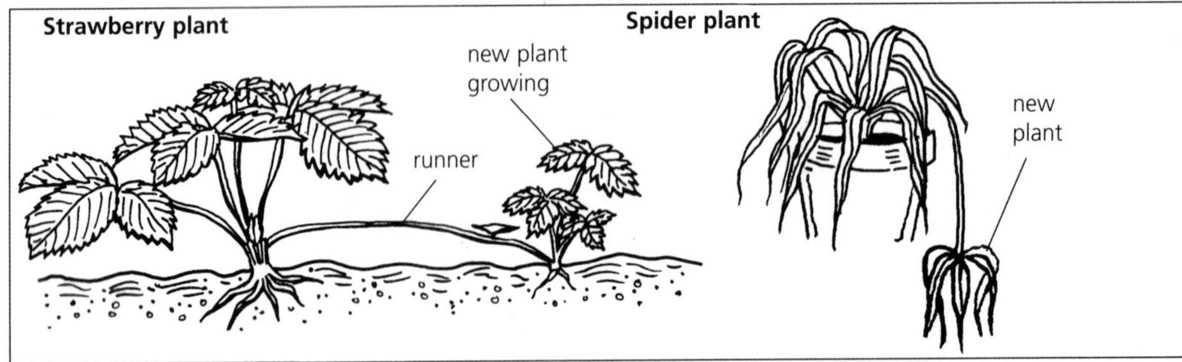

In **sexual reproduction** two parents are involved. One produces the male sex cells (**gametes**) and the other the female gametes. During sexual reproduction the male and female gametes join together at **fertilisation** to form a **zygote** which develops into the offspring. The offspring are **not** identical to the parents.

The result of sexual reproduction is offspring who are similar but not identical to their parents. This is because they have a mix of characteristics from both parents. We say that they **inherit** these characteristics.

Inherited information

The information which shapes our characteristics is carried in the nucleus of all cells. The nucleus of a cell contains **chromosomes**.

Each species of plant or animal has a different number of chromosomes in their cells. Human body cells have 46, arranged in 23 pairs.

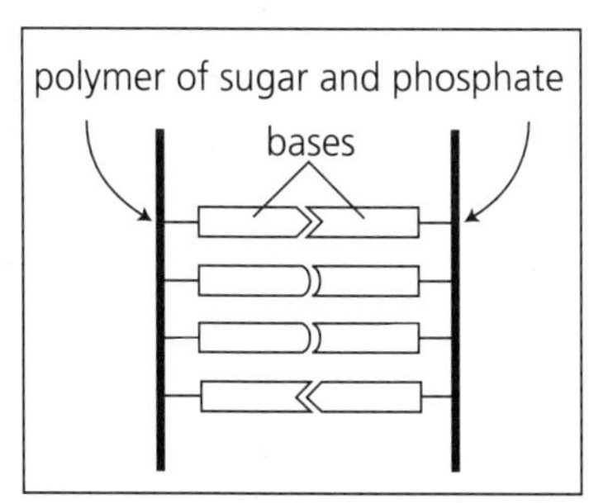

Chromosomes are made of very long polymer molecules called **DNA** (deoxyribonucleic acid). DNA has two long chains of sugar and phosphate molecules linked by pairs of **bases**. Different pairs of bases make up a code to control chemical reactions in the cell. Each chromosome is divided into thousands of sections called **genes**. One set of genes controls eye colour, another hair colour and so on.

The gametes which made you carried some of your parents' genes which mixed together at fertilisation. So you may have similar characteristics to your parents, but in different combinations.

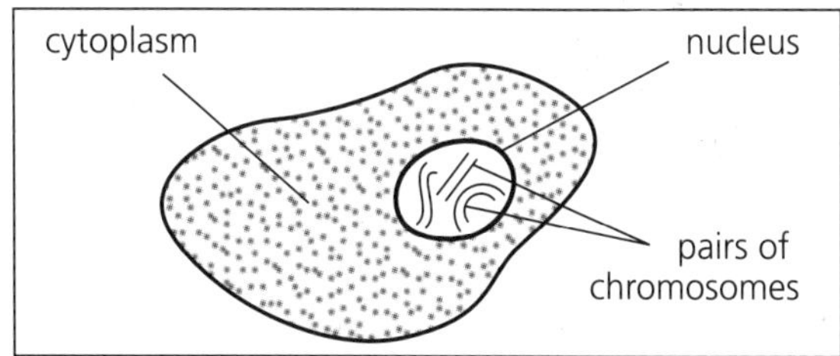

Environmental variation

Your characteristics are also affected by your environment. For example, inherited information may make you tall, but if you are well fed as a child you may be even taller. Your intelligence and sporting ability may also be a combination of hereditary and environmental factors.

Plants are also changed by their environment. If an acorn is planted in open ground it will be a large tree after 20 years. If it is planted in a Bonsai pot with its shoots and roots cut back every year it will be a miniature one.

Now do this

1 What is a species?

2 Name the **two** causes of variation and give an example of each type.

3 Describe the structure of a chromosome.

Inheritance

Cell division

In asexual reproduction cells divide by **mitosis**. Mitosis results in the production of two cells which are genetically identical to the original parent cell. Therefore this type of cell division is also used for growth and repair.

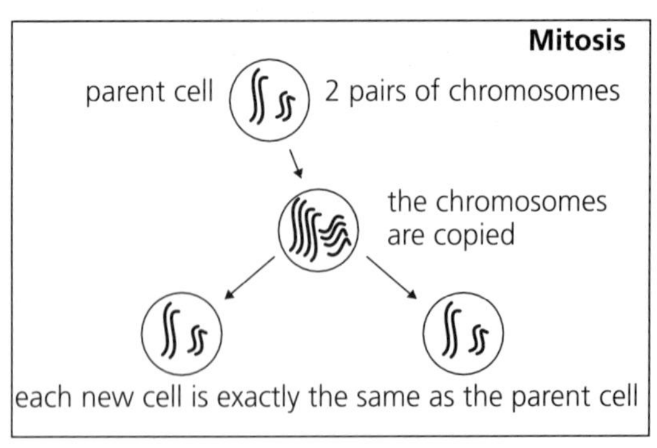

In sexual reproduction gametes are produced by **meiosis**. Meiosis produces gamete cells with only *half* the number of chromosomes of ordinary cells. The pairs of chromosomes split so each gamete has one half of a pair.

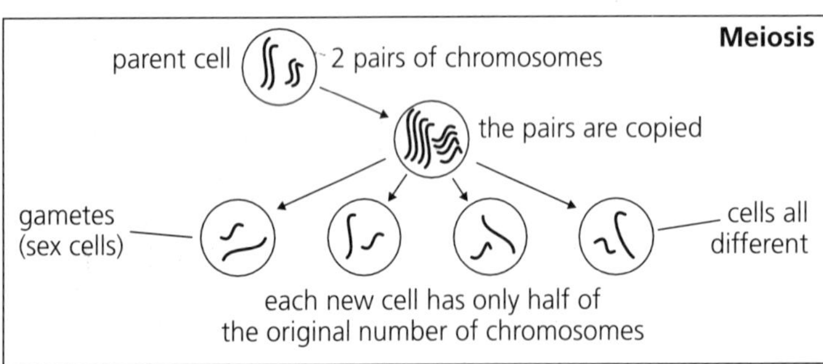

A human gamete has only 23 chromosomes. When male and female gametes fuse at fertilisation the zygote has a full set of 46 chromosomes.

haploid = half the chromosome number

diploid = the full chromosome number

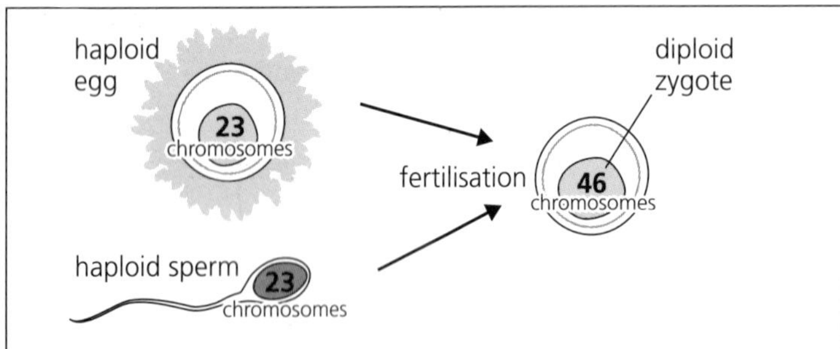

Now do this

1 A cat cell has 38 chromosomes. How many chromosomes do its gametes contain?

Meiosis leads to variety

Meiosis leads to a large number of different gametes. For example, if a cell contained just three pairs of chromosomes, it could produce eight different gametes.

Remember – gametes are haploid, they only contain one of each pair of chromosomes.

We have 23 pairs of chromosomes so just imagine how many different combinations we might have!

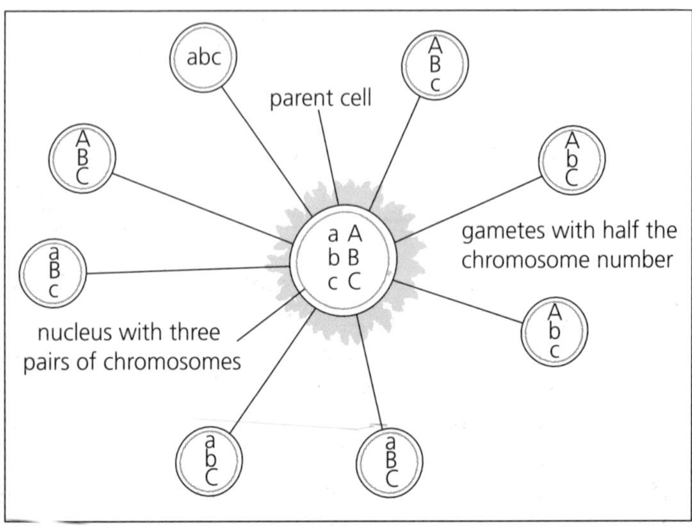

Passing on genes

Each chromosome in most pairs carries genes for the same characteristics. So you carry two genes for every characteristic, one on the chromosome from your mother and the other on the chromosome from your father.

Many genes have several different versions called **alleles**. For example, there are blue and brown alleles for eye colour. Each chromosome in a pair might have a different allele of a gene.

If you inherit a blue allele from each parent you will have blue eyes. But if you inherit one blue allele and one brown allele you will have brown eyes because the brown allele is 'stronger' than the blue one. Strong alleles are called **dominant** and the weak alleles are called **recessive**. We show a dominant allele by a capital letter and a recessive allele by a small letter. For eye colour, we can represent the dominant brown allele as B and the recessive blue allele as b. If both the alleles are the same, BB or bb, the individual is called **homozygous**. If the alleles are different, Bb, the individual is called **heterozygous**.

The alleles you inherit are called your **genotype**. How you look because of this is called your **phenotype**. A person with the phenotype of blue eyes can only have one genotype, bb. A person with the phenotype of brown eyes could have a genotype of BB or Bb. If you know the genotype of the parents you can work out what their offspring's phenotypes are likely to be. For example, if one parent is BB for brown eyes and the other is bb for blue eyes, we can work out the possible combinations of their alleles with a genetic diagram, **a**.

a genetic diagram for cross of two parents homozygous for brown and blue eyes

Gametes	B	B
b	Bb	Bb
b	Bb	Bb

all offspring have brown eyes

b genetic diagram for cross of two parents heterozygous for brown eyes

Gametes	B	b
B	BB	bB
b	Bb	bb

three brown-eyed, one blue-eyed offspring

Genetic diagram **b** shows the offspring of one of these children with another Bb individual.

Working out the probabilities

The way a characteristic is inherited can be studied by breeding two individuals and observing the characteristics in their offspring. This is called a **monohybrid cross** because it only follows the inheritance of one characteristic. We can make predictions about the probable outcome of a monohybrid cross.

The probability of two brown eyed people with the Bb genotype producing a blue eyed bb child is 1 in 4, or 25 %. This means that when they have a child, there is a 25 % chance that it will have blue eyes.

Deciding a baby's sex

One pair of your chromosomes decides your sex. There are two types of sex chromosome, the **X chromosome** and the **Y chromosome**. Gametes have either an X or a Y chromosome. If two gametes with X chromosomes fuse the offspring is female (**XX**). If a gamete with an X and one with a Y fuse the offspring is male (**XY**).

??? Now do this

2 Explain what ratio of offspring would be expected from a cross between a blue eyed and a heterozygous brown eyed individual.

3 Tongue rolling is an inherited characteristic. The 'tongue rolling' allele is dominant (T). Draw a genetic diagram to show the offspring of a Tt mother and a tt father.

Genes in action

Sex linkage

When an allele is on the X chromosome it is said to be **sex linked**. Some recessive alleles on the X chromosome are responsible for inherited human disorders such as red-green colour blindness and haemophilia.

Gametes	X	X^C
X	XX	X^CX
Y	XY	X^CY

X Normal X chromosome

X^C Chromosome with allele for colour blindness

Y Normal Y chromosome

A female has two X chromosomes therefore she can have three different genotypes relating to colour blindness:

- XX normal female
- X^cX carrier female with normal phenotype
- X^cX^c colour blind female

However a male has only one X chromosome and so he can only have two different genotypes:

- XY normal male
- X^cY colour blind male

A female can carry a recessive allele on one of her X chromosomes without being affected. However if a male has the allele on his X chromosome, he will have the disorder. For example a normal sighted woman carrying one allele for colour blindness (X^cX) and her unaffected partner (XY) can have a colour blind son (X^cY) (see above).

Haemophilia is a disorder where your blood does not clot properly. There are two alleles for blood clotting – one normal and one faulty. They only appear on the X chromosome. The normal one is dominant.

A male has only one X chromosome and if it has the faulty allele he suffers from haemophilia. Females have two X chromosomes and so have two alleles for blood clotting. If they have a normal one it will 'override' the faulty one. This is why it is rare for females to have haemophilia.

Now do this

1. What is meant by a 'sex linked' disorder?
2. Explain how two normal parents could produce a son with haemophilia.
3. Explain whether these parents could also produce a daughter with haemophilia.

Artificial selection

We take advantage of variation when we **selectively breed** animals and plants. This involves picking those individuals with the characteristics we want and breeding them. The best offspring are selected and bred. This is repeated over many generations to establish a genetically stable breeding pool.

We selectively breed for many reasons. In animals we may want better yields of milk or meat, less aggression or a more attractive appearance. In plants we may want better yields of grain or fruit, better flavour or resistance to disease.

Genetic engineering

Selective breeding involves sexual reproduction. It is therefore time consuming and unreliable because we cannot control which genes a gamete contains. The random combination of chromosomes during meiosis gives rise to genetic variation, which might produce offspring without the desired characteristics. It is also limited to living things within the same species. This means that you cannot breed a cow with a giraffe for example to try and produce a long necked cow able to feed over hedges! Genetic engineering involves the transfer of genetic material (DNA) from one organism to another. Genes from one species can be placed inside the cells of a different species, and the outcome is known.

Genetic engineering in action

1 The desired gene is identified.

2 The gene is removed and isolated using special enzymes (which act like scissors).

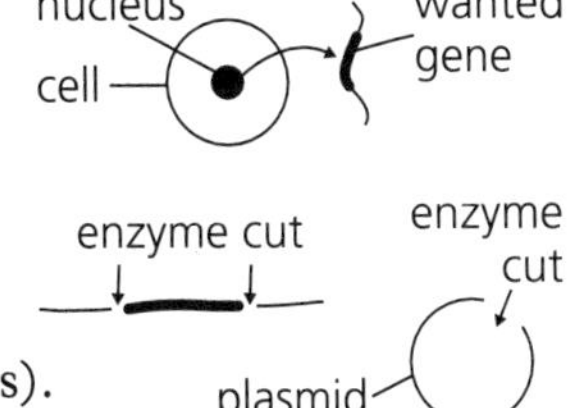

3 The gene is joined to a circular piece of DNA from a bacterium. This is called a plasmid.

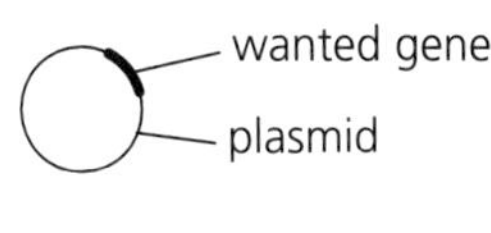

4 The plasmid containing the gene is taken up by bacteria.

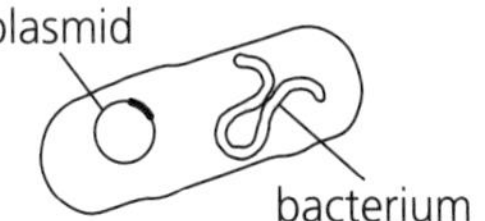

When the bacteria breed, they make lots of bacteria each containing a copy of the plasmid and the gene. The gene is then collected and inserted into the genetic material of the host organism.

Inserting the gene for human insulin into a microbe has led to microbes capable of producing large amounts of human insulin.

Crop plants can be given a gene which prevents them being attacked by various insects.

Selective breeding	Genetic engineering
Advantages: • gradually produce living things with more and more desirable characteristics **Disadvantages:** • time consuming • the outcome is not predictable	**Advantages:** • the outcome is known • once set up it is quicker than selective breeding • can be used to make large amounts of insulin which would otherwise be unavailable • can transfer genes from one species to another **Disadvantages:** • expensive to set up and develop • worries about the transferred gene escaping into other species, e.g. crossing into closely related weed species • worries about the effect of eating these genetically altered individuals • ethical worries, including the concern that it may move on to humans, leading to the engineering of selected human characteristics

When a genetically engineered plant cell has been produced, it is made to divide by mitosis to produce a lot of identical cells. These are grown in a sterile, nutrient medium to produce lots of genetically identical (**cloned**) plantlets. This growing procedure is called **micropropagation** and the plants may be used to take cuttings to produce even more genetically identical individuals.

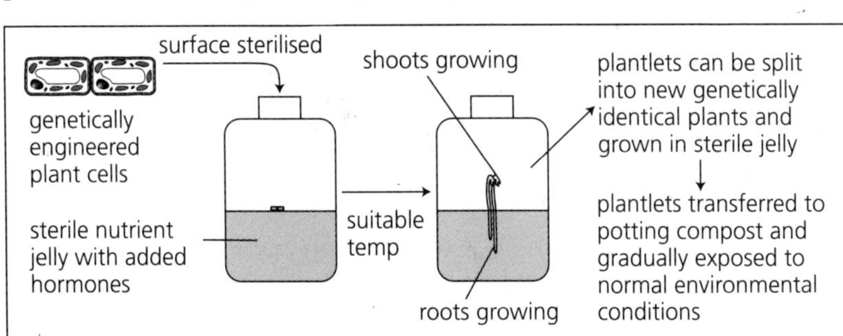

Now do this

4 Explain why selective breeding is still used a lot for animals, but not so much for plants.

5 What does genetic engineering mean?

Evolution

Mutations lead to change

Meiosis makes lots of different combinations possible in the genetic code.

Sometimes there are changes to the genetic code. These changes are called **mutations**.

Some mutations are harmful because the allele they change can no longer work properly. The altered allele producing haemophilia is an example of this. But, some mutations are beneficial. Ionising radiation and some chemicals may increase the probability of genetic mutation.

Mutation to the rescue

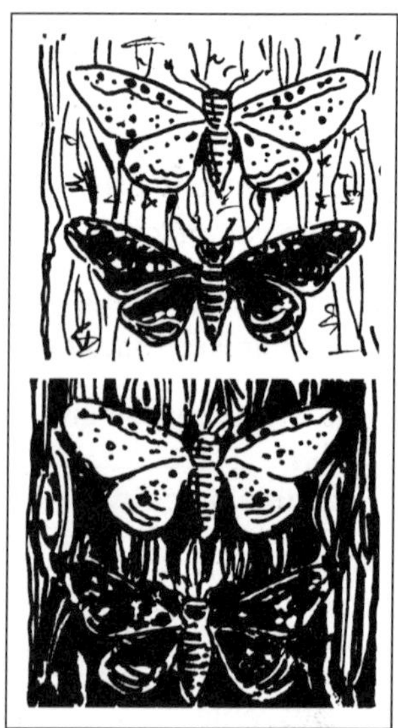

Before the Industrial Revolution trees had pale bark and the pale, peppered moth was well hidden as it rested on the tree trunks.

As the industrial revolution progressed, the bark turned black as it became coated with smoke and soot. The peppered moth was now easily seen and large numbers were eaten by birds.

A chance mutation produced a black peppered moth which could easily hide against the darkened bark. The black peppered moths gradually increased in number because they were more likely to survive and breed, passing the mutant black allele on to their offspring.

By the start of the twentieth century, most of the peppered moths were black – the allele had spread through the population!

What is the link between mutation and evolution?

Animals and plants have gradually developed from much simpler forms over many millions of years. This process is called **evolution**.

Evolution is the result of **natural selection**. This means that those animals and plants that adapt best to their surroundings (environment) will have the best chance of surviving and growing in numbers, just as the black peppered moth did.

The evidence for evolution

We only know about evolution from the fossils that have been found. Fossils are the remains of dead organisms which have become preserved in rock.

The fossil record shows that living things evolve over a very long period of time.

Evolution of the modern horse

	50 million years ago. Small terrier sized animal, avoided predators by hiding behind shrubs and bushes. Non specialised teeth for eating juicy vegetation. Short legs with splayed out toes to enable it to move across the soggy marsh lands.
	Over thousands of years the marshlands and boggy woodlands have dried out to be replaced with vast grasslands. This favoured a change to more specialised teeth designed for grinding tough grass, with a consequent lengthening of the face; speed became important as a means of avoiding predators, therefore this favoured a longer leg with straighter, stiffer backs; the dry, hard grasslands favoured reduction of the splayed foot to a single hoof.

Now do this

1 What is a mutation?
2 Give **one** example of an unwanted mutation, and **one** example of a useful mutation.
3 What does evolution mean?
4 What is a fossil?
5 Explain how the change from pale coloured peppered moths to black ones can be considered an example of natural selection.

Death of a species

Sometimes a species dies out because its environment changes so quickly and drastically that it has no time to adapt. For example, the Dodo was a large flightless bird which lived on an island. It had no predators on the island and flourished there. When people first landed on the island, they discovered that the Dodo was good to eat. They hunted it. Because it could not fly, it could not escape. Soon there were no more Dodos left, they had become **extinct**. They could not adapt quickly enough to the arrival of people.

When we selectively breed organisms we can reduce the amount of genetic variation they contain. This is called reducing their gene pool. If the gene pool becomes too small, any changes in the environment may prove disastrous because there is insufficient variation in the gene pool for the organisms to adapt to the change. Sometimes this happens in the wild, if for example a population becomes very small, there may not be enough variation in the gene pool for the population to adapt to any changes. This is why conservationists are concerned even when it sounds like there is a reasonably large number of breeding pandas left in the wild.

Exam questions

1 Petal shape in poppies is controlled by a single gene with two alleles.

One allele produces smooth, regular shaped petals, and the other allele produces smaller petals with jagged edges.

When a plant breeder crossed the two poppies, all the offspring had smooth regular petals.

a Which of the poppy alleles is dominant? [1]

b Write down what you understand by the term recessive allele. [1]

c Draw a genetic diagram to show the cross the breeder carried out. [4]

d Explain what would be produced if the breeder crossed two of these smooth, regular petal poppies. Use a genetic diagram to help you. [4]

The poppies with the jagged edged petals are very attractive.

e Explain as fully as you can how the breeder could be sure of producing more jagged poppies. [3]

[13 marks]

2 The figure shows a family tree.

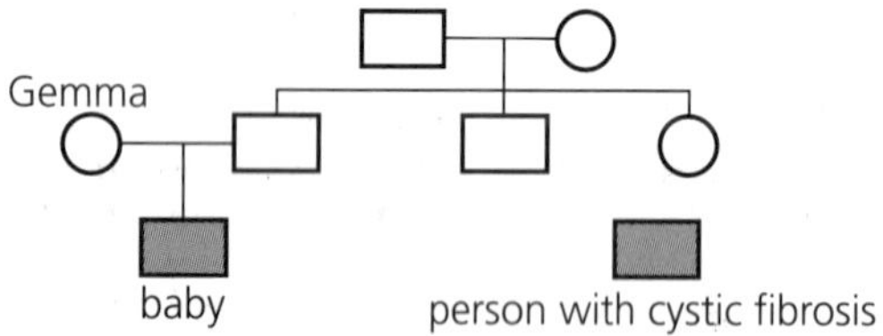

Gemma has been told that her baby has cystic fibrosis. Doctors know that it is an inherited disorder. Neither Gemma nor her partner have cystic fibrosis.

a Using suitable symbols, draw a genetic diagram to show how the baby has inherited cystic fibrosis. [4]

b Gemma would like to have another baby but is worried that it might also inherit cystic fibrosis. What is the probability of her next child inheriting the disorder? [1]

c Haemophilia is another inherited disorder. Explain why males are far more likely to inherit haemophilia than females. [3]

Both inheited disorders are caused by mutations to the genetic code.

d What is the genetic code of an individual? [2]

e Name **two** possible causes of a mutation. [2]

[12 marks]

3 The figure shows different stages in the process of genetic engineering.

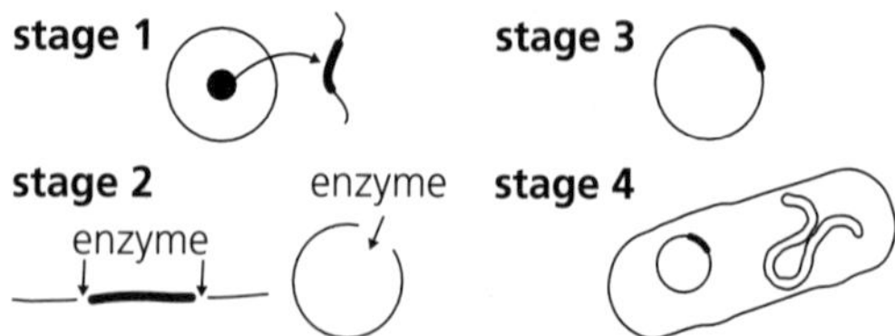

a What does genetic engineering mean? [1]

b Look at the figure and explain what is happening at each stage of the process. [6]

c Genetic engineering is used commercially to produce human insulin. Briefly outline the process. [3]

d Some people consider genetic engineering to be the only way we can hope to feed the increasing world population, whereas others view it as an evil which has to be stopped at all costs. Discuss these two extreme views. [6]

[16 marks]

4 Haemophilia is a sex-linked characteristic. People with haemophilia are unable to clot their blood properly.
It is caused by a recessive allele.

a What do you understand by the term sex linked characteristic? [1]

b What is a recessive allele? [2]

Look at the family tree.

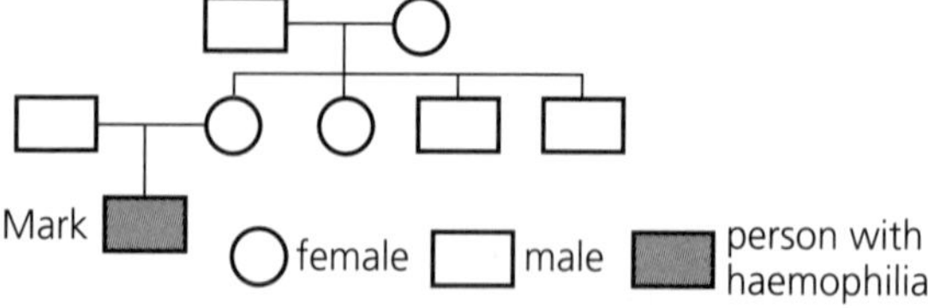

c Explain who Mark inherited his haemophilia from. [2]

d If Mark was able to have children, would he be able to pass his haemophilia on to his son? Explain your answer. [2]

e Mark's father has a daughter who does not have haemophilia. What is the probability that his next child will be a girl? [1]

[8 marks]

Living things in their environment

You will have met these ideas in the units *Evolution*, *Balancing acts*, *Keeping healthy*, *Waste not, want not* and *Energy for today and tomorrow*. This section is divided into four spreads.

Adaptation and competition

Surviving the environment

Have you ever asked yourself why polar bears do not live in the Sahara desert?

Living things are not randomly scattered across the planet. They are found in areas where they are most suited to the prevailing physical conditions. For example, polar bears have thick, white fur coats and plenty of insulating fat. This makes them suited to life in cold areas – their coat and fat will keep them warm; their white colour will help them to blend in with the snow and so catch their food more easily. Polar bears are **adapted** to life in areas where the physical factors include very low temperatures and plenty of snow and ice.

Other animals and plants are adapted to different physical factors. Blood worms contain a red oxygen carrier similar to the haemoglobin found in our blood. It enables them to live in water containing very little oxygen. Camels and cacti are adapted to live in areas where there is very little water available. Cacti conserve water in their swollen stems and reduced leaves, camels store water as fatty deposits in their humps.

Keeping warm

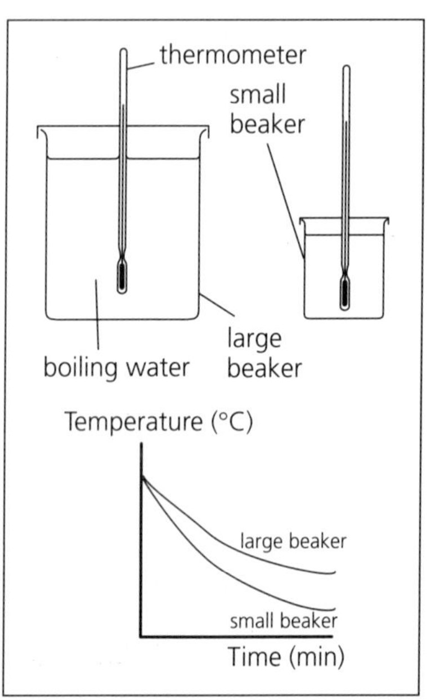

Even body size is important. The larger the body, the greater the surface area of skin through which heat can be lost. However, large, fat bodies have larger volumes and therefore do not lose heat so easily.

You can do an experiment to show this. Fill a large beaker and a very small beaker to the top with boiling water. Record the temperature of the water in each beaker over the next 20 minutes. The large beaker will stay hotter. This is because although it has a larger surface area over which heat can be lost, it also has a much larger volume of hot water in it.

Some animals reduce heat loss by huddling together. This reduces the surface area exposed to the cold surroundings.

Competition

Different species have different needs for food, warmth and shelter, according to the environment they are adapted to live in. However, all animals need warmth, moisture, and a good food supply in order to survive. The number of animals in an area depends on how much of all these resources is available. When a population becomes too large for the resources in its area it stops growing.

Living things also **compete** against each other for these resources. The size of a population of one species often depends on how well it competes against other populations for what it needs.

Predators for example the arctic fox, are animals which eat other animals (**prey**). The prey of the arctic fox is the snow shoe hare.

Predators depend upon prey so if the numbers of prey in a habitat go down, then some predators will starve and the number of predators will also go down.

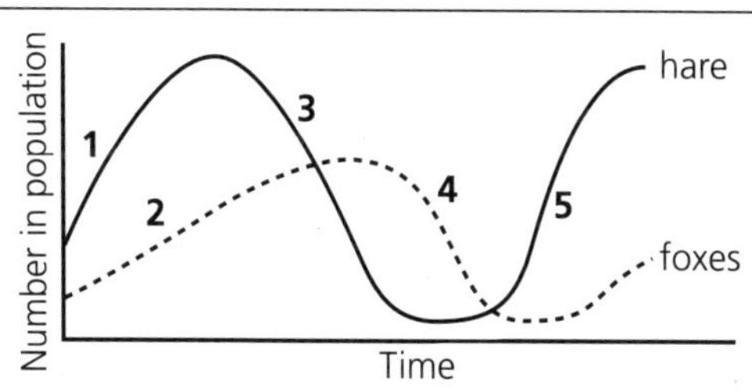

1 Snow shoe hare has plenty of food therefore breeds and increases in number.
2 More hares means more food for arctic foxes, therefore foxes breed and their numbers increase.
3 More foxes eating more hares means hare numbers decreases.
4 Fewer hares therefore some foxes starve.
5 Fewer foxes therefore not so many hares eaten and hare numbers start to increase again.

Now do this

1 Camels have long, thin legs. Suggest how this might adapt them to living in a hot area.

2 List **three** physical factors which affect the environment. For each factor, give an example of an organism adapted to live in it.

3 List **three** things which animals might compete for.

4 Explain why predator and prey population numbers change over a period of time.

How do bacteria grow?

Like most other living things bacteria need a good supply of food, warmth, moisture and no competition to grow rapidly. Bacteria reproduce by splitting into two and their numbers can increase rapidly in the right conditions. When bacteria invade a new environment, their population goes through a series of different phases which can be shown as a growth curve:

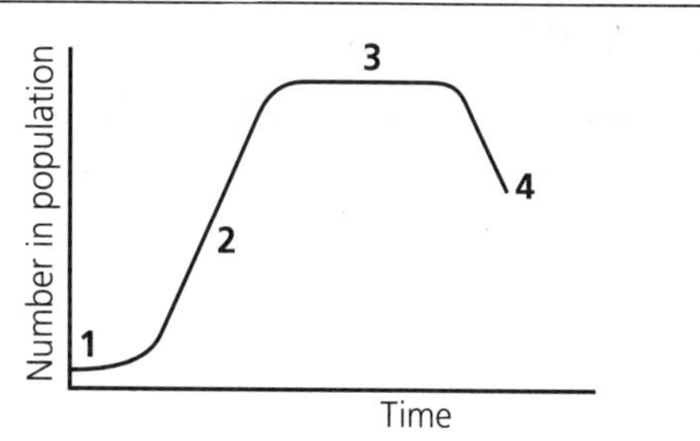

1 Lag phase – bacteria newly arrived, not very numerous, settling in to new environment
2 Log phase – bacteria reproducing rapidly
3 Death is equal to birth rate therefore the population enters a stationary phase
4 Senescence – accumulation of waste products or running short of food, may cause the population to decrease

Most bacteria are harmless to us and some are very useful. But some bacteria are very dangerous to us. Unfortunately our bodies, food and houses often provide ideal conditions for breeding.

Waging war against bacteria

Over the last 150 years people have learned a lot about how to control bacteria using chemicals and good hygiene. Now we can combat harmful bacteria by:

- cleaning floors and surfaces in kitchens, toilets and hospitals with disinfectants
- using antiseptics on wounds to kill bacteria before they can get into the body
- using antibiotics and immunisation to attack bacteria in our bodies
- methods of food storage which stop bacteria growing on food, including canning, freezing, refrigerating, drying and chemical preservatives
- good sanitation, with drinking water cleaned and treated with chlorine and sewage properly treated.

Now do this

5 Why do you think freezing food will stop bacteria growing?

Humans and the environment

The human population is growing rapidly, and this affects our environment in many ways.

Food production

More land is needed for growing human food and this often destroys the homes of other plants and animals.

Farmers use various chemicals to produce more food:

- **herbicides** to kill weeds which compete with their crop for space and nutrients
- **pesticides** to kill pests which eat their crop whilst it is growing or in storage
- **fertilisers** to provide extra nitrates and minerals for the crop to grow.

These chemicals can harm the environment.

- Herbicides may kill plants which are an important part of a food chain. Animals which normally feed on them either die or find something else to eat, possibly the crop itself!
- Pesticides may kill non-pest organisms either directly or through the food chain.
- Phosphates and nitrates in fertilisers can run off into rivers and streams where they cause **eutrophication**, by making algae and water plants grow faster.

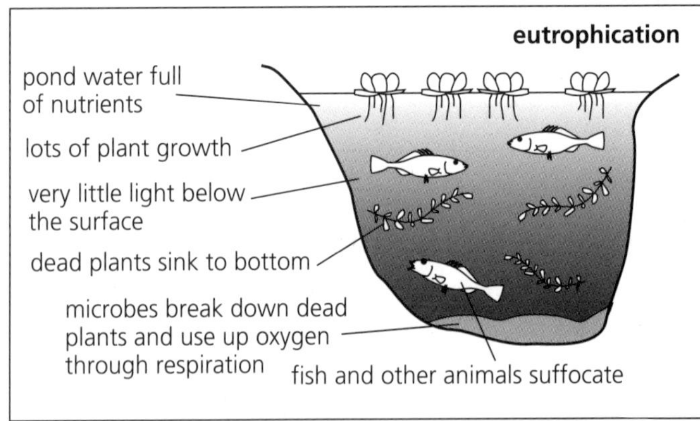

What else does an increasing population need?

The growing human population also needs more living space, more fossil fuels for energy, and more jobs. The price of this is growing amounts of waste materials, sewage and pollution.

The waste problem

Waste may be dumped, burned, recycled or reused.

- Dumping waste requires large areas of land. Most of the waste rots down but it produces methane gas which is very explosive. This has to be carefully handled. There is also a danger of waste leaking from tips and polluting local waterways.
- Burning requires special furnaces but some of the energy released can be used for heating buildings. Care is needed to prevent harmful fumes or dust pollution.
- Glass, paper, aluminium cans and some plastics can be recycled. This saves on raw materials but sometimes needs special reprocessing plants which can be expensive.
- Plastic carrier bags, toys and clothes are some of the things we could reuse.

Now do this

1. Describe **three** ways in which farmers can improve the yield of their crops.
2. Explain the process of eutrophication and its effect on waterways.
3. List **one** advantage and **one** disadvantage of burning and recycling waste.

Sewage

Our sewers carry mainly water with human waste, soaps, detergents, soil, paper and dissolved materials. This is called **sewage** or waste water. As the population increases, so does the amount of sewage.

Water companies treat waste water before putting it back into rivers or the sea. The treatment removes all the harmful bacteria, but does not necessarily remove all dissolved chemicals. If these get into waterways in large quantities, they can kill large numbers of other plants and animals and possibly affect our drinking water.

If untreated sewage gets into the waterways it is a very powerful pollutant because it contains high levels of nitrates and phosphates. These can cause eutrophication in waterways. Indeed, one indicator of water quality is its levels of dissolved oxygen, nitrates and phosphates.

Clean water

Clean water contains a lot of dissolved oxygen and many different species of animals can live in it.

There are some animals such as fish, stonefly larva and mayfly larva which can only survive in clean water. They are called **indicator species** because their presence in water shows that it is clean.

When water is polluted, the oxygen level drops and the range of animals present also drops. Poor quality water has its own indicator species: sludge worms and rat-tailed maggots.

stonefly larva

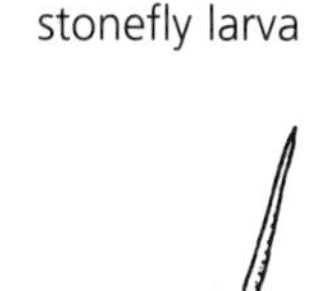

rat-tailed maggot

Now do this

4 A sample of river water contains water beetles, fish, snails and stonefly larvae. Is the water clean or polluted?

5 Why does the level of dissolved oxygen decrease if there are high levels of phosphates and nitrates present in a waterway?

Industrial pollution

Many industrial processes pollute air and water. Sometimes this can be very dramatic, for example when a large oil liner is holed and a huge oil spillage kills wildlife for miles around. However, most industrial pollution is less dramatic but going on all the time all over the earth.

The main forms of pollution are:

- the release of gases such as carbon dioxide and sulphur dioxide when industries or transport vehicles burn fossil fuels
- the release of chemical waste products directly into the air or surrounding waterways.

These can reduce the numbers and types of animals and plants in the polluted area.

Now do this

6 Name **two** gases which pollute the air.

Energy and nutrient transfer

All animals rely on plants for their energy, even if they do not eat them directly. Animals may eat other animals but there is always an animal which eats plants (a **herbivore**) at the end of the line. Animals which eat meat are called **carnivores**. Animals which eat both are called **omnivores**.

Green plants make their own food (glucose and starches) using energy from the Sun. They are called **producers** because they make (produce) their own food. Other living things are called **consumers** because they have to get their food by eating (consuming) green plants or other animals.

These feeding relationships can be drawn as a **food chain**. Some of the energy captured from light by plants is passed along the food chain as plants and animals are eaten. The Sun is the source of energy for **all** food chains.

The arrows in a food chain **must** point towards the animal that is eating because it shows the direction the energy is moving in.

grass → rabbit, means the rabbit eats the grass

grass ← rabbit, means the grass eats the rabbit!

Each feeding level is called a **trophic level**. Energy is lost from each trophic level through respiration and excretion. Not all the energy in an organism is necessarily available as not all the available food at each trophic level is consumed. When we eat meat, we do not eat the skin, hooves, bones and assorted other bits.

Food webs

Most living things eat more than one type of food so we usually link food chains together into a **food web** which shows all the feeding relationships.

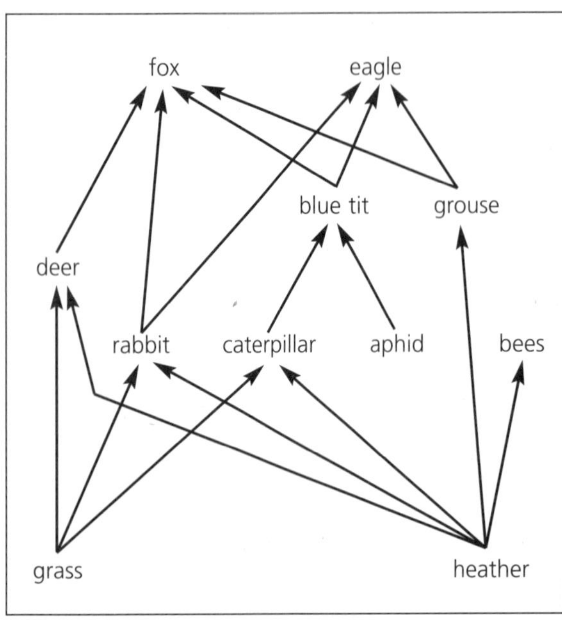

Now do this

1 On a moorland the main plant is heather which is eaten by lots of animals including rabbits, grouse, bees and deer. There are also several fox families and a pair of eagles which survive by hunting the grouse and rabbits.

a Name **one** moorland producer, **one** primary consumer and **one** predator.

b Draw **two** food chains using some of the living things mentioned in the passage.

c Explain what would happen to the grouse population if the rabbits were to die from myxamatosis.

Pyramids of numbers

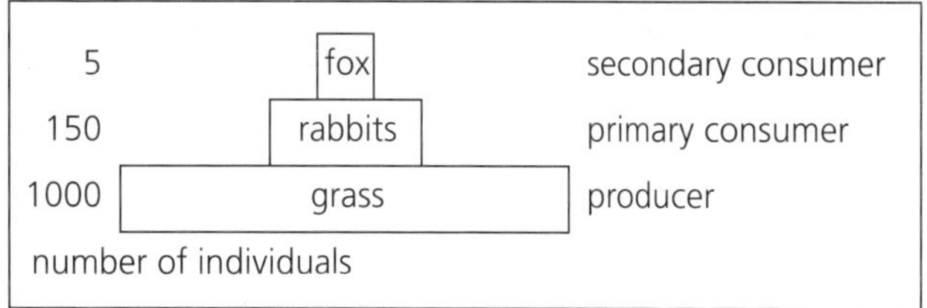

Another way of showing feeding relationships is as a **pyramid of numbers**. Here, each feeding level is represented by a block. The size of the block represents the number of individuals.

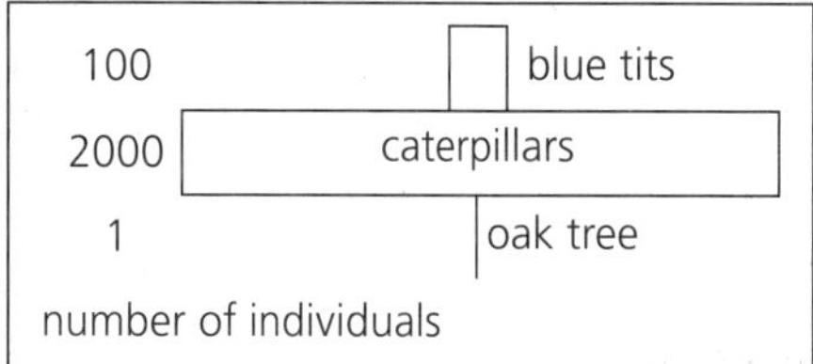

But it does not always work.

Don't be put off, always put the producer at the bottom and arrange the other feeding levels above it keeping to the order in which they appear in a food chain.

Pyramid of biomass

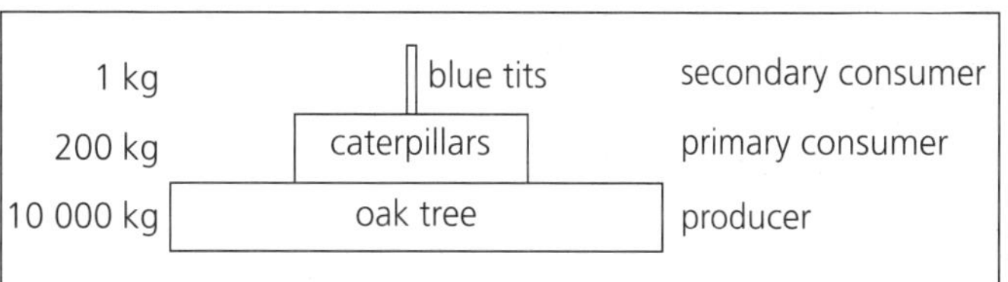

A more accurate way is to produce a **pyramid of biomass**. Here the size of the blocks represents the biomass of the animals and plants feeding at that level, rather than the number. Biomass is the dry mass of an organism (that is, with all the water removed). The dry mass is used to construct the pyramid.

Managed ecosystems

An ecosystem is a small part of the global environment, for example, a field, a wood or the North Sea. As the population grows there is an ever increasing demand for food and humans must either exploit existing ecosystems more efficiently or create new ecosystems.

An area of land can produce more plant food, and feed more people, than if the same area is used to produce meat. To accommodate some people's wish to have meat in their diet, farmers use intensive farming techniques in which animals are reared indoors where they can be fed and checked for disease regularly. This improves the efficiency of energy transfer from one trophic level to the next because it reduces the amount of energy needed for respiration (movement and heat loss are controlled indoors). But the food the animals eat still has to be grown outside and this requires a reasonably large area of land.

We are also attempting to control existing ecosystems more efficiently by legislation and policing policy aimed at protecting the fish supplies in the North Sea. The minimum mesh size of the fishing nets has been set to protect small, immature fish from being caught. Areas have been designated as 'no fishing' zones to allow fish to breed and replenish their numbers. Fishermen now have quotas setting out the maximum number of fish they may catch in a year.

Fish farms is another example of an artificial ecosystem to enhance food production. In Scotland, salmon are kept in large, penned off areas where they can be fed and disease monitored. The breeding fish are separated from the youngsters which are marketed when they reach a desired size. There are problems with disease and with predators such as seals.

Now do this

2 Describe **two** ways that intensive farming techniques reduce energy loss between trophic levels.

Recycling useful materials

What happens to all the waste and dead animals and plants produced in a food chain?

They are used for food by living things called **decomposers**. Decomposers are very important because materials need to be broken down (**decay**) so that the nutrients they contain can be used again by other living things. Decomposers include some bacteria and fungi.

Living things are mostly made up of carbohydrates and proteins. Both of these have carbon, hydrogen, oxygen. Proteins contain nitrogen as well. These are called **organic** compounds and all their elements are recycled to form new life.

An example of this recycling can be seen in the **carbon cycle**.

In the carbon cycle:

- decomposers in the soil release carbon dioxide into the air as they respire
- plants and animals release carbon dioxide into the air as they respire
- some of the carbon dioxide dissolves in the seas
- plants use some of the carbon dioxide in the air to make carbohydrates and proteins (photosynthesis)
- animals get their carbohydrates by eating plants
- animals and plants die and decomposers feed on them releasing carbon dioxide.

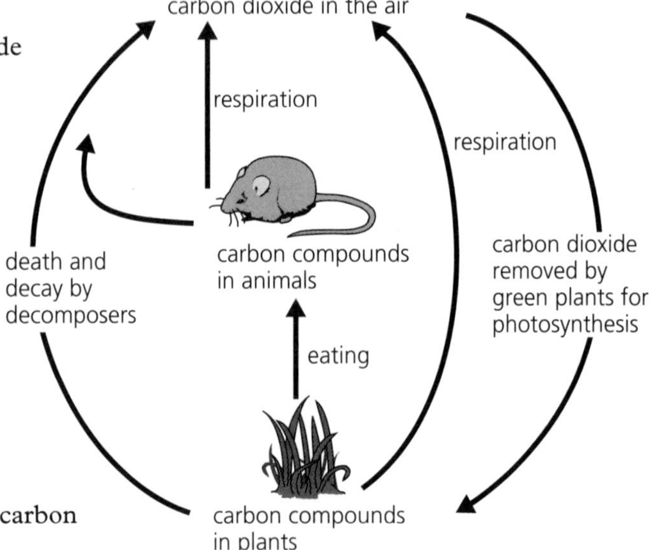

There are also two other important sources of carbon dioxide:

- acid rain attacks carbonate rock releasing carbon dioxide
- combustion of fossil fuels releases carbon dioxide into the air.

Upsetting the cycle

Carbon dioxide is a **greenhouse gas** which causes heat to be trapped in the atmosphere, leading to **global warming**. This has the possible consequences of:

- ice caps melting
- increased sea levels
- loss of low lying habitats
- changing weather patterns.

Now do this

1. Name **two** groups of living things which can act as decomposers.
2. Why are decomposers so important?
3. Give **two** ways in which carbon dioxide is removed from the atmosphere.

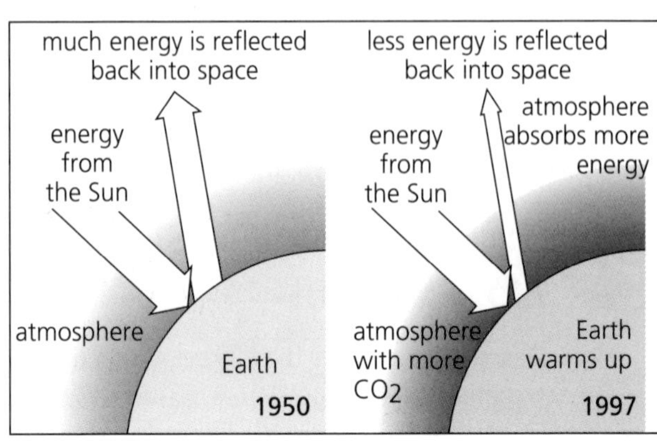

The nitrogen cycle

Although the atmosphere contains a large amount of nitrogen, atmospheric nitrogen must be changed into soluble nitrates and nitrites before it can be used by most living things.

- Nitrogen fixing bacteria convert atmospheric nitrogen into amino acids and proteins. Some of these bacteria are free-living in the soil and others live in the root nodules of leguminous plants, e.g. clover, beans, peas.
- Lightening converts atmospheric nitrogen into nitrates.
- Plant roots absorb nitrates from the soil and convert them into amino acids and proteins.
- Decay bacteria convert proteins and urea into ammonia.
- Nitrifying bacteria add nitrates to the soil by converting ammonia into nitrates.
- Farmers artificially boost the nitrate content of soil by adding fertilisers.
- Farmers can boost the nitrate content of soil by ploughing plant remains, especially leguminous plant remains, back into the soil so they can decay.

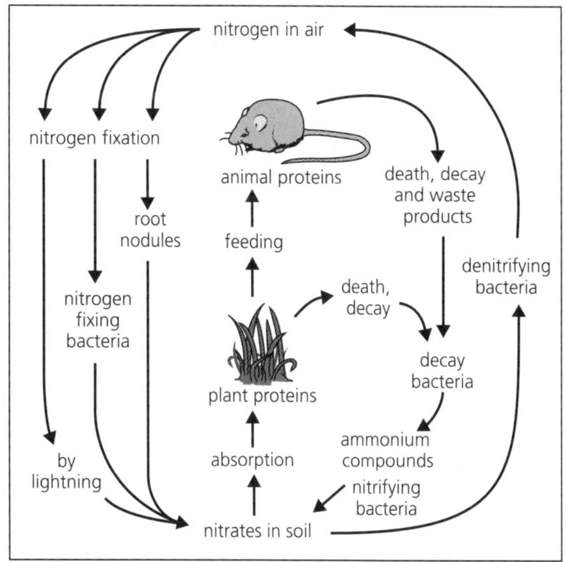

Now do this

4 The nitrogen cycle involves nitrogen fixing bacteria, denitrifying bacteria and nitrifying bacteria. Explain the **three** different roles they have in the cycle.

5 Explain why traditional farming techniques included crop rotation in which every five years a field would be planted with beans and instead of cropping the beans, the farmer would plough them back into the soil.

Busy bacteria

Gardeners can make use of decomposing bacteria in their compost heaps. These bacteria need a good supply of food, which is the material they decompose, moisture, warmth and plenty of oxygen. In these conditions, they will rot down garden rubbish to form nutrient-rich compost.

On a larger scale it is possible to rot down animal and vegetable matter and keep the air out. The bacteria which do this produce 'biogas' which is mostly methane and can be used to generate electricity.

Some countries even use bacteria to break down (ferment) sugar-rich crops to produce alcohol which can then be used as a fuel to run cars for example.

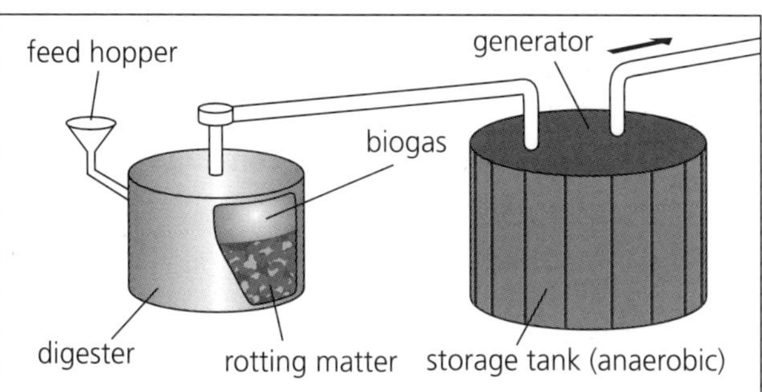

Now do this

6 What is the main gas in 'biogas'?

7 Explain why compost heaps will not normally produce 'biogas' but landfill sites do.

Exam questions

1 In America some farmers keep their pigs in indoor pens. The floors of these pens are metal slats which allow urine and waste to drop through into a reservoir.

In some areas, nitrate rich material from these reservoirs has seeped out into local waterways, causing widespread nitrate pollution and eutrophication.

Explain fully the effect of eutrophication on a waterway. [6]

[6 marks]

2 The graph shows how a population of bacteria in a sore throat changed over a period of five days.

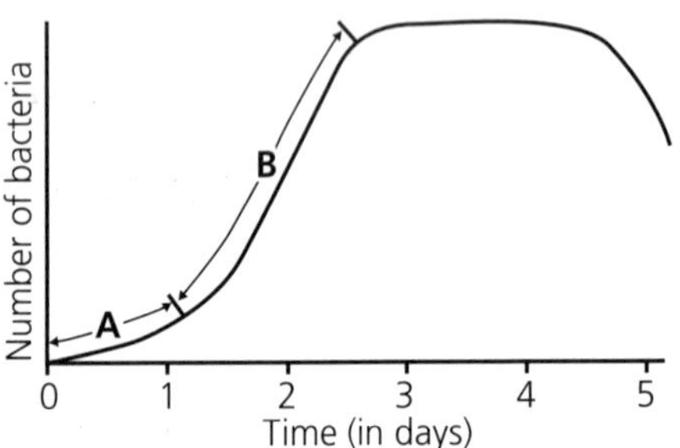

a During which time was the population of bacteria increasing most rapidly? [1]

b How do bacteria increase in numbers? [1]

c Explain what is happening in the stages labelled A and B. [4]

d List **three** conditions the throat had which made it an ideal place for the bacteria to grow. [3]

e Suggest why the population of bacteria drops towards the end of the five days. [1]

[10 marks]

3 Look at the diagram of the nitrogen cycle.

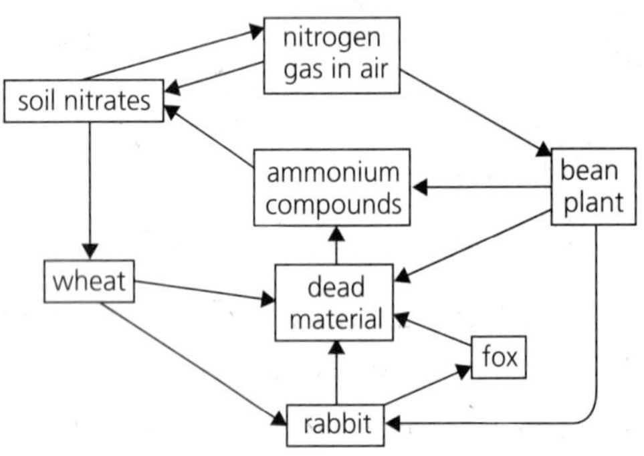

Bacteria play an important part in the nitrogen cycle.

a What type of bacteria convert atmospheric nitrogen into nitrates in the soil? [1]

b What type of bacteria convert ammonium compounds into soil nitrates? [1]

c Explain why a good crop of wheat would require the addition of nitrate fertiliser while a crop of beans grown in the same field would not need the addition of nitrate fertiliser. [4]

d Draw a pyramid of biomass for the organisms shown in the nitrogen cycle above. [3]

[9 marks]

4 The diagram shows some of the ways in which carbon can be recycled.

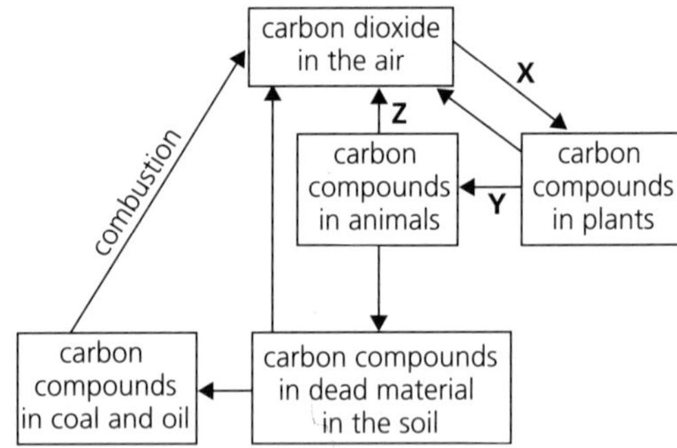

a Name the processes represented by the arrows, labelled X, Y and Z. [3]

b Name **one** group of organisms which help break down dead organisms and return carbon dioxide to the air? [1]

c Scientists have become concerned that carbon dioxide levels in the air have been rising for some years. State and explain **one** possible reason for this rise. [2]

d Explain how higher levels of carbon dioxide may contribute to the 'greenhouse' effect. [3]

e Suggest **three** possible consequences of the 'greenhouse' effect. [3]

[12 marks]

Classifying materials

You will have met the ideas in this section when you worked on the units *Atmosphere*, *Construction materials*, *Mining and minerals*, *Food for thought*, *Burning and bonding*, *Transporting chemicals* and *Seeing inside the body*. This section is divided into five spreads.

Particles and change

How are particles arranged in solids, liquids and gasses?

How do elements make molecules?

What is the difference between a mixture and a compound?

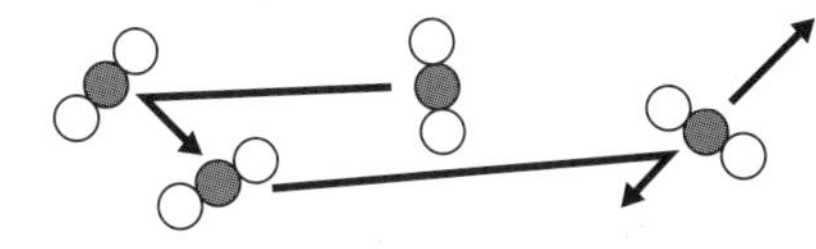

Mixtures and change

How can we separate mixtures?

What are physical and chemical changes?

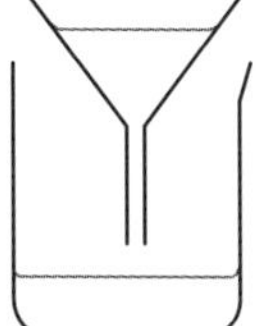

Symbols and equations

How do you write the symbol for an element?

What does a chemical formula tell you?

How do you balance an equation?

$C + O_2 \rightarrow CO_2$

What are atoms made of?

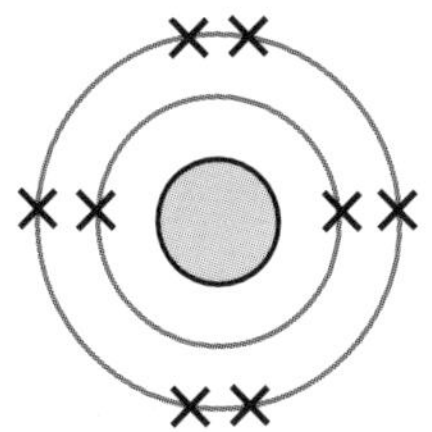

How do the bits of an atom fit together?

What are isotopes?

What are electron shells?

Bonding, molecules and giant structures

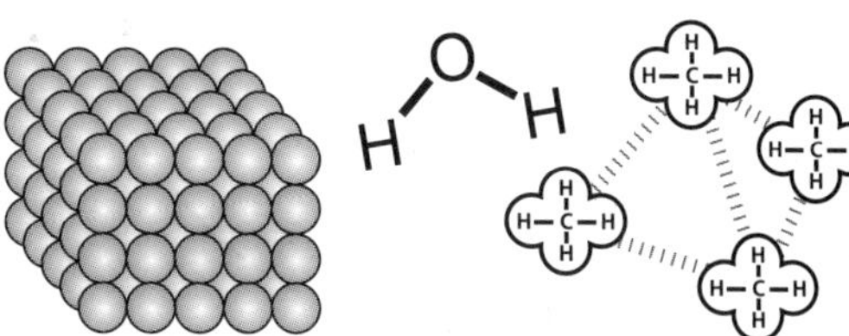

How do atoms stick together?

How does the structure of a compound affect its properties?

Particles and their behaviour

Everything is made of very small particles which are too small to see. The particles are always moving; the hotter they are the more they move. Forces between the particles hold the particles together. Particles are arranged in different ways in solids, liquids and gases.

Solids

The particles are close together. The particles stay in the same places, so solids keep their shape – even though the vibrations increase as the solid gets hotter. You can't move the particles any closer, so solids can't be compressed into a smaller space. Forces between the particles are strong.

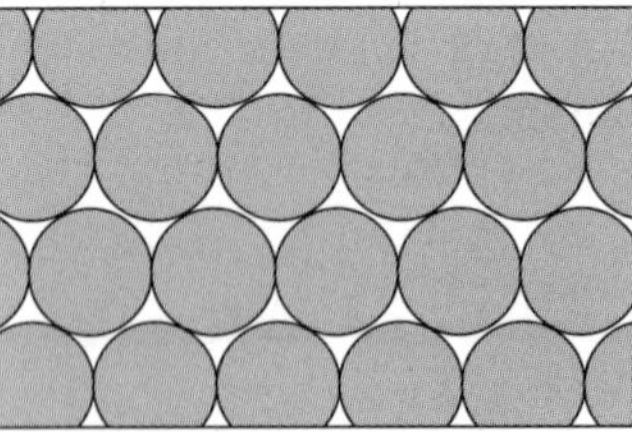
particles in a solid

Liquids

Usually the particles are **slightly** further apart than in a solid. They can move about, so liquids do not have a fixed shape. You still can't move the particles any closer, so liquids can't be compressed into a smaller space. As a liquid gets hotter, the particles move faster.

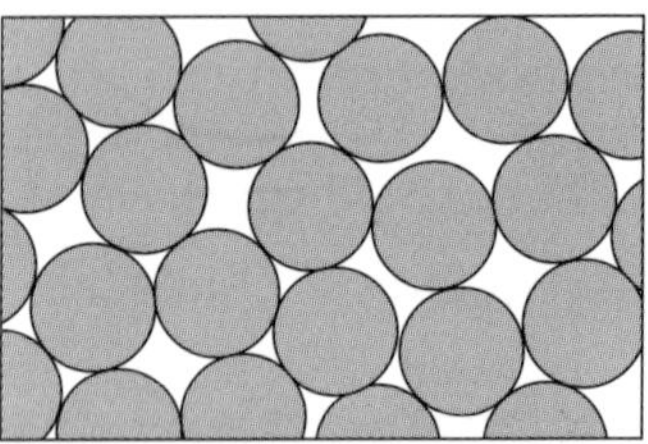
particles in a liquid

Examiner's tip

Draw liquid particles close together!

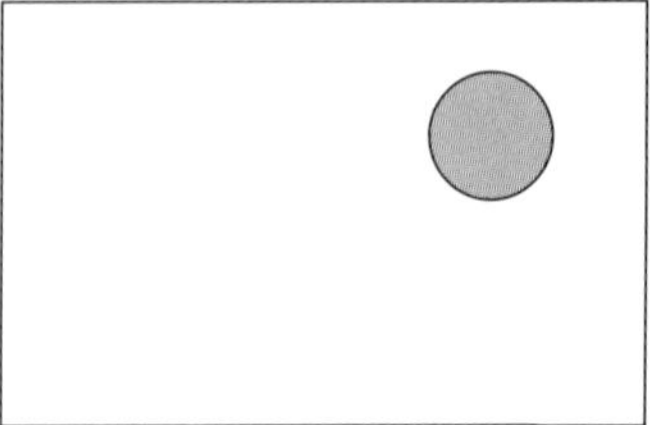
on this scale the nearest gas particle is on the next page!

Gases

The particles are *very* far apart. This means that gases have no shape and it is easy to compress them into a small space. The forces between the particles are very weak, so they don't stick together.

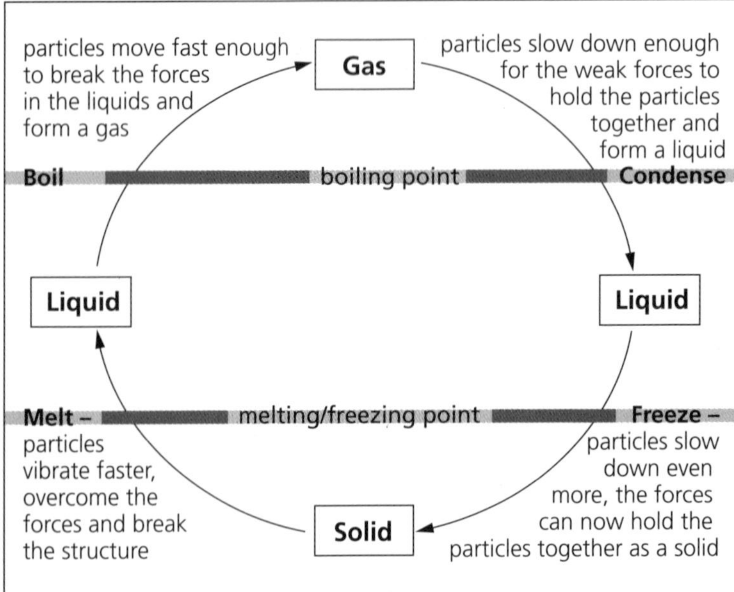

Now do this

1 Give **two** ways in which the behaviour of particles in a liquid is similar to particles in a gas.

2 Why are solids hard?

3 Describe what happens to the particles inside a solid when the solid is heated until it melts.

4 Use your understanding of forces between molecules to explain why water at 60 °C does not boil but water at 100 °C does boil.

Atoms, elements and molecules

The particles inside everything are made of **atoms**. There are 104 different types of atom. Each different type of atom is a different **element**. Some common elements are hydrogen, carbon, oxygen, sulphur, iron.

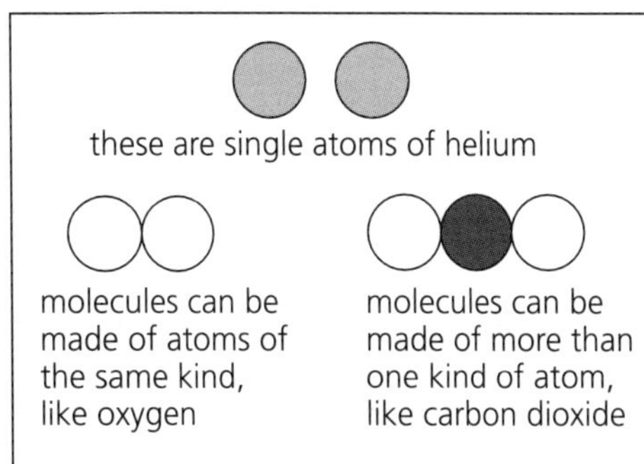

Some particles are just single atoms on their own. Sometimes groups of atoms bond together to make **molecules**. Molecules can be made from atoms of one element or from atoms of several different elements. You can also get enormous groups of atoms called giant structures – you will come across these later.

Compounds and chemical bonds

Atoms of different elements can join together to make **compounds**. Compounds are always made from more than one element. The atoms inside a compound are held to each other by **chemical bonds**.

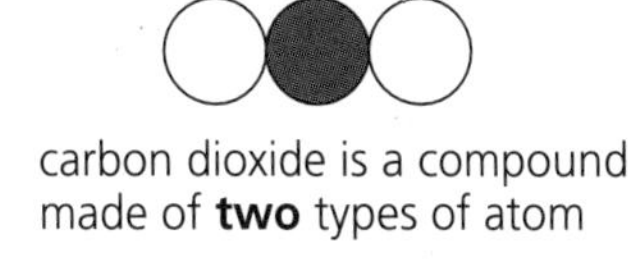

Mixtures

Substances can be mixed together without joining up. When this happens they do not form compounds, they stay as **mixtures**. For example, air is a mixture of gases including oxygen and nitrogen. Sea water is a mixture of water and salt – the salt is dissolved in the water but it does not form a compound with the water. Substances in a mixture do not join, so they are easy to separate out.

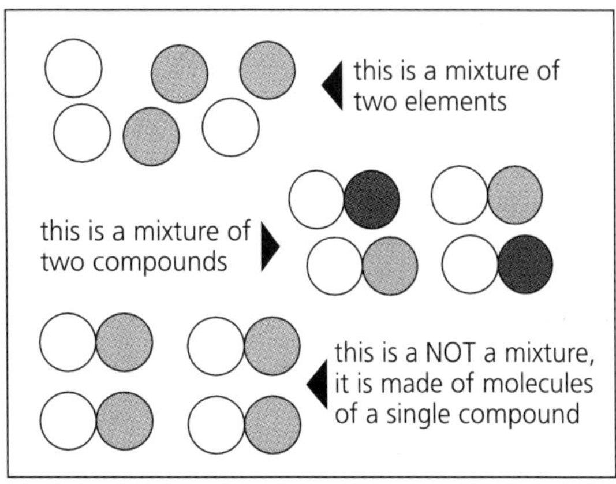

Now do this

5 Which are the compounds in this list?
hydrogen, hydrogen sulphide, oxygen, sugar, nitric acid, carbon.

6 Which are the mixtures in this list?
salt and sand; sodium chloride; sugar; water; salty water.

Mixtures and changes

Separating mixtures

Substances in a mixture are not joined together, so you can separate them out again using one of these methods.

Many mixtures are made of a solid dissolved in a liquid. A solid that dissolves in a liquid is **soluble**. One that won't dissolve is **insoluble**. The liquid that it dissolves in is a **solvent**. The solvent with the substance dissolved in it is a **solution**. Water is a very useful solvent, it will dissolve lots of chemicals.

Filtration

If you have a liquid with an insoluble solid in it you can filter out the solid. You can use this to get sand from a mixture of sand and salty water.

Evaporation and crystallisation

You can use this technique to get a soluble solid back out of a solution. Gently heat the mixture so that the liquid evaporates into the air and the solid stays behind as crystals.

You could you use this to get **salt** out of salty water.

Distillation

You can use this to get a pure liquid out of a solution.

Put the liquid into a flask instead of a beaker. When the liquid evaporates, the flask stops the hot vapour escaping into the room and it sends the vapour through the condenser instead.

You could use this to get **pure water** from salty water.

flask
thermometer
cooling water out
3 the vapour is pure, all the solid has stayed behind
condenser
4 the pure vapour condenses into pure liquid
2 the liquid boils
1 start with a solution – the solid is dissolved in the liquid but you can't see it
HEAT
cooling water in
5 the pure liquid collects in the beaker

Fractional distillation

Solutions made of two liquids cannot be separated by normal distillation – both liquids will evaporate when you heat the solution. You have to use a fractionating column instead. Crude oil is a mixture of liquids which is separated in this way – see the section on fuels.

Chromatography

You can use chromatography to see how many chemicals there are in a solution.

Put a drop of solution on a strip of filter paper and dip the end in water. As the water goes up the paper the chemicals separate and each moves a different distance up the paper. You could use this to see how many coloured dyes there are in black ink.

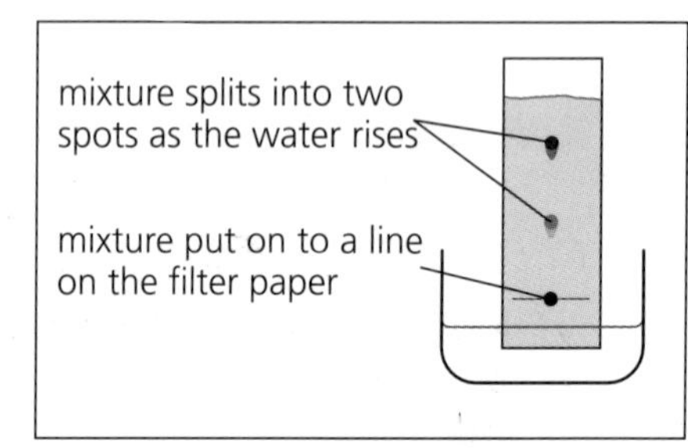

Now do this

1 Here are some separation problems. Some can be done by using just one of the techniques in the table. Others will need more than one method. Copy the table and tick the techniques that you need for each separation.

	Technique		
	Dissolve	**Filter**	**Evaporate**
1 To get solid salt out of salty water (like the sea)			✓
2 To get sand from sand mixed with salty water		✓	
3 To get solid salt from sand mixed with salty water		✓	✓
4 To get solid salt from sand mixed with salt crystals	✓	✓	✓

Physical changes

water ↔ steam

When water boils it changes from a liquid into steam. It is easy to change steam back into liquid water. The molecules inside the water move further apart when it boils but the molecules do not change, no new substance has been made. This is called a **physical change**. Dissolving is another physical change.

Chemical changes

When carbon burns in oxygen the carbon and oxygen turn into a new substance, carbon dioxide. This is a **chemical reaction**.

The carbon and oxygen in the carbon dioxide are held together by **chemical bonds**.

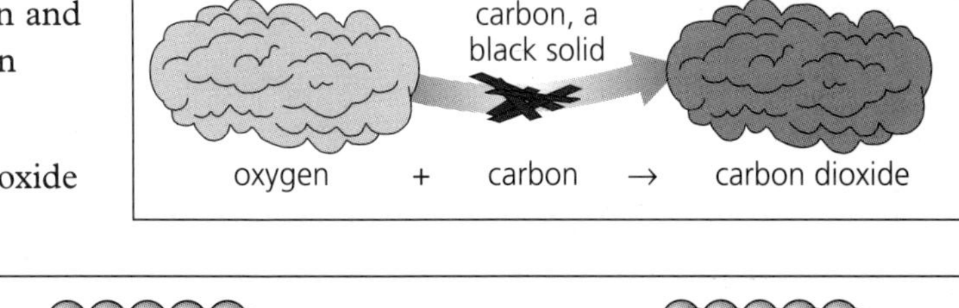

When clay is heated there is a chemical reaction as the clay turns into brick.

Once a reaction has happened it is very difficult to reverse it.

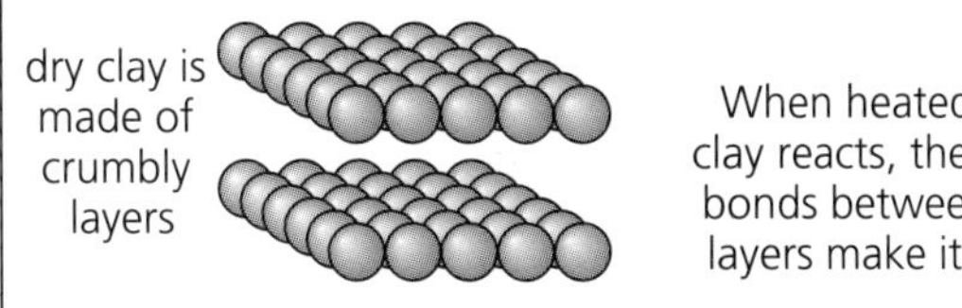

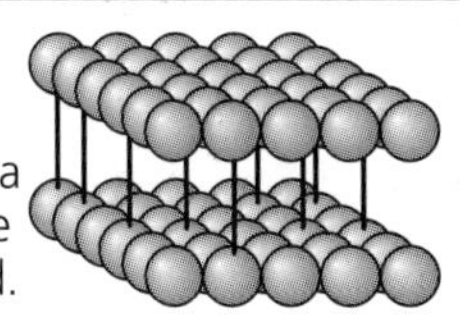

Reactions which get hotter as they take place are **exothermic**.
Reactions which get colder as they take place are **endothermic**.

The reaction between carbon and oxygen is a combustion reaction – they burn! Combustion reactions always get hot, they are exothermic.

Examiner's tip

Most chemical reactions either give out heat or they need heating to make them start – this is one sign that a chemical reaction is taking place.

Now do this

2 When you put iron filings into copper sulphate solution, the solution gets warm, it changes colour, and it is difficult to get the iron filings and copper sulphate back again. What are the **two** clues that tell you that this is a chemical change?

Symbols and equations

Symbols for the elements

Elements have symbols of either one or two letters.

If the symbol has one letter, that letter must be a capital. For example, H is hydrogen.

If the symbol has two letters, the first letter is a capital and the second letter is a little letter. For example, Al is aluminium.

Formulae for compounds

The formula for a compound tells us which elements are inside the compound. It also tells us how many atoms of each element are in the compound.

molecule diagram	formula
H—H	H_2

The formula of a hydrogen molecule is H_2.
It is made of two hydrogen atoms bonded together.

molecule diagram	formula
H—Cl	HCl

The formula of hydrogen chloride is HCl.
It is made one atom of hydrogen and one atom of chlorine bonded together.

If the molecule of a compound contains different numbers of atoms inside it, write the numbers after each symbol in the formula.

molecule diagram	formula
H—O—H	H_2O

The formula of water is H_2O.
It has two atoms of hydrogen and one atom of oxygen bonded together. See how the '2' comes after the 'H' in H_2O.

NH_4NO_3 is a formula that looks more complicated. It is made of two atoms of N, four atoms of H and three atoms of O.

Now do this

1 Write out and complete this table for these compounds: HCl, H_2O, CH_4, CO_2, $AlCl_3$, H_2SO_4, $C_6H_{12}O_6$.

Formula	Number of atoms in the formula	Number of different elements

2 Write down the formula of the hydrogen sulphide molecule shown in this diagram. **H—S—H**

3 Write down the formula of ammonia shown in this diagram.

4 Write down the formulae for these metal compounds (the chemical bonds are not shown):

magnesium chloride (Mg Cl Cl);
iron oxide (Fe Fe O O O).

5 Here are some substances called alkanes. Write down the formulae of each one.

What is a chemical equation?

When sodium combines with chlorine, the two substances turn into sodium chloride – something totally new. For changes like this chemical reaction to happen the bonds inside the chemicals must break up and new ones must form. This isn't easy, so chemical reactions are very difficult to undo. Most chemical reactions either need heating to start or give out heat as they happen – one sign that a chemical reaction is taking place.

A **chemical equation** tells us what happens in a chemical reaction. The chemicals at the start are the **reactants**, and they change into the **products**.

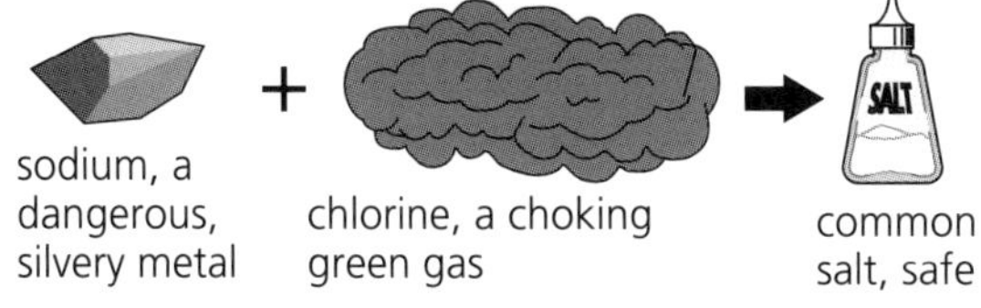

sodium	+	**chlorine**	→	**sodium chloride**
reactant	+	**reactant**	→	**product**

Balancing equations

All the atoms inside the reactant molecules end up inside the product molecules, so equations always have the same number of atoms on each side of the equation.

For example, hydrogen gas and chlorine gas will react with each other.

hydrogen + chlorine → hydrogen chloride

Hydrogen and chlorine molecules are both made of pairs of atoms, so the symbol equation *might* look like this

$H_2 + Cl_2 \rightarrow HCl$ **NOT BALANCED**

But this means that there are two atoms of hydrogen and two of chlorine on the left but only one of each on the right. To balance this up we write

$H_2 + Cl_2 \rightarrow 2HCl$ **BALANCED**

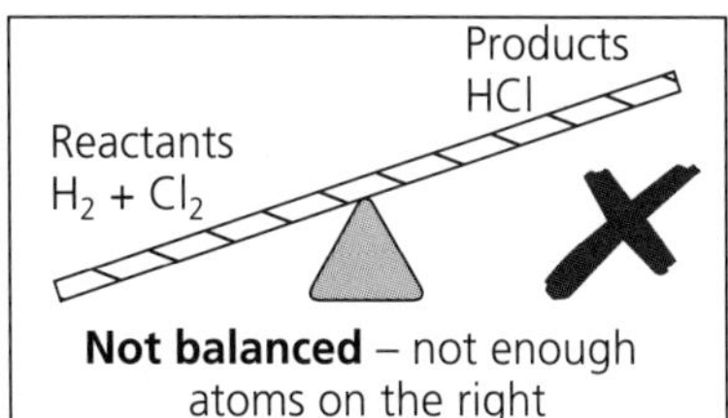

Not balanced – not enough atoms on the right

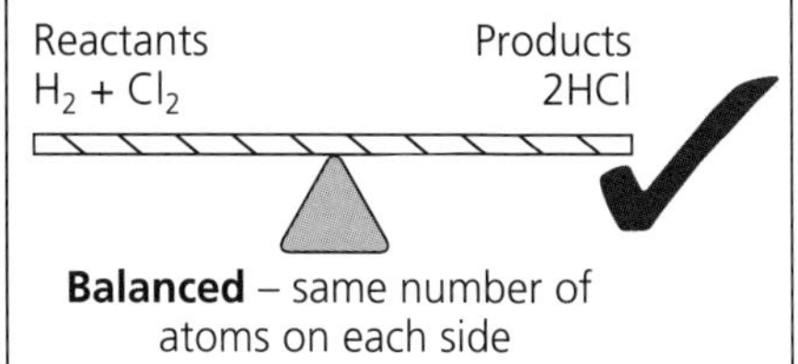

Balanced – same number of atoms on each side

Examiner's tip

You can only change the numbers *in front of* a formula. Never change any other numbers in the equation!

Now do this

6 Copy and complete these equations – the lines represent missing numbers:

H_2	+	Cl_2	→	2 HCl		
Mg	+	2 HCl	→	$MgCl_2$	+	H_2
C_3H_8	+	$5O_2$	→	3 CO_2	+	4 H_2O
C_2H_4	+	3 O_2	→	$2CO_2$	+	$2H_2O$

What are atoms made of?

An atom is made of a tiny positive nucleus surrounded by shells of electrons.

Atoms are neutral. Their negative and positive charges cancel out. This means that the number of electrons must be the same as the number of protons.

The nucleus is made of protons and neutrons. Protons have positive charge, neutrons are neutral. They are both heavy particles.

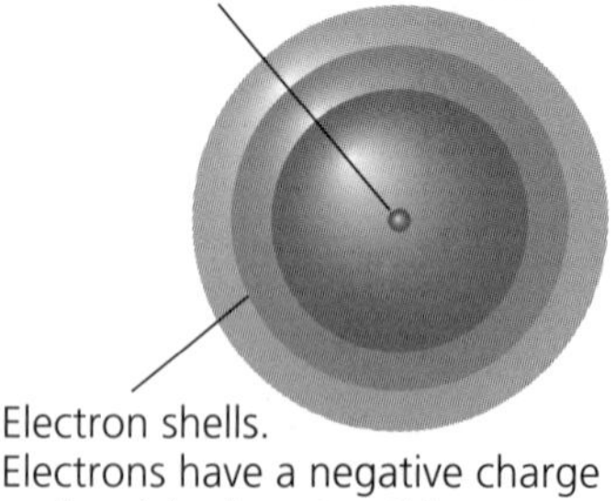

Electron shells. Electrons have a negative charge and weigh almost nothing.

Name	Charge	Mass	Where found
proton	+1	1	inside the nucleus
neutron	0	1	inside the nucleus
electron	–1	0	outside the nucleus, in shells

The number of protons in an atom is called the **atomic number**. It tells you which element you have. If an atom has one proton, the element is hydrogen. If it has two protons it is helium.

The mass of an atom is made up of all the protons and neutrons, because both are heavy particles. Add together the numbers of protons and neutrons to make the **mass number**. The electrons don't weigh enough to matter.

A hydrogen atom is the only element whose nucleus doesn't contain any neutrons, so its mass number is just 1, the same as its number of protons.

We write all this information in a standard way.

The number of neutrons is the mass number minus the atomic number.

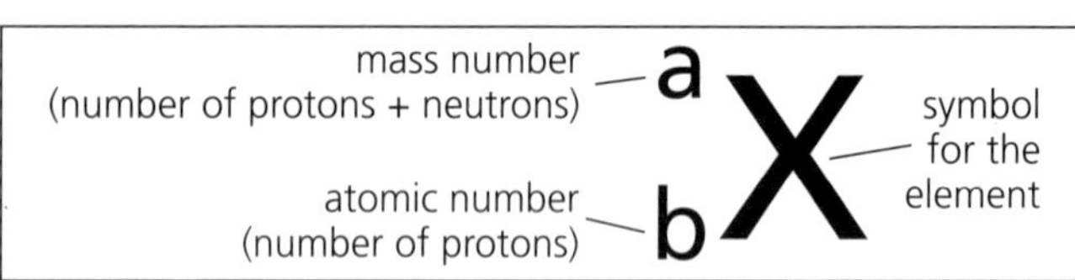

Isotopes

Many elements have more than one mass number. These different forms of the same element are called **isotopes**.

$^{35}_{17}Cl$ has 17 protons, so it is chlorine. Work out how many neutrons it must have (mass number – proton number). You should have the answer 18 neutrons.

$^{37}_{17}Cl$ has 17 protons, so it is chlorine. Work out how many neutrons it must have (mass number – proton number). You should have the answer 20 neutrons.

The only difference between them is the number of neutrons in the nucleus. This makes one isotope heavier than the other, but otherwise it doesn't have much effect.

Now do this

1. How many protons are in $^{56}_{26}Fe$?
2. How many neutrons are in $^{56}_{26}Fe$?
3. What is the difference between $^{16}_{8}O$ and $^{18}_{8}O$?

How are the electrons arranged in an atom?

Electrons fit into shells around the nucleus. Two electrons fit into the first shell, then up to eight electrons fit into the next shell. Eight electrons give a stable arrangement for all shells after the innermost one.

Sodium has eleven electrons, so its electrons go into three shells to make the arrangement 2,8,1. This means that there are two electrons in the first shell, eight in the next and one in the outer shell.

When two atoms react with each other it is the their outer shells which touch. This makes the electrons in each outer shell very important. The outer electrons move between the atoms to form stable outer shells, this is what makes a reaction happen.

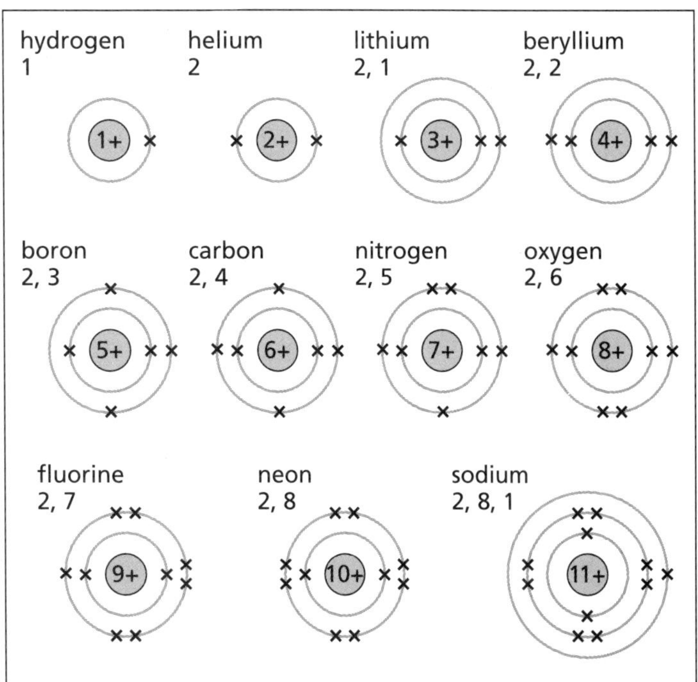

Ions

If an element only needs to lose or gain a few electrons to get eight, the element will form an **ion**. The atom loses or gains electrons so that the outer shell ends up with eight electrons. If more than two electrons need to move then the elements don't usually form ions when they react, they share electrons instead.

Elements whose atoms *gain* electrons to form ions

If there are 7 electrons in the outer shell, they gain one electron → X^- ion.

If there are 6 electrons in the outer shell, they gain two electrons → X^{2-} ion.

Elements whose atoms *give away* electrons to form ions

If there is 1 electron in the outer shell, they give away one electron → X^+ ion.

If there are 2 electrons in the outer shell, they give away two electrons → X^{2+} ion.

Now do this

4 The atomic number of nitrogen is 7.
- **a** How many protons has it got?
- **b** How many electrons has it got?
- **c** How are the electrons arranged?

5 The atomic number of sodium is 11. What is its electron arrangement?

6 The atomic number of potassium is 19. What is its electron arrangement?

Examiner's tip

Atoms which gain electrons form negative ions.

Atoms which give away electrons form positive ions.

Bonding, molecules and giant structures

Ionic bonding

Ions with opposite charges will hold each other together. This is **ionic bonding**. Compounds of metals with non-metals are held together by ionic bonding. Metals form positive ions, non-metals form negative ions.

We can use 'dot and cross' diagrams to show how these ions are made – this one is for sodium chloride, salt.

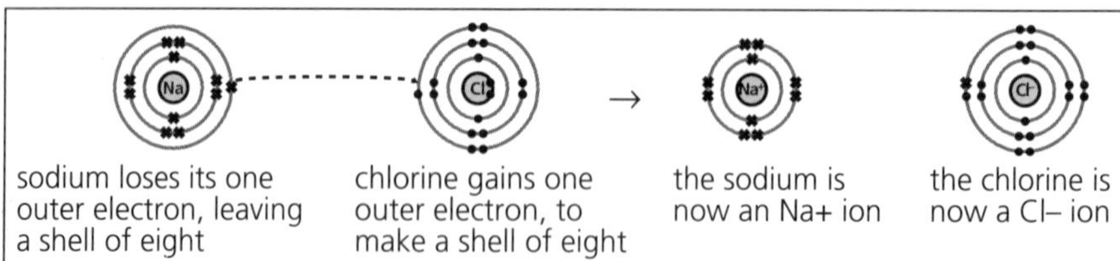

Ionic giant structures

Ionic bonds are very strong forces. Compounds with ionic bonds form enormous groups called **giant structures**. Giant structures have high melting points because all the strong forces holding the particles together are difficult to break. Salt has a giant structure. If you melt an ionic giant structure, or dissolve it in water, its ions will be able to move so it will conduct electricity.

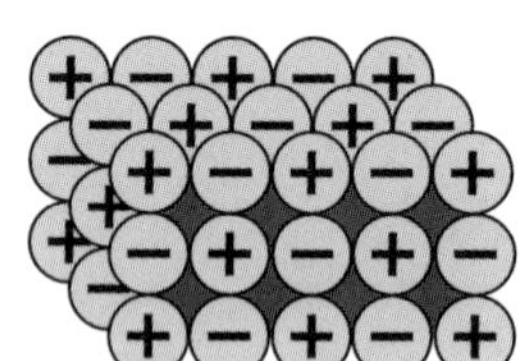

Covalent bonding

When non-metals react with each other they also make stable outer shells, but they share pairs of electrons to achieve this. This is **covalent bonding**, and it is just as strong as ionic bonding. Covalent compounds do not contain charged particles, so they do not conduct electricity when melted.

The hydrogen molecule, H_2, has a single covalent bond. The outer shell of each hydrogen atom needs two electrons to make it stable.

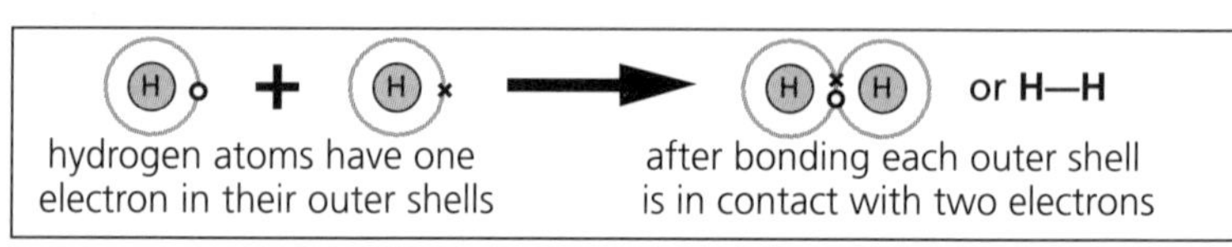

The chlorine molecule, Cl_2, has a single covalent bond. The outer shell of each chlorine atom needs eight electrons to make it stable.

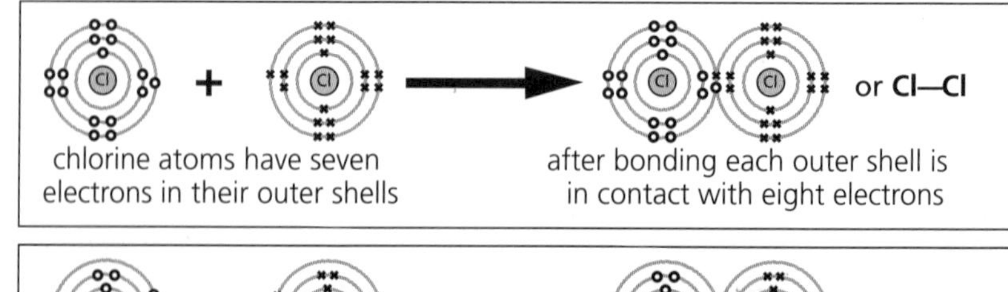

The oxygen molecule, O_2, has a double covalent bond. The outer shell of each oxygen atom needs eight electrons to make it stable.

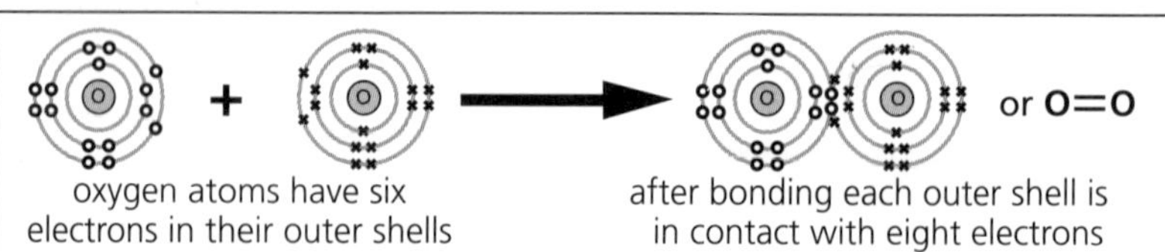

Now do this

1 Draw 'dot and cross' diagrams for the following molecules.

H–O–H water, H_2O

H–C(H)(H)–H methane, CH_4

O=C=O carbon dioxide, CO_2

N≡N nitrogen, N_2

Molecules and giants

Covalent compounds can form giant structures, or they can form small molecules. Ionic compounds form giant structures only.

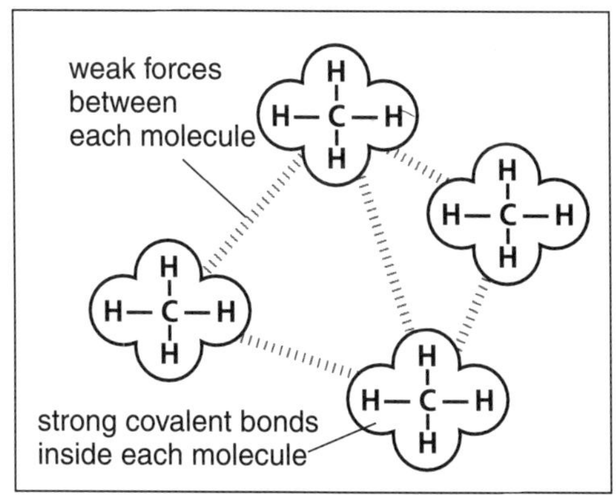

Covalent molecules

Molecules have strong covalent bonds on the inside – these hold the molecule together. Molecules have very weak forces on the outside – these hold one molecule to another molecule. The weak forces make it easy to separate one molecule from another, so substances made of molecules have low melting and boiling points.

Covalent giant structures

Sometimes all the atoms inside a structure are held together with covalent bonds, there are no weak forces. This makes a **covalent giant structure**. As the covalent bond is just as strong as the ionic bond, the structure will have very high melting and boiling points.

Carbon is important because it is an element that can form two different giant structures, diamond and graphite.

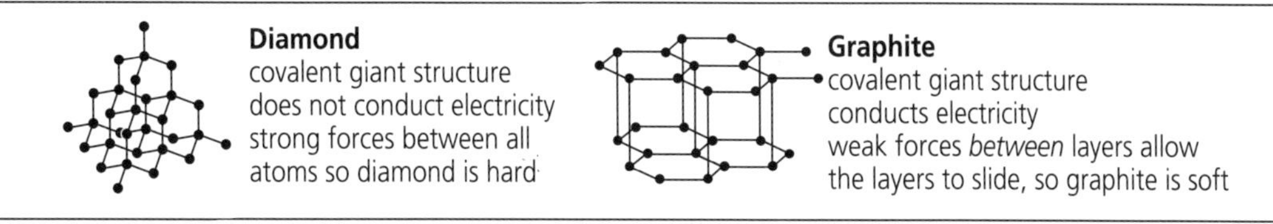

Diamond
covalent giant structure
does not conduct electricity
strong forces between all atoms so diamond is hard

Graphite
covalent giant structure
conducts electricity
weak forces *between* layers allow the layers to slide, so graphite is soft

How can you tell if it is a molecular structure?

- low melting point (less than 200 °C)
- does not conduct electricity
- most do not dissolve in water

How can you tell if it is a covalent giant structure?

- high melting point
- usually hard, though graphite is soft.
- graphite is the only common covalent giant structure that will conduct electricity, the rest don't
- insoluble

How can you tell if it is an ionic giant structure?

- high melting point
- hard
- solid will not conduct electricity, liquids will
- many are soluble in water giving solutions that conduct electricity

Metal elements are held together by a third type of strong force, **metallic bonding**. The metal atoms form ions in a sea of electrons. The negative electrons hold the positive metal ions together.

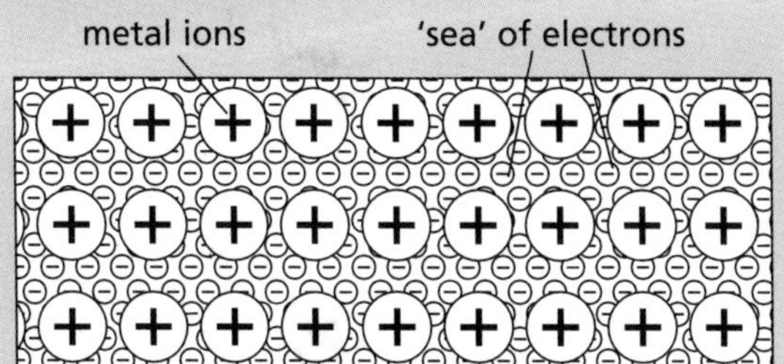

Now do this

2 A solid melts at 100 °C. What type of structure has it got?

3 A solid melts at 1000 °C. What sort of structure has it got?

4 What sort of forces hold the atoms together inside a molecule of hydrogen?

5 What sort of forces hold one molecule of hydrogen to another molecule of hydrogen?

Exam questions

1 Every winter our roads are kept free of ice by lorries which go out every night spreading a combination of sodium chloride and grit. The sodium chloride melts the ice, making a solution of sodium chloride in water. Unfortunately this makes the iron inside cars rust more quickly.

a Two sets of mixtures are mentioned above. What are they? [2]

b Two compounds are mentioned. What are they? [2]

c One element is mentioned. What is it? [1]

[5 marks]

2 Bobby seals up the end of a bicycle pump, then pushes on the plunger.

The pump is full of air.

a Which of these diagrams could show the particles in air?

A 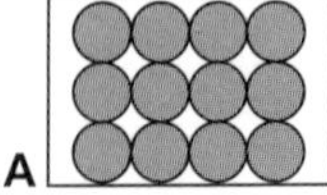 B 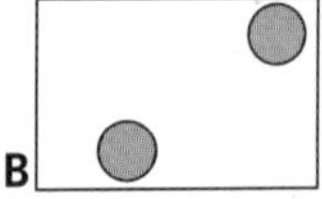 C 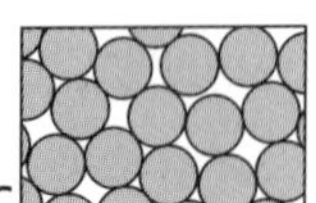 [1]

b i What will happen to the plunger when you push it? [1]

ii Use ideas about particles in gases to explain why. [2]

c i If the pump is full of water, what will happen to the plunger when you push it? [1]

ii Use ideas about particles in liquids to explain why. [2]

[7 marks]

3 The table shows some information about three different solids.

	X	Y	Z
Melting point	high	high	low
Does it dissolve in water?	no	yes	no
Does the solid conduct electricity?	no	no	no
Does the melted substance conduct electricity?	no	yes	no

a i Which two substances are giant structures?

ii How can you tell? [3]

b i Which substance is ionic?

ii How can you tell? [2]

[5 marks]

4 Iron will react with chlorine to make iron chloride. The equation for this is

$2Fe + 3Cl_2 \rightarrow 2FeCl_3$

a What is the formula of iron chloride? [1]

b How many different types of element are inside iron chloride? [1]

c How many atoms of iron are used in the equation? [1]

d How many atoms of chlorine are used in the equation? [1]

e Use your knowledge of structures to explain how the atoms in a solid lump of pure iron are held together. [2]

[6 marks]

5 Calcium oxide (CaO) will combine with water to make calcium hydroxide ($Ca(OH)_2$). Nothing else is formed.

a Write a word equation for this reaction. [1]

b Write a balanced chemical equation for this reaction [2]

[3 marks]

6 When methane (CH_4) burns in oxygen (O_2), carbon dioxide and water are produced.

a Write a word equation for this reaction. [1]

b Write a balanced chemical equation for this reaction [3]

[4 marks]

7 Almost all atoms are made of protons, neutrons and electrons.

a Which of these particles are inside the nucleus of an atom? [1]

When the nuclear power station at Chernobyl released radioactive dust into the air, some of the dust contained the radioactive isotope $^{60}_{27}Co$. The normal isotope of cobalt is $^{59}_{27}Co$.

b How many neutrons are in an atom of $^{60}_{27}Co$? [1]

c What is the mass number of the radioactive isotope? [1]

[4 marks]

8 Selenium (Se) atoms have six electrons in their outer shell.

What will be the formula of a selenium ion? – Explain how you worked it out. [2]

[2 marks]

Changing materials

You will have met the ideas in this section when you worked on the units *Making use of oil*, *Burning and bonding*, *Mining and minerals*, *Construction materials*, *Restless Earth*, *Atmosphere*, *Energy today and tomorrow*. Other units contain smaller amounts of material, such as *Food for thought*, *Transporting chemicals*, *Seeing inside the body* and *Waste not, want not*. This section is divided into ten spreads.

Acids and pH

How do acids react?
How do you measure acidity?

Oil and the alkanes

How is oil made?
What are the hydrocarbons?

Combustion and pollution

What happens when a hydrocarbon burns?
What types of pollution are caused?

Alkenes and plastics

What are alkenes?
What can we use them for?
Recycling plastics

The Earth's surface

What is the Earth made of?
What are plate tectonics?
What are the three types of rock?
How are rocks recycled?

What do rocks tell us about the past?

How did rocks form?
How can we tell past climates from the rocks?
How can we get ores out?

Metals from minerals

How can we extract metals?
How do we use the reactivity series?
Where should you site an industry?

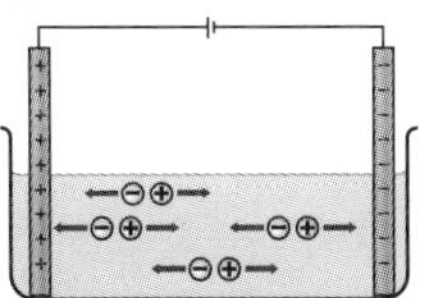

Electrolysis and metals

What is electrolysis?
Extracting aluminium and copper
How do we extract iron?
Why does iron rust?

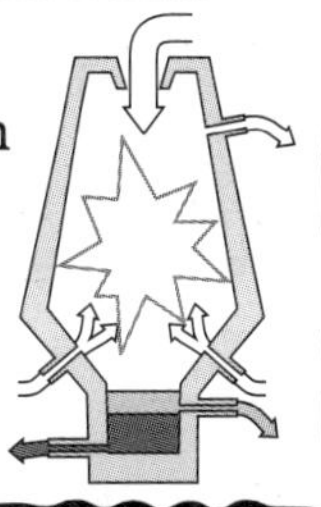

Atmosphere

What is the atmosphere made of?
How was it formed?
How is carbon recycled?
How is water recycled?

Chemical calculations

What is relative atomic mass?
How do you calculate the mass of a chemical in a reaction?
How do you calculate a chemical formula?

Acids and pH

Natural acids are all around us. Acids in orange juice and vinegar give a sharp taste, acids in nettles and bee stings hurt us, acids in our stomachs help digest our food.

How acidic is it?

An indicator such as damp litmus will tell you if something is acidic – it will turn from blue to red. The pH scale tells us more, it tells us how strongly acidic something is.

very acidic					slightly acidic		NEUTRAL ↓	slightly alkaline					very alkaline	
0	1	2	3	4	5	6	7	8	9	10	11	12	13	14

The pH scale

Acids from the lab such as hydrochloric acid or sulphuric acid have a pH of about 1, so they are very acidic. Lemon juice and vinegar are much less acidic with a pH of around 4. Sodium hydroxide is very alkaline and has a pH of about 14, but baking soda is slightly alkaline at around pH 8.

Examiner's tip

Low pH = Acid
7 = Neutral
High pH = Alkali

Bases, alkalis and neutralisation

Substances which **neutralise** acids (destroy acid properties) are called **bases**. Bases which dissolve in water (such as sodium hydroxide) give alkaline solutions and are called **alkalis**. Metal oxides are usually basic. Sodium hydroxide is an alkali.

When acids react with alkalis they produce a **salt** and water. Acids always form salts when they react. Some fertilisers are salts that are made by neutralising acid with ammonia.

ACID	+	ALKALI	→	SALT	+	WATER
H_2SO_4	+	$2NaOH$	→	Na_2SO_4	+	$2H_2O$
sulphuric acid	+	sodium hydroxide	→	sodium sulphate	+	water

Ammonia and fertilisers

Ammonia forms an alkaline solution. This alkali will neutralise acid to make salts such as ammonium sulphate and ammonium nitrate. These salts make good fertilisers.

ACID	+	ALKALI	→	SALT	+	WATER
HNO_3	+	NH_4OH	→	NH_4NO_3	+	H_2O
nitric acid	+	ammonium hydroxide	→	ammonium nitrate	+	water
H_2SO_4	+	$2NH_4OH$	→	$(NH_4)_2SO_4$	+	H_2O
sulphuric acid	+	ammonium hydroxide	→	ammonium sulphate	+	water

Now do this

1. What pH numbers are alkaline?
2. What pH number is neutral?
3. Which is most acidic, pH 3 or pH 6?
4. Bee stings are acidic. Choose the best substance from the list under the pH scale that would neutralise a bee sting.
5. Which fertiliser is made if you react ammonium hydroxide with sulphuric acid?

Acids and metals

Many metals react with acids. The acid gives off its hydrogen and the rest of the acid turns into a salt.

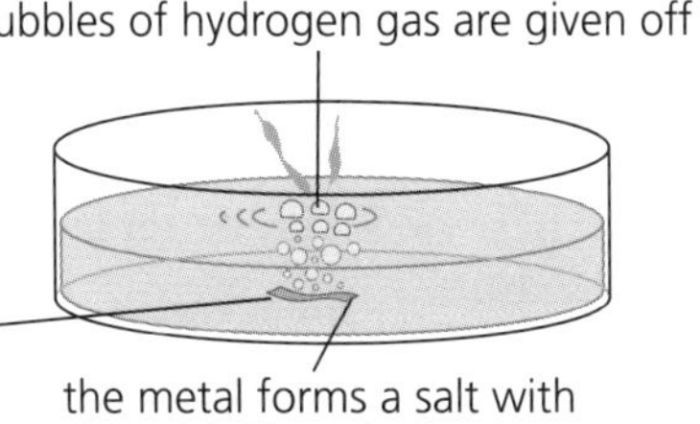

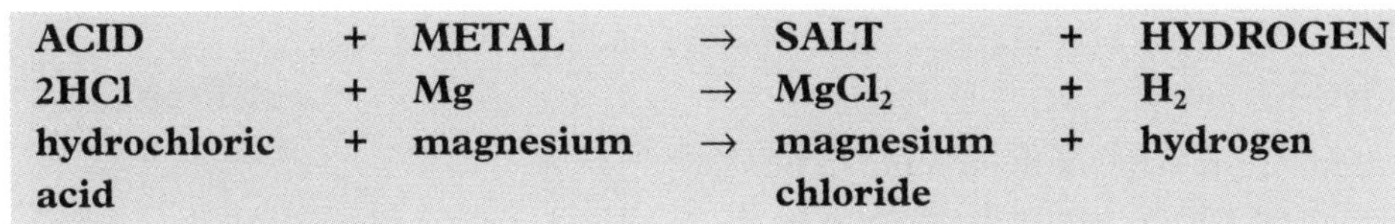

ACID	+	METAL	→	SALT	+	HYDROGEN
2HCl	+	Mg	→	$MgCl_2$	+	H_2
hydrochloric acid	+	magnesium	→	magnesium chloride	+	hydrogen

Not all metals react with acids. Metals such as copper and silver are not reactive enough to be attacked by acids.

Acid and carbonates

Carbonates react with acids to produce a salt, carbon dioxide gas and water.

ACID	+	CARBONATE	→	SALT	+	WATER	+	CARBON DIOXIDE
2HCl	+	$CaCO_3$	→	$CaCl_2$	+	H_2O	+	CO_2
hydrochloric acid	+	calcium carbonate	→	calcium chloride	+	water	+	carbon dioxide

Limestone, chalk and marble are all made of calcium carbonate, $CaCO_3$. Many important buildings are made of limestone. These are attacked by acid rain (acids dissolved in rainwater), especially in the middle of large cities where there is a lot of pollution. Oxides of nitrogen from car exhausts create nitric acid in rain. Sulphur dioxide from burning coal creates sulphuric acid in rain.

You will have reacted marble chips with acid in the laboratory to demonstrate the effect of acid on limestone buildings.

bubbles of carbon dioxide gas are given off

the lumps of carbonate dissolve

the carbonate forms a salt with the acid. The salt dissolves

Now do this

Marble chips are made of calcium carbonate.

6 What gas is formed when you add acid?

7 What would you see when you added the acid?

8 The marble chips get smaller as they react.
Where does the calcium part of the marble chips end up?
Where does the carbon part of the marble chips end up?

9 What is formed when acid rain attacks iron?
What is formed when acid rain attacks marble?

10 Which of these metals will not react with acids?
calcium, copper, iron, magnesium, silver

Oil and the alkanes

Coal, oil and natural gas were formed millions of years ago, they are **fossil fuels**. Once they have been used up they cannot be replaced, they are **non-renewable**.

Wood or sugar-cane are sources of fuels. These fuels can be replaced by growing more wood or sugar-cane. They are **renewable**.

Oil is not just a fuel, we can make useful chemicals out of it. It is a **chemical feedstock**.

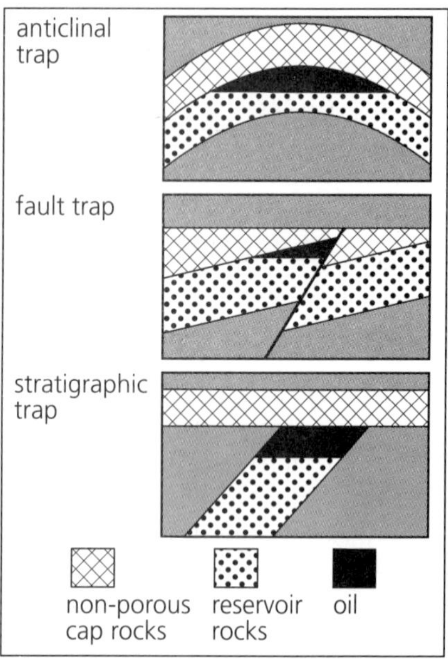

Oil and natural gas

When microscopic sea creatures die some of them settle to the sea bed and are covered in sediment which eventually turns to rock. The solid sediments keep out air, and the pressure and temperature of the layers of rock forms oil from the dead creatures.

The oil soaks up through porous reservoir rocks until it reaches a layer that it can't soak through. If the oil is trapped in the porous rocks it forms an **oil reservoir**. There are several rock formations that trap oil. These rock formations can be identified by measuring how sound waves reflect off the different layers of rock. This is called **seismic surveying**. Oil workers then drill down through the rock layers, bringing up 'cores' of rock. These cores show, in order, the different rock types. Any oil will also show up.

What is crude oil made of?

Crude oil is made of a mixture of compounds which boil at different temperatures. These can be separated by **fractional distillation**. The crude oil is boiled and the mixture of vapours goes up the fractionating column. The column gets cooler nearer the top. As each vapour reaches the part of the column that is just below its own boiling point, that vapour condenses. The highest boiling point liquids condense low down the column where it is hottest, and the lowest boiling point liquids rise up to the cooler part. The column has an exit point for each liquid.

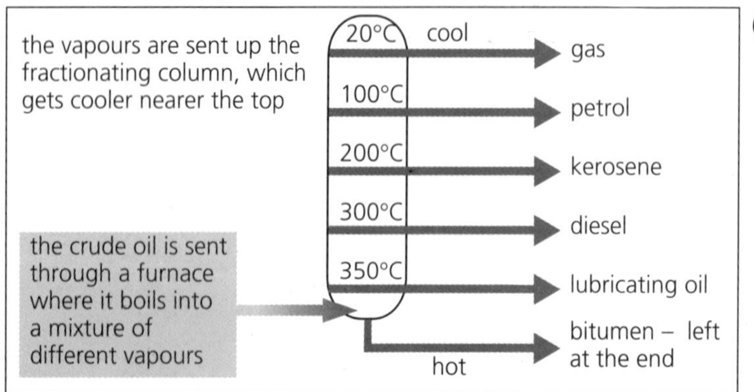

Now do this

1 What are the boiling points of diesel fuel, petrol and kerosene?

2 Why does petrol leave the fractionating column higher up than kerosene?

Many of the compounds in crude oil are made of carbon and hydrogen only, they are called **hydrocarbons**. Hydrocarbons have different numbers of carbon and hydrogen atoms inside their molecules. The more carbon atoms there are, the higher the boiling point.

There are different groups of hydrocarbons, two groups that you need to know are the **alkanes** and the **alkenes**.

Alkanes

The first alkanes in the group are:

methane ethane propane

The carbon atoms in the alkane molecules are linked by single bonds only, so we say that they are **saturated**. Each carbon has four bonds, each hydrogen has one bond.

Alkanes are covalent molecules, so there are weak forces between the molecules. (See *Bonding, molecules and giant structures*, page 62.) As the molecules get bigger, there are more weak forces between the molecules. This makes the boiling points of the alkanes increase as they get bigger. It also makes them harder to burn and more viscous.

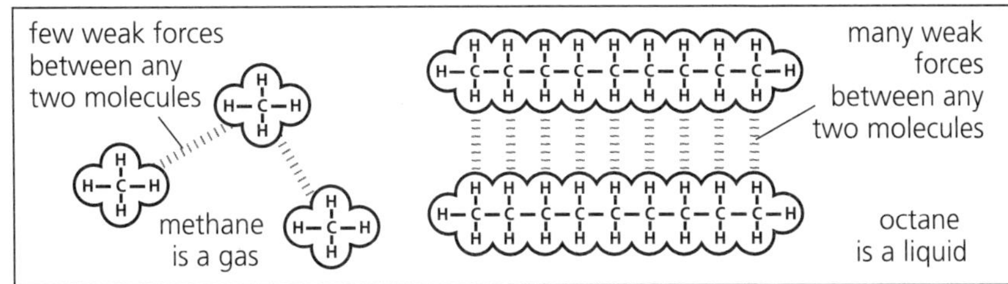

Examiner's tip

Don't confuse the forces *between* molecules with the bonds between atoms *inside* a molecule.

Alkane molecules do not always form straight chains. These two alkanes both have the formula C_4H_{10}. Count up the atoms to check! The first is a straight chain and the second is branched chain molecule. Can you see the branch? Molecules with different arrangements of atoms but which have the same overall formula are called **isomers**.

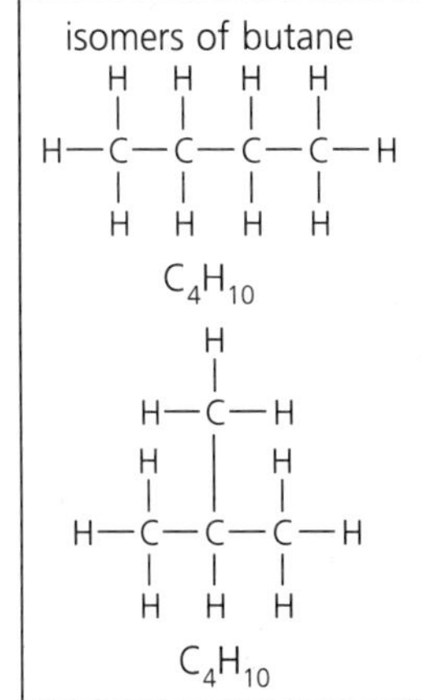

Using alkanes

Methane is an alkane. We call it Natural Gas or Biogas. It is more than a fossil fuel because it can also be produced from decayed organic matter such as animal and plant remains, so it is a renewable resource. Farms and sewage works often produce methane from waste. Rubbish in landfill sites generates methane which must be piped away safely to avoid the risk of explosion.

Methane is used in cookers and gas fires. Propane is bottled gas, it is used in some houses with no gas supply. Larger alkanes are used for petrol and diesel fuel.

Cracking alkanes

There aren't enough small alkanes in crude oil to make all the petrol we want, so we 'crack' the larger alkane molecules using a catalyst, high temperatures and high pressure.

Cracking also produces hydrogen, which is used in the Haber process, and alkenes, which are another type of hydrocarbon. Alkenes are used to make plastics.

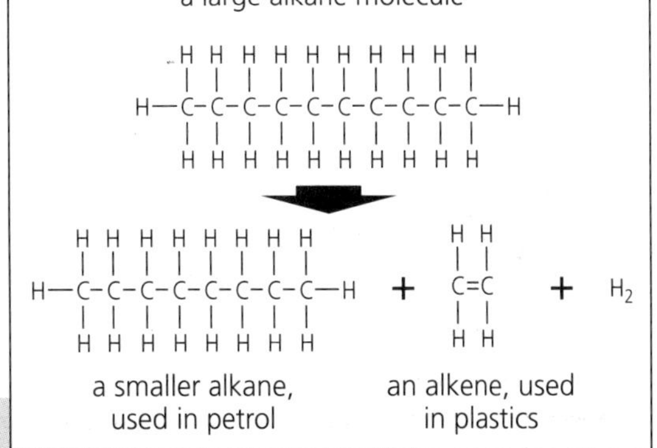

Now do this

3 Draw the structures of the three possible isomers with the formula C_5H_{12}.

Combustion and pollution

Hydrocarbons make good fuels because they transfer a lot of energy.

Chemical energy is transferred to movement energy when a fuel burns in a car engine. Chemical energy from burning natural gas heats up your food on a gas stove.

Oxidation

When something reacts with oxygen to make an oxide we say that it has been **oxidised**. This is an **oxidation** reaction. Burning is an oxidation reaction.

When a hydrocarbon burns with plenty of oxygen the hydrogen atoms form water and the carbon atoms form carbon dioxide.

> **Examiner's tip**
>
> When a hydrocarbon burns, the hydrogen atoms always form water. What the carbon atoms form depends on the amount of oxygen available.

For example, when the methane in a gas cooker burns

methane	+	**oxygen**	→	**carbon dioxide**	+	**water**
CH_4	+	$2O_2$	→	CO_2	+	$2H_2O$

The chemicals get hot, this is an **exothermic** reaction.

If the room is sealed up so not enough oxygen can get in, the carbon in the hydrocarbons will form carbon monoxide instead of carbon dioxide. Carbon monoxide is poisonous and can kill. Gas cookers and some gas fires are only safe if the room is well ventilated.

methane + oxygen → carbon monoxide + water

If the oxygen levels drop further, the hydrogen atoms in the methane still react to make water but the carbon stops burning, it forms soot.

methane + oxygen → carbon + water

Flash points

Liquid fuels such as petrol won't burn. When petrol catches fire it is the petrol vapour that burns. The lowest temperature at which a fuel will give off enough vapour to burn is its **flash point**. Diesel fuel has larger molecules than petrol. With more very weak forces between the molecules diesel has a higher flash point.

Now do this

1. Write a word equation to show what happens when methane burns in oxygen.
2. Why is using a gas ring not safe in a sealed room?
3. Propane is C_3H_8. Write a balanced chemical equation to show what happens when propane burns in oxygen.
4. Why is it more difficult to set fire to diesel fuel than petrol?

Carbon dioxide and the greenhouse effect

Ultra-violet rays from the Sun go through the Earth's atmosphere and heat up the Earth's surface. The warm Earth gives off infra-red radiation which leaves the Earth.

Greenhouse gases in the atmosphere absorb some of this infra-red radiation. This makes the Earth get warmer.

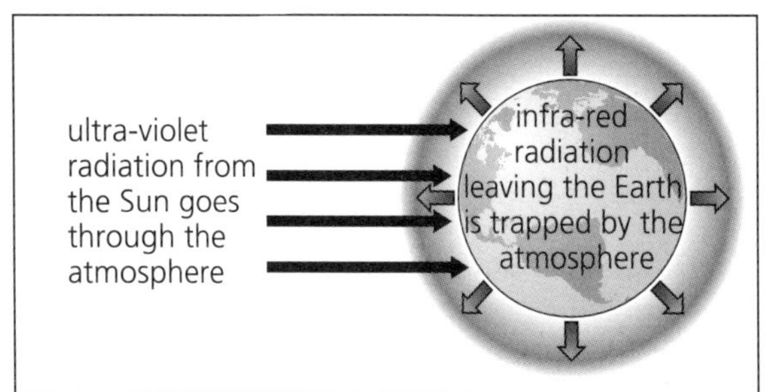

The major greenhouse gas is carbon dioxide. Because we burn millions of tonnes of oil and coal every year carbon dioxide is being produced faster than it is being removed. This is slowly making the Earth warmer. Another greenhouse gas is methane, which is produced by farm animals and from rotting vegetation.

Pollution from burning fuels

Petrol burns *inside* car engines, where the supply of oxygen is limited (car engines are called internal combustion engines). This means that carbon monoxide is formed along with soot and unburned fuel, which all come out in the exhaust. The high temperature in the engine also forms nitrogen oxides. All these gases can cause pollution.

Fossil fuels such as coal and oil contain small amounts of sulphur. When the fuel burns sulphur turns into sulphur oxides. These oxides dissolve in rain water to make sulphuric acid or acid rain. Acid rain attacks buildings made of limestone, and also changes the soil slightly, which harms animals and plants.

High temperatures in engines form nitrogen oxides. If there is too much nitrogen oxide and unburnt hydrocarbons in the air, the sunlight can make them react with the air. This makes photochemical smog. **Smog** is a mixture of irritant gases that make your eyes water and cause severe breathing problems. Other polluting gases are nitrogen oxides, unburnt hydrocarbons and carbon monoxide. Catalytic converters in car exhaust systems turn these gases into nitrogen, carbon dioxide and water, which are less harmful.

Now do this

5 Use your understanding of the radiation hitting the Earth and leaving the Earth to explain the greenhouse effect

6 Explain how fossil fuels are responsible for acid rain.

7 Give **two** problems caused by acid rain.

Alkenes and plastics

Alkenes

The carbon atoms in the alkane molecules are linked by single bonds, so we say that they are **saturated**. The other important group of hydrocarbons is the **alkenes**. The alkenes all have a double bond between two carbon atoms, so we say that they are **unsaturated**.

This is ethene, C_2H_4. It is the simplest of the alkenes. It is *not* the same as ethane. Ethene has a double bond, ethane doesn't.

$$\begin{matrix} H & & H \\ | & & | \\ C & = & C \\ | & & | \\ H & & H \end{matrix}$$

ethene

You can test for an unsaturated compound using bromine water. Unsaturated compounds will turn bromine water from orange to colourless. Saturated compounds have no effect on bromine water.

$$\begin{matrix} H\ H \\ |\ \ | \\ C{=}C \\ |\ \ | \\ H\ H \end{matrix} + \underset{\text{orange}}{Br{-}Br} \rightarrow \underset{\text{colourless}}{\begin{matrix} H\ H \\ |\ \ | \\ Br{-}C{-}C{-}Br \\ |\ \ | \\ H\ H \end{matrix}}$$

Plastics

The double bond in alkenes is very important as other chemicals such as bromine can join on to the double bond – this is called an **addition reaction**. In addition reactions the double bond turns back to a single bond.

Alkenes are often used to make plastics. Plastics are made of small molecules or **monomers**, which are joined together to form long chain molecules called **polymers**. Polymerisation often needs high pressures and a catalyst.

monomer	+	monomer	+	monomer	+	monomer	→	polymer
(M)	+	(M)	+	(M)	+	(M)	→	–(M)–(M)–(M)–(M)–

The alkenes are good monomers. The double bond allows the alkene molecules to add on to each other to make long chains – this is **addition polymerisation**. Ethene is the monomer used to make poly(ethene) or polythene.

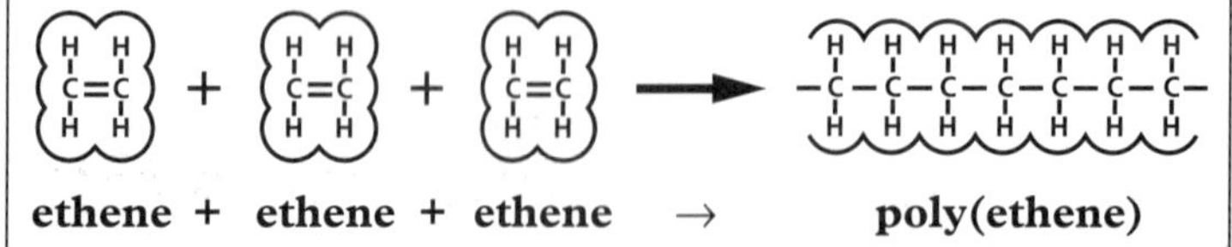

Examiner's tip

This is an addition reaction, the double bond disappears.

Different alkenes make different types of plastic which are used to do different jobs.

Polythene is cheap and flexible, so it is used to make polythene bags.

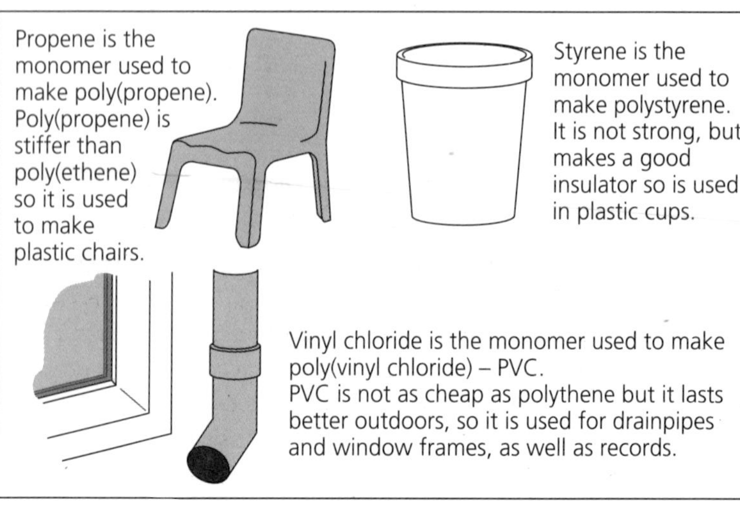

Now do this

1 Write the formula of ethene.

2 What makes ethene different from ethane?

3 The vinyl chloride monomer is $\begin{array}{cc} H & Cl \\ | & | \\ C & = C \\ | & | \\ H & H \end{array}$ Draw three links of the polymer.

4 Draw the structure of the monomer which would produce this polymer:

$$\begin{array}{cccccccccccccccc} H & CN & H & CN & H & CN & H & CN & H & CN & H & CN & H & CN & H & CN \\ | & | & | & | & | & | & | & | & | & | & | & | & | & | & | & | \\ -C- & C- & C- & C- & C- & C- & C- & C- & C- & C- & C- & C- & C- & C- & C- & C- \\ | & | & | & | & | & | & | & | & | & | & | & | & | & | & | & | \\ H & H & H & H & H & H & H & H & H & H & H & H & H & H & H & H \end{array}$$

Thermosoftening plastics

Plastics such as polythene, polypropene and PVC go soft when you heat them, they are all thermosoftening plastics. They are made of long chains. When you heat them the chains can move and slide past each other, so it is easy to turn the plastic into new shapes. PVC is used as the flexible insulation in electric wires.

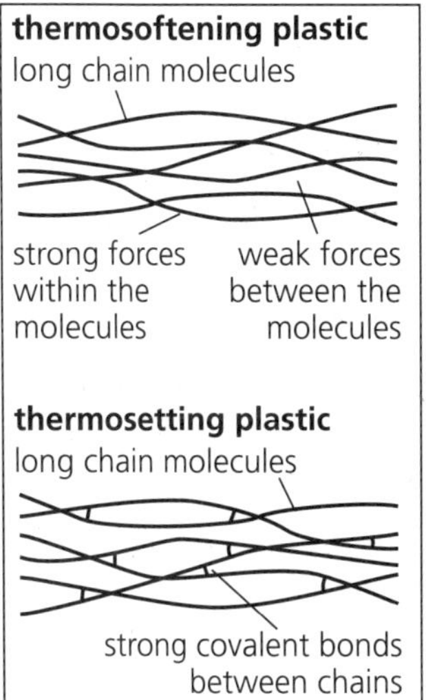

Thermosetting plastics

Thermosetting plastics do not soften as they get hotter. They stay solid, and go black or even burn if you heat them for long enough. They are also made of molecules which have long chains, but their chains are held to each other by **cross-links**. The cross-links stop the molecules sliding past each other, so they stay stiff and solid.

'Plastic' light switches are made out of a thermosetting polymer.

Throwing plastics away

Plastics do not rot, they are not attacked by decomposers in the soil. Plastics are **non-biodegradable**. A few modern **biodegradable** plastics have now been produced which will rot when they are thrown away.

We can get rid of waste plastics in special incinerators. They burn the plastic and we can use the heat produced. Plastics often give off poisonous fumes when they burn. The incinerators have to stop the fumes getting into the atmosphere, which makes them expensive.

We can also recycle some plastics and so save the oil that they were made from and we do not have to use more oil to make new plastic.

Alkenes and margarine

Margarine and butter are both made from fat containing tiny droplets of water. The fat in butter comes from milk, the fat in margarine comes from plant oils. Plant oils are too runny to make a good margarine. The oils are runny because they contain a C=C double bond. They are alkenes. Margarine makers react this double bond with hydrogen. This turns the double bond back to a single bond, which stops the margarine from being too runny.

Now do this

5 What happens to a thermosoftening plastic when you heat it?

6 Give **one** advantage of recycling waste plastic.

7 Give **one** problem of recycling waste plastic such as drinks bottles.

8 What is reacted with plant oils to make margarine?

The Earth's surface

What is the Earth made of?

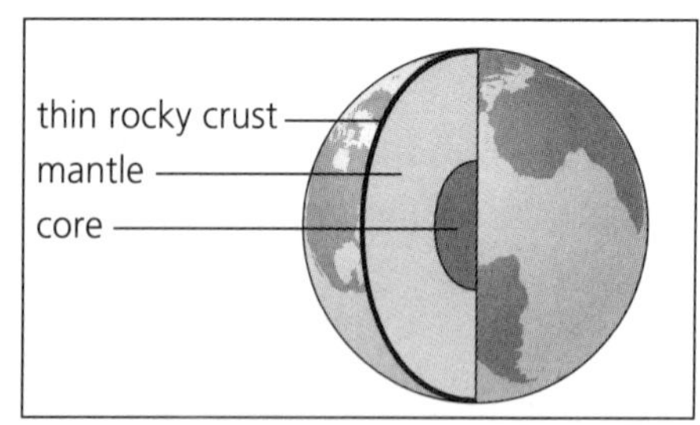

- The top layer of the Earth is a thin rocky **crust**.
- The **mantle** is under the crust. It is made of very hot solid rock that can slowly move. It can melt into **magma**.
- In the middle of the Earth is the **core**. The Earth's core is even hotter and is liquid.

Plate tectonics

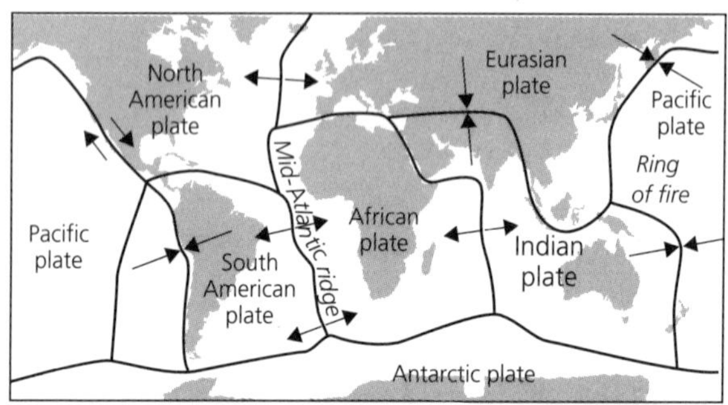

The thin rocky crust of the Earth is made up of large, slowly moving sections called **plates**. The plates move a few centimetres each year and they may be moving away from each other or towards each other. The forces created where the plates move against each other are so strong that earthquakes, volcanoes and mountain ranges occur at the edges of the plates.

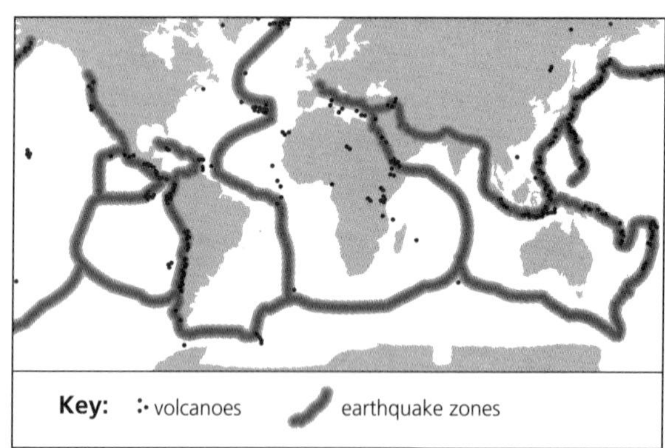

The Atlantic Ocean is getting wider by at least a centimetre every year. This is because the plates are moving apart, leaving a gap down the centre of the ocean floor. Magma flows into the gap, making a ridge of new rocks. This is called **sea floor spreading**. There are earthquakes and sometimes volcanoes on the sea floor.

When two plates move together, one plate is forced underneath the other. The plate that it is pushed down into the mantle melts and forms magma. The plate on the surface buckles and gets pushed up into mountain ranges.

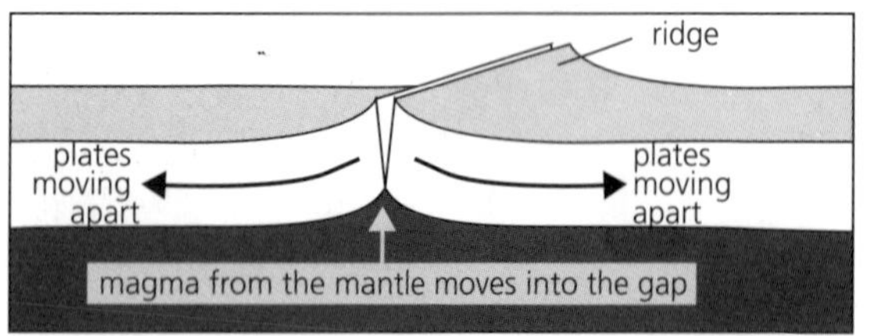

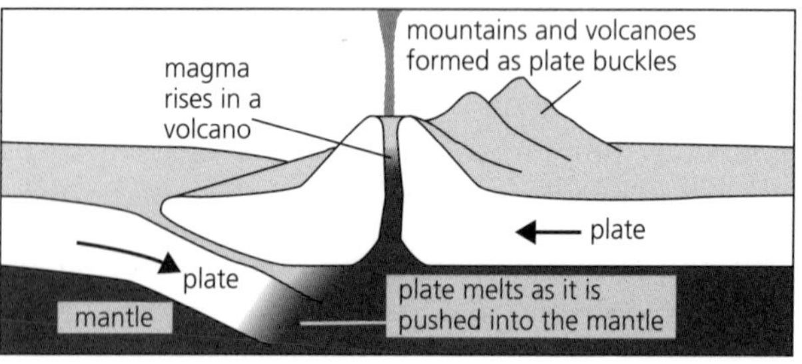

The liquid rock (magma) rises to the surface and makes volcanoes.

The moving crust also causes earthquakes. Most earthquakes are very minor, but some can be much more powerful. The place on the surface above the centre of an earthquake is the **epicentre**. The epicentres of most earthquakes are near the edges of plates.

Now do this

1 When two plates push into each other, one plate stays on the surface and the other plate disappears.
  a Where does this plate go?
  b What happens to the rocks of that plate?

2 What problems are likely to happen in countries where there are two plates that are pushing into each other?

Types of rock

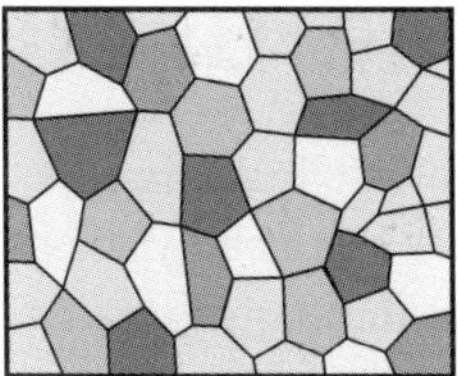
igneous – slow cooling, large interlocking crystals

There are three types of rock – igneous, sedimentary and metamorphic.

Igneous rocks are made from magma which has cooled down and solidified. It usually forms interlocking crystals of different **minerals**. Granite and basalt are igneous rocks.

Sedimentary rocks are small pieces of older rock, for example sand or mud, which settle and form layers. As the sediments build up, the layers at the bottom are compressed by the weight of the layers above them, which helps turn them into a solid rock. Often, chemicals soaking through the rock layers will also cement the grains together into a solid. Limestone, sandstone and mudstone are sedimentary rocks.

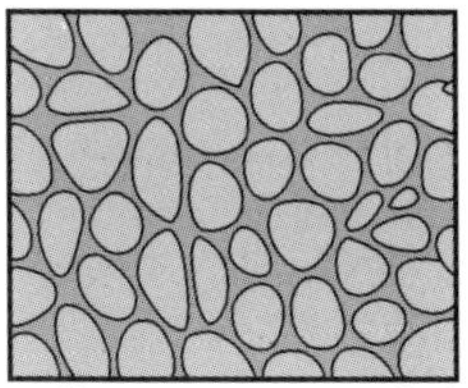
sedimentary – rounded grains and fossils

Metamorphic rocks are rocks which have changed after they were originally formed. This is usually caused by high temperature or pressure from other rocks. The final rock depends on what you start with and what happened to it. Marble and slate are metamorphic rocks.

Examiner's tip

Fossils are only formed in sedimentary rocks.
Distorted fossils *may* still be present if the sedimentary rock changes to metamorphic.
Fossils are *never* present in igneous rocks.

The rock cycle

Rocks are continually being broken down into pieces which are then carried away by wind, streams and rivers. This is called **erosion**.

Eventually the pieces settle, are buried and solidify into layers of sedimentary rock. Earth movements can then bring the rock back to the surface so that it is weathered all over again. Earth movements can bring any of the three types of rock up to the surface, where they will be weathered and eventually form sedimentary rock.

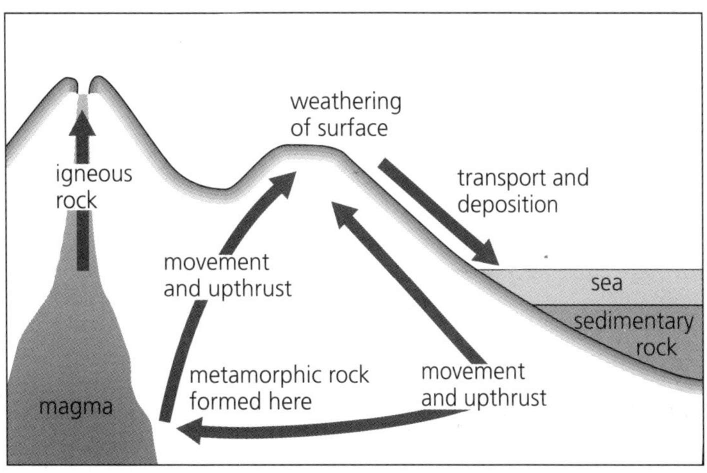

Now do this

3 What would you look for to decide if a rock is igneous?

4 Suggest **two** features that may be found in sedimentary rocks that you would not expect to find in igneous rock.

5 Deposits of igneous rock are often surrounded by metamorphic rock. Suggest why.

Useful rocks

Rocks tell us what the world was like at the time that they were formed. They give us clues about how they were formed, where they formed, and sometimes even what the climate might have been like at the time.

How fast did an igneous rock form?

As igneous rocks cool they form crystals. Large crystals are only produced if the crystals grow very slowly. Crystals which form rapidly are always much smaller.

Basalt is an igneous rock which is made of very small crystals, so it must have cooled rapidly. This means that the molten rock got to the Earth's surface where it could lose heat rapidly.

Granite is an igneous rock made of large crystals, so it must have cooled down very slowly. This tells us that it was underground when it cooled, well insulated from the Earth's surface.

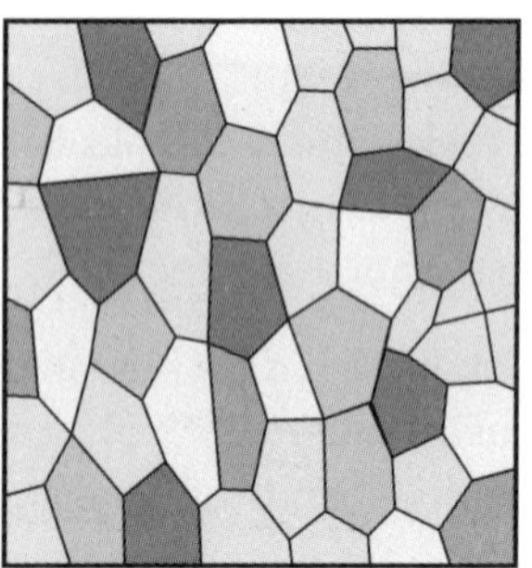

igneous – slow cooling, large interlocking crystals

igneous – rapid cooling, small interlocking crystals

How old are sedimentary rocks?

Usually the oldest rocks form the bottom layer and the youngest rocks form the top layer. The thicker the layer of rock, the longer it took to form.

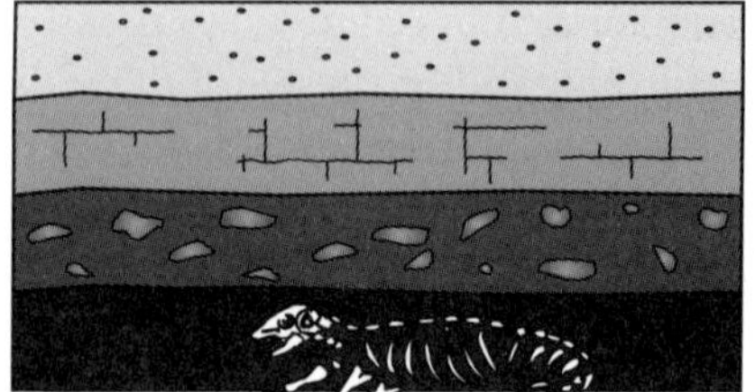

What was the area like when a rock was forming?

Chalk is a sedimentary rock made from sea shells. The area where it formed must have been under water.

Coal is formed when fern trees collapse and are buried in mud. The area where coal formed must have been swampy.

Sandstone is made in places where there is a lot of sand. This might mean that the area was a desert when the sandstone was formed.

Salt deposits are formed when a lot of salty water evaporates. Salt forms in very hot areas where there are also shallow seas. The seas evaporate, leaving beds of salt behind.

Now do this

1. Granite is made of large crystals. What does that tell you about the way it cooled? Explain how that tells you that granite formed underground.
2. There are underground layers of salt in Cheshire. What does that tell you about that area in the past?
3. Beachy Head is famous for its chalk cliffs. The cliffs are 150 metres high. What does this tell you about that area in the past?

Using rocks

The rocks of the Earth's crust are very useful to us. We can dig some rocks out of the ground and use them straight away to make useful substances. Most rocks can't be used straight away. The useful part of the rock, the mineral, is usually mixed in with other bits of rock that we don't want. This combination of mineral and other rock is called an ore. Often the mineral inside the rock is a metal compound such as a metal oxide (or a metal sulphide).

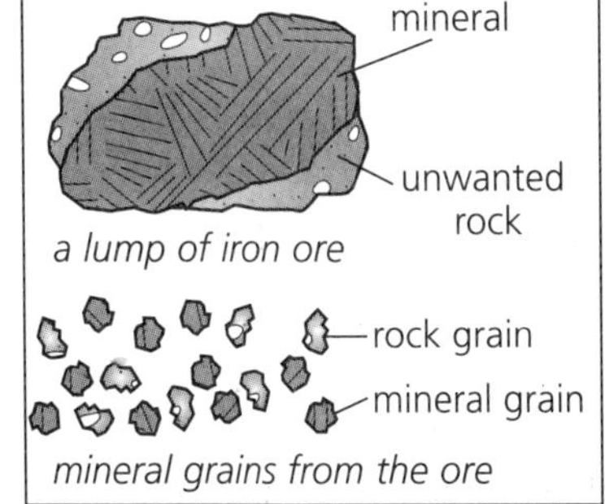

a lump of iron ore

mineral grains from the ore

Extracting minerals from ores

Ores are mixtures, so a method for separating mixtures is used.

A lump of ore from a mine will have the mineral that we want and also unwanted rock. We grind the ore into small grains. This gives a **mixture** of different bits of mineral and rock.

If the mineral grains are heavier than the rest of the rock you can use panning to separate the two. You swirl the mixture in a shallow dish of water making the lighter rock grains wash over the edge leaving the heavy mineral grains in the bottom of the dish. This is the way that prospectors used to 'pan for gold' in the gold rush.

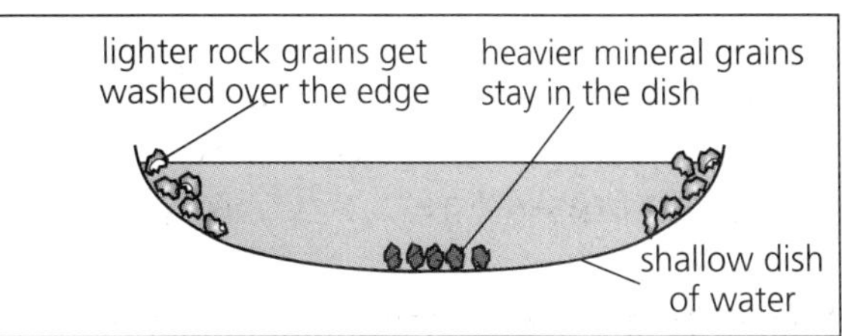

Where should we look for minerals?

Minerals are not always easy to detect. Iron ore is magnetic, so we can use a compass. Other minerals change the electrical conductivity of the ground. Sometimes a mineral in the ore will dissolve slightly and affect the plants that grow on the surface. Prospectors sometimes know where to look for minerals just by changes in the vegetation!

Uses for calcium carbonate

Calcium carbonate is the mineral in limestone and in chalk. It is pure enough not to need separating. It used as stone for buildings and for roads, or to make cement or other chemicals. It is also put on to fields to neutralise acid soil (remember the reaction between acid and marble chips?).

If a lump of limestone is heated very strongly it goes powdery and changes into calcium oxide (quicklime). The limestone breaks down when it gets very hot. This is called **thermal decomposition**.

calcium carbonate → calcium oxide + carbon dioxide
$$CaCO_3 \rightarrow CaO + CO_2$$

Calcium oxide will react with water to make calcium hydroxide (slaked lime).

calcium oxide + water → calcium hydroxide
$$CaO + H_2O \rightarrow Ca(OH)_2$$

Calcium oxide and calcium hydroxide are alkaline, so they will react with acids. They are also both used to make other chemicals.

Now do this

4 Once a metal ore has been mined it is usually ground into small pieces. Explain why.

5 Give **three** uses for limestone.

6 Write a word equation to show what happens when limestone is heated.

Metals from minerals

Using reactivity to get metals from their minerals

Many minerals are a compound of a metal with oxygen or sulphur. For example, iron oxide is a mineral in iron ore. To get metals out of their minerals we have to remove the oxygen.

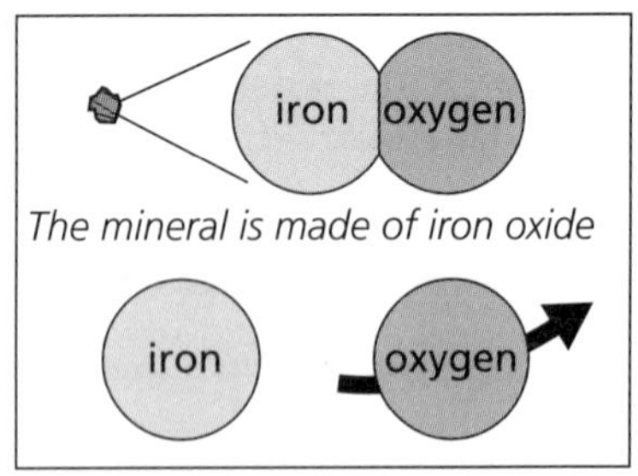

The mineral is made of iron oxide

Any reaction that takes oxygen away from an oxide is called a **reduction** reaction.
We can do this by using a more reactive element to take away the oxygen.
The least reactive metals only combine weakly with oxygen, or do not react at all.
The most reactive metals combine strongly with oxygen, so they will steal oxygen out of other compounds, leaving the less reactive metal behind. The reactive metal has **displaced** the less reactive metal.

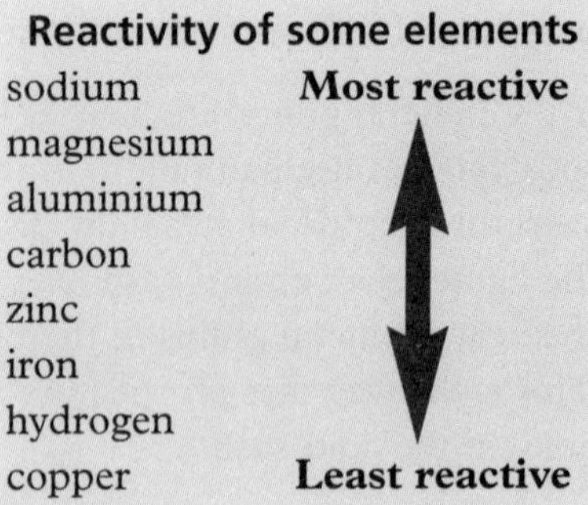

Aluminium powder is so reactive that it displaces iron from iron oxide, it steals the oxygen from the iron oxide. The reaction gets so hot that the iron melts. This is the Thermit reaction.

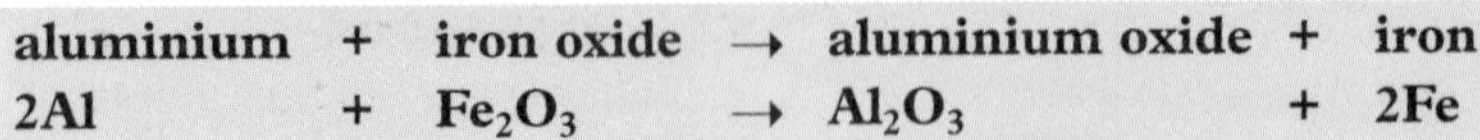

aluminium	+	**iron oxide**	→	**aluminium oxide**	+	**iron**
2Al	+	**Fe_2O_3**	→	**Al_2O_3**	+	**2Fe**

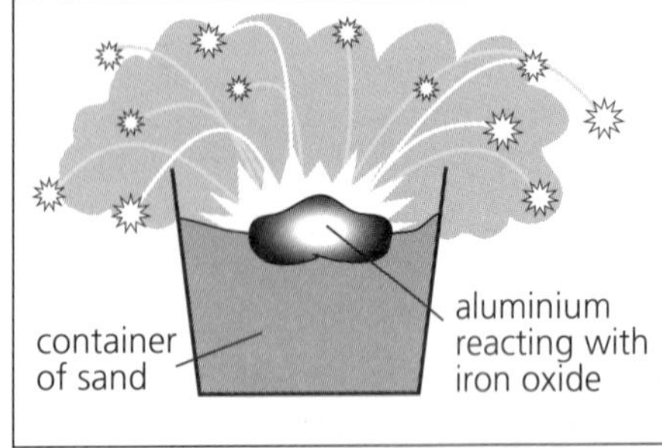

Now do this

1. Complete the equation

   aluminium + iron oxide → ? + ?

2. Complete the equation

   aluminium + copper oxide → ? + ?

3. Look at this list:
   iron oxide, copper oxide, sodium oxide.

   a Which of these will hydrogen react with?

   b What will be formed in the cases that do react?

Magnesium is more reactive than copper, it displaces copper from copper compounds.

It can steal oxygen out of copper oxide leaving the copper.

magnesium	+	**copper oxide**	→	**magnesium oxide**	+	**copper**
Mg	+	**CuO**	→	**MgO**	+	**Cu**

It can steal sulphate out of copper sulphate leaving the copper.

magnesium + copper sulphate → magnesium sulphate + copper
Mg + $CuSO_4$ → $MgSO_4$ + Cu

copper sulphate solution
magnesium ribbon becomes coated with copper

Carbon is also used to reduce metal oxides. Carbon is more reactive than iron and zinc, so it will take oxygen away from iron oxide and from zinc oxide. When carbon steals oxygen from iron oxide, iron is left behind. When carbon steals oxygen from zinc oxide, zinc is left behind.

carbon + zinc oxide → zinc + carbon dioxide
C + 2ZnO → 2Zn + CO_2

Where should you site an industry?

Different industries have developed in different parts of the country. There are always reasons for this, even if the reasons are now out of date!

Any industry needs:
- raw materials – from local mines or they might have to come from far away.
- energy – if a lot of energy is needed the industry must be near a coalfield or power station
- transport system – any form of transport is expensive, so industries need to keep it down to the minimum. Railways are good for moving bulk quantities, nearby motorways make it easier to transport goods all over the country. The industry might have to be near a port if it uses materials from other countries
- workers – if there is a similar industry in the area it will be easier to get people who understand how to do the jobs.

Not in my backyard?

Any company which wants to extract minerals has to get permission. The people who live nearby might want the company to go ahead, or they might oppose it.

Reasons for
- we need minerals to make the tools and chemicals that help us to live
- there will be jobs with the company
- local economy will improve – more food and equipment will be bought at the local shops.

Reasons against
- might ruin an area of natural beauty
- minerals might dissolve in water seeping through the mine and pollute streams and rivers
- increased traffic
- noise and dust may upset farm animals.

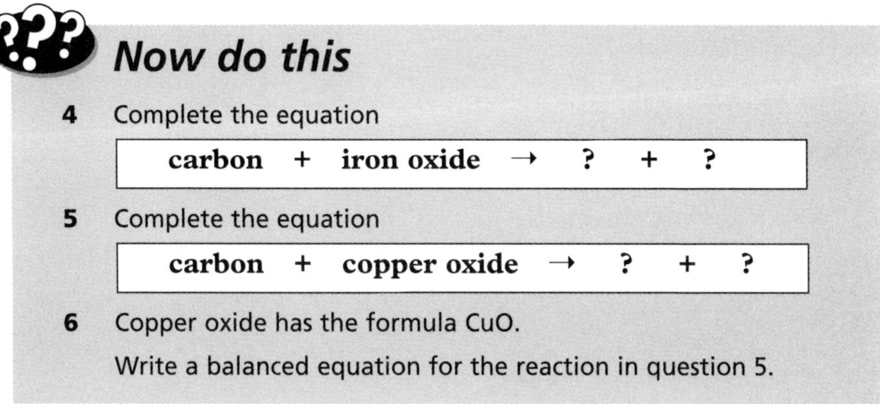

Now do this

4 Complete the equation

carbon + iron oxide → ? + ?

5 Complete the equation

carbon + copper oxide → ? + ?

6 Copper oxide has the formula CuO.

Write a balanced equation for the reaction in question 5.

Electrolysis to extract metals

We can use electricity to split ionic compounds apart, this is **electrolysis**.

Ionic compounds don't conduct electricity when they are solid but they do conduct if they are melted or dissolved. An electric current is a movement of charge. In an ionic solid the ions are held in place, so they can't move. In liquids the ions can move, so the current is carried by the ions. Ionic liquids are called **electrolytes**.

Ions are attracted by the oppositely charged electrode. The **cathode** is negative; it attracts positive ions. When the positive ions reach the cathode they pick up electrons from the cathode and turn into neutral atoms. Metal ions are always positively charged, so they are always attracted to the negative cathode.

The **anode** is the positive electrode; it attracts negative ions. When negative ions reach the anode they usually give their extra electrons to the anode and turn into neutral atoms.

Electrolysis is very useful for extracting metals that are too reactive for carbon to reduce. Even water can be electrolysed if it is impure. The water contains H^+ and OH^- ions, which produce hydrogen at the cathode and oxygen at the anode during electrolysis.

negative ions are attracted to the anode...
positive ions are attracted to the cathode...
anode
cathode
...where they turn into neutral atoms
...where they turn into neutral atoms

Using electrolysis to extract aluminium

Aluminium ore contains aluminium oxide. It melts at a high temperature, so a substance called cryolite can be added, which lowers the melting point and saves energy. The carbon lining of the tank is connected to an electricity supply to make the cathode. Carbon anodes are lowered into the molten mixture of aluminium oxide and cryolite.

Aluminium ions are positive, so they are attracted to the negative cathode and are neutralised. Molten aluminium collects at the bottom of the tank. Oxygen is formed at the anodes, reacting with the carbon anodes to make carbon dioxide.

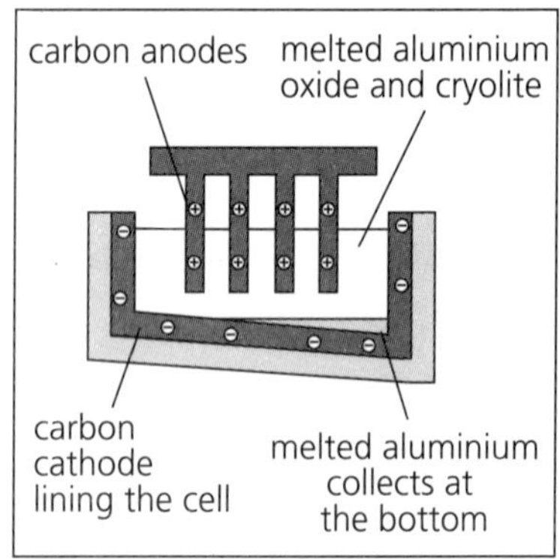

At the cathode: $Al^{+++} + 3e^- \rightarrow Al$ **At the anode:** $O^{--} \rightarrow \frac{1}{2}O_2 + 2e^-$

Using electrolysis to purify copper

The copper to be purified is made into an anode. Pure copper is used as the cathode. During electrolysis the copper dissolves from the impure anode and plates on to the cathode. The pure copper cathode becomes thicker as more copper sticks on to it.

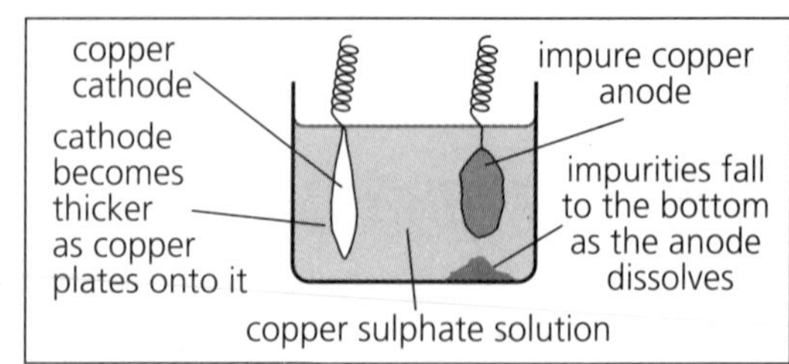

At the cathode: $Cu^{++} + 2e^- \rightarrow Cu$ **At the anode:** $Cu \rightarrow Cu^{++} + 2e^-$

Now do this

1 Write an equation for what happens at the cathode when water is electrolysed.

2 Write an equation for what happens at the anode when melted aluminium oxide is electrolysed.

Iron

Extracting iron by reduction

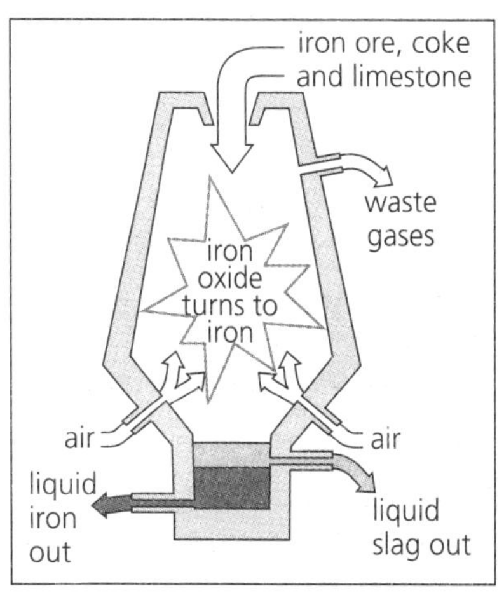

Iron ore is made of iron oxide. Iron is extracted from iron ore using carbon in a blast furnace. The carbon reacts with some of the air to make carbon monoxide inside the blast furnace, and the carbon monoxide goes on to reduce the iron ore.

Iron ore and coke are put at the top of the furnace and air is pumped in through the holes at the side. There is so much heat given out in this reaction that the iron melts and collects at the bottom of the furnace. Limestone is used to react with impurities in the iron ore and turn them into liquid slag. The slag floats on top of the iron and is drained out of the furnace before the liquid iron is run out.

Carbon and oxygen form carbon monoxide:

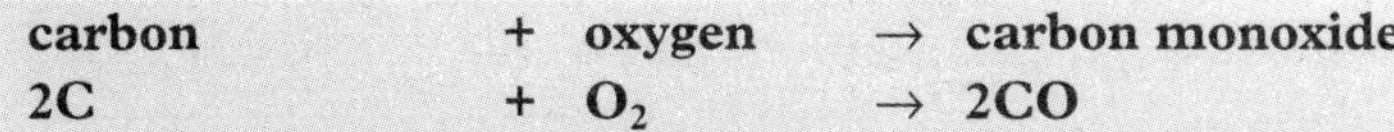

carbon	+	**oxygen**	→	**carbon monoxide**
2C	+	**O_2**	→	**2CO**

Carbon monoxide takes the oxygen from the iron oxide:

carbon monoxide	+	**iron oxide**	→	**carbon dioxide**	+	**iron**
3CO	+	**Fe_2O_3**	→	**2Fe**	+	**$3CO_2$**

Rusting iron

When iron rusts it reacts with oxygen in the air to make iron oxide. Any reaction where oxygen is added to something is an **oxidation** reaction. Rusting is the reaction of iron with oxygen, but water is needed as well.

Iron ships at the bottom of very deep oceans don't go rusty; there is plenty of water but there isn't enough oxygen dissolved in the water. Iron objects in a dry desert don't go rusty; there is oxygen in the air but there is no water.

Rusting happens much faster if salt is present. Cars rust quickly in the winter because of the salt which is put on the roads.

Stopping the rust

- Painting – makes an air-tight layer of paint. The iron rusts once the paint is scratched.
- Galvanising – makes an air-tight layer of zinc, a reactive metal. The iron is protected even if the zinc is scratched because zinc is more reactive than iron.
- Alloying – stainless steel is an alloy made of iron with a small amount of other metals such as chromium added to it. The chromium atoms form a protective layer at the surface of the iron. If the surface is scratched, a new protective layer forms again.

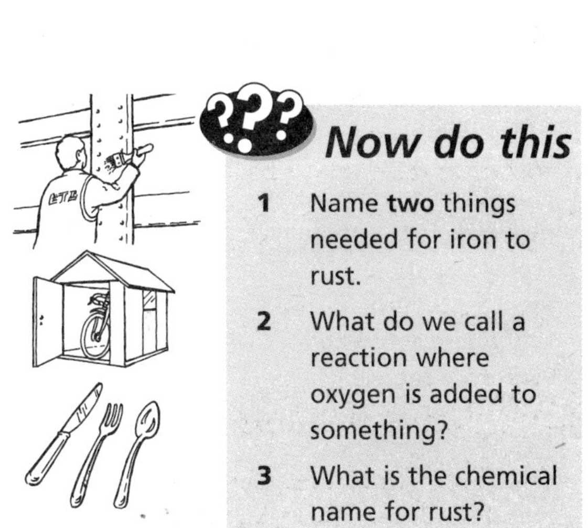

Now do this

1 Name **two** things needed for iron to rust.

2 What do we call a reaction where oxygen is added to something?

3 What is the chemical name for rust?

The atmosphere

All planets have an atmosphere, though sometimes it is hard to detect.

Atmospheres on different planets contain different gases. The Earth is the only planet with an atmosphere that we can breathe. As you go up through the atmosphere the pressure gets less.

The Sun is the major energy source for the Earth, and this has enormous effects on the atmosphere.

Our atmosphere is a mixture of gases

Oxygen is one of the two most important gases in air, but it does not make up a large amount of the air. The air is made of approximately:

- 80 % nitrogen – which does very little
- 20 % oxygen – a most important gas
- small amounts of other gases, including carbon dioxide
- 0.04 % carbon dioxide – the other important gas.

Our atmosphere also contains large amounts of water vapour, but the amount changes with the weather.

Examiner's tip

Carbon dioxide in the atmosphere is vital for plant photosynthesis, notice how little there is of it!

Amounts of nitrogen and of oxygen don't change because they are being replaced at about the same rate as they are being used up. We think that levels of carbon dioxide are increasing *very* slowly because it is being made slightly faster than it is being used up.

Carbon dioxide is recycled

Carbon dioxide from the atmosphere is taken in by plants during photosynthesis – this uses the energy from the Sun. Carbon goes from the plants to the animals when the animals eat the plants.

Carbon dioxide is dissolved in the oceans and is used by organisms to make their shells. Carbon dioxide goes back into the air when:

- plants and animals respire
- plants and animals decay
- plants such as trees burn (combustion)
- fossil fuels burn
- acid rain reacts with carbonate rocks such as chalk.

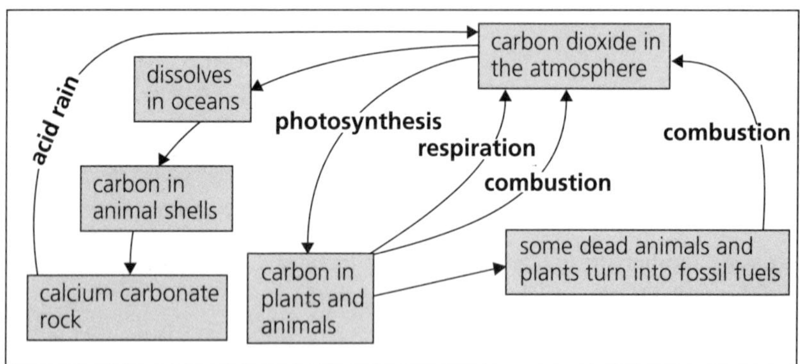

Now do this

1 What is the approximate percentage of carbon dioxide in the atmosphere?

2 What is the approximate percentage of oxygen in the atmosphere?

3 What are the **two** main processes that put carbon dioxide into the atmosphere?

4 What are the **two** main processes that remove carbon dioxide from the atmosphere?

Water is also recycled

Water goes through a cycle in a similar way to carbon dioxide. Enormous amounts of water are spread throughout the whole of the atmosphere as invisible water vapour, as well as the visible droplets which make the clouds. The water cycle is driven by energy from the Sun.

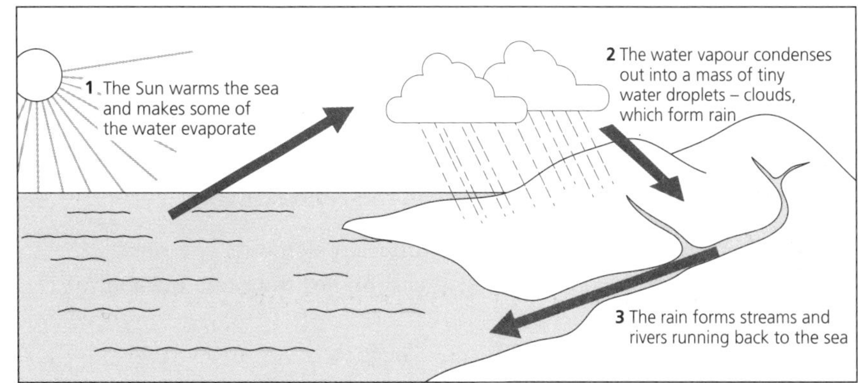

Where did the atmosphere come from?

Billions of years ago there was no oxygen in the Earth's atmosphere. Life did not exist. The atmosphere was formed by volcanoes which were producing ammonia, methane, carbon dioxide and water.

Three billion years ago the first simple plant life appeared. The plants turned the carbon dioxide and water into food and oxygen – photosynthesis had started.

The amount of oxygen in the atmosphere increased, and the different types of living things increased, until the living things were using up the oxygen as fast as it was being made. This now keeps the amount of oxygen constant.

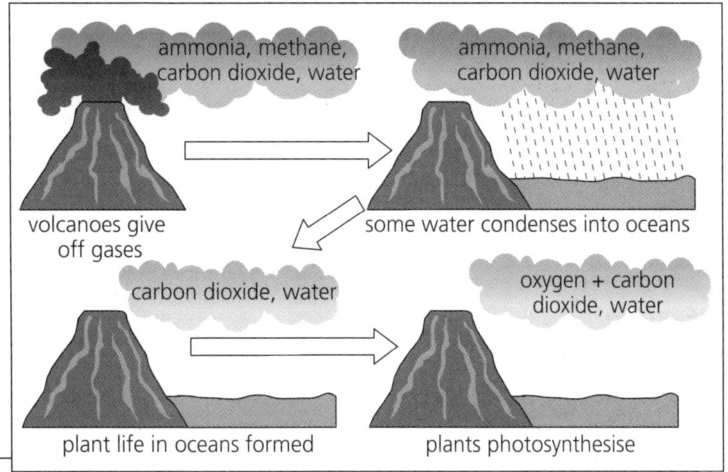

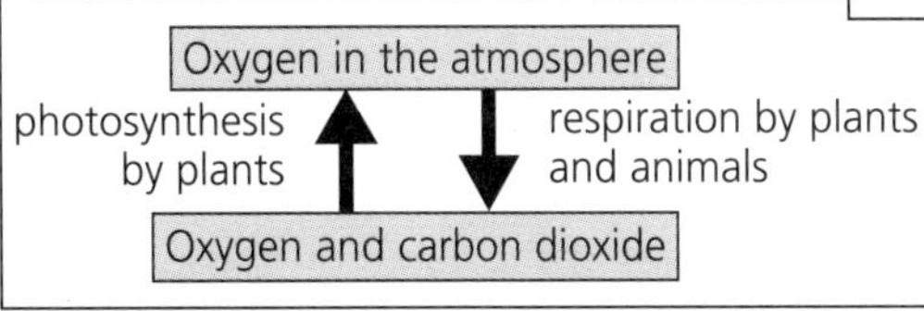

For details of the **greenhouse effect** go to page 71.

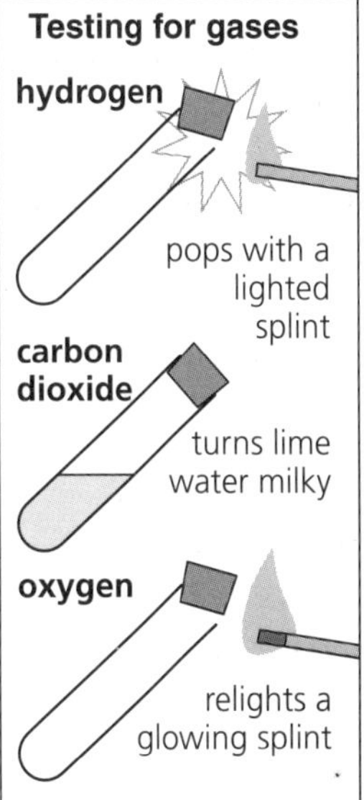

Now do this

5 Where did the original atmosphere of the Earth come from?

6 Three billion years ago there was almost no oxygen gas in the Earth's atmosphere. The oxygen atoms were present inside other gases.

Suggest the **two** gases in the atmosphere at the time which contained the oxygen.

7 Explain why oxygen started to appear.

8 Why doesn't the amount of oxygen in the atmosphere change?

Chemical calculations

How much do we need?

To measure out chemicals we find their mass. Atoms of different elements have different masses. You can see what the masses are by looking at their **relative atomic masses** given in the table opposite. Relative atomic masses are also given on the Periodic Table.

To get the same numbers of atoms of different elements you need different masses. For example, 12 g of carbon has the same number of atoms as 64 g of copper.

Some relative atomic masses			
hydrogen	H	=	1
carbon	C	=	12
nitrogen	N	=	14
oxygen	O	=	16
sodium	Na	=	23
sulphur	S	=	32
chlorine	Cl	=	35.5
iron	Fe	=	56

Now do this

You have 1 g of hydrogen.

1 You want the same number of atoms of carbon. What mass of carbon do you need?

2 You want twice as many atoms of carbon. What mass of carbon do you need?

Formula masses

When we find the mass of substances made of more than one atom, we have to add up the masses of all the atoms inside the formula. This is called the **formula mass**.

Now do this

3 What is the formula mass of NH_3?

4 What is the formula mass of H_2O?

5 What is the formula mass of NaOH?

Calculating amounts of chemicals used in reactions

A If you know the other masses in the equation

When chemicals react, their atoms join together in different ways. All the atoms at the start of the reaction are still there at the end. This means that the mass of the chemicals is the same at the end of the reaction.

Worked example

Q 12 g of carbon reacts completely with 32 g of oxygen to form carbon dioxide. How much carbon dioxide is formed?

$$C + O_2 \rightarrow CO_2$$

$$12\,g + 32\,g \rightarrow ?g$$

A (12 g + 32 g) = **44 g of CO_2**.

You can do these calculations even if the mass is in tonnes. The two sides of the equation must add up to the same mass, it doesn't matter if it is grams or in tonnes!

Now do this

6 40 g of oxygen reacts with hydrogen to make 45 g of water.

$$2H_2 + O_2 \rightarrow 2H_2O$$

How much hydrogen was needed?

7 100 tonnes of $CaCO_3$ will form 56 tonnes of CaO. How much CO_2 will be made?

$$CaCO_3 \rightarrow CaO + CO_2$$

B Using formula masses and a balanced equation

If you can't just add up all the masses in an equation, you will have to use formula masses. Make sure that the equation is balanced properly!

Worked example

Q The reaction of carbon with oxygen is shown in this equation.

$$C + O_2 \rightarrow CO_2$$

How much oxygen will react with 24 g of carbon?

A Put the formula masses into the equation.

$$C + O_2 \rightarrow CO_2$$
$$12\,g + 32\,g \rightarrow 44\,g$$

24 g of carbon is 2 formula masses, so it will need $2 \times 32 =$ **64 g of oxygen**.

Now do this

8 The reaction of ethene with hydrogen is shown in this equation:

$$C_2H_4 + H_2 \rightarrow C_2H_6$$

How much hydrogen will react with 14 g of ethene?

9 Sodium carbonate forms sodium chloride when it is neutralised by hydrochloric acid.

$$Na_2CO_3 + 2HCl \rightarrow 2NaCl + CO_2 + H_2O$$

How much sodium chloride is produced by 10.6 g of sodium carbonate?

C How to find a formula from reacting masses

Examiner's tip

Show lots of working. Even if you get the answer wrong you may get marks for working and for units.

Worked example

Q Ammonia is made from 28 g of nitrogen and 6 g of hydrogen. What is the formula of ammonia?

A The relative atomic mass of a nitrogen atom is 14.
The relative atomic mass of a hydrogen atom is 1

How many lots of 14 g of nitrogen atoms are there?	How many lots of 1g of hydrogen atoms are there?
28/14 = 2	6/1 = 6
So for every 2 atoms of nitrogen …	… there are 6 atoms of hydrogen.
For every 1 atom of nitrogen …	… there are 3 atoms of hydrogen.

The formula of ammonia is NH_3.

Now do this

10 5 g of hydrogen react with 64 g of sulphur to make hydrogen sulphide. What is the formula of hydrogen sulphide?

11 An oxide of sulphur is made of 8 g of sulphur and 8 g of oxygen. What is the formula of the sulphur oxide?

Exam questions

1 Crude'oil is a mixture of alkane molecules. We can separate these molecules by fractionation (fractional distillation).

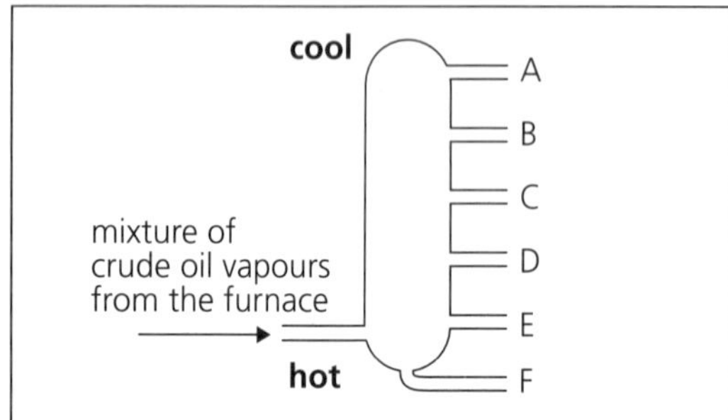

a i Which fraction is most likely to be a gas at room temperature? [1]

ii Which fraction is made up of the largest molecules? [1]

iii Use your knowledge of forces between molecules to explain why some fractions are gases at room temperature but other fractions are liquids. [4]

b Hexane (C_6H_{14})can be cracked into a smaller alkane (propane,C_3H_8), an alkene (propene, C_3H_6), and hydrogen.

i Write a word equation for this reaction [1]

ii Suggest a chemical test that would show you if a chemical was propene or propane. Say what you would see in each case. [3]

c Once crude oil has been refined it is sent out by tanker or by pipeline to where it is needed.

i Under what circumstances might it be best to use tankers? [1]

ii Suggest **one** disadvantage of tankers. [2]

d Alkenes can be used to make plastics

Use this table about different plastics to answer the next question.

Type of plastic	Information
acrylic	flexible, will take up dyes
polycarbonate	rigid, tough and transparent
polythene	flexible, easily formed into thin sheets, very cheap
PVC	can be rigid, tough, fairly cheap

Which plastic would be best for making

i Plastic drainpipes? [1]

ii Different coloured clothes? [1]

iii Plastic bags to put shopping in? [1]

iv Safety spectacles? [1]

e Some plastics are thermosetting, they do not soften when they are heated. Thermoplastic substances will soften when they are heated. Explain why one softens and the other does not. Draw diagrams of the molecules to show what you mean. [3]

[20 marks]

2 Some people use paraffin stoves to heat their rooms. Paraffin molecules are made of hydrogen and carbon atoms only. When the paraffin burns it makes water vapour and another chemical.

a What do we call chemical reactions that give out heat? [1]

b Write a word equation to for the combustion of paraffin in a well ventilated room. [2]

c Why is it dangerous to burn paraffin stoves if the room is not well ventilated? [2]

[5 marks]

3 Geologists think that a particular type of rock from South America was made from molten magma which came to the surface and quickly cooled.

a What do we call rocks formed when molten magma solidifies? [1]

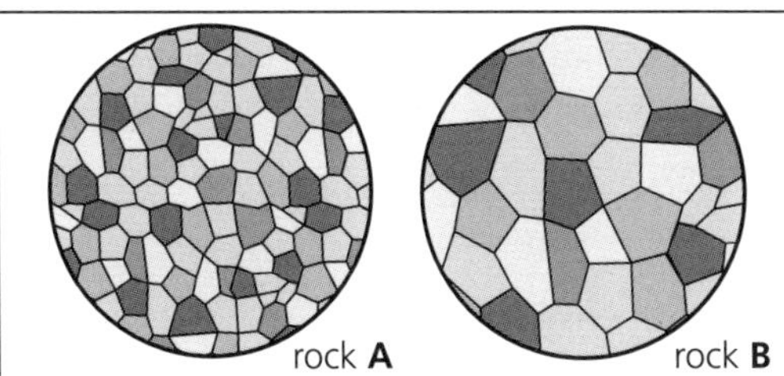

b What can you say about where rocks A and B were when they cooled?

Explain how you can tell. [4]

c There is an identical type of rock in Africa. Geologists think that the two rocks were formed very close to each other. Use ideas about plate tectonics to explain why they are so far apart. [2]

Some of the rock from South America turned into another type of rock which had rounded grains inside it.

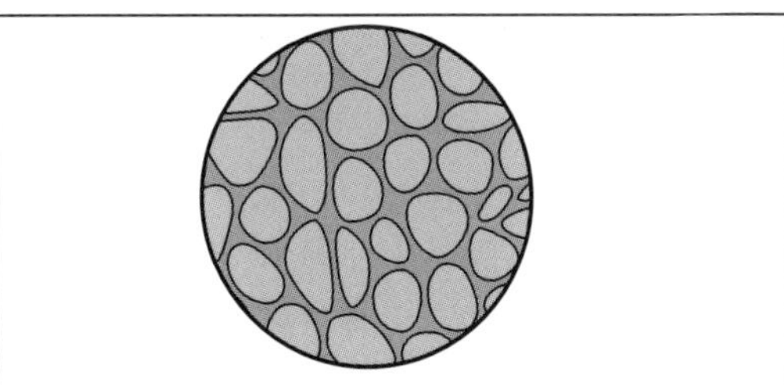

d Suggest how the first type of rock could have turned into the second type of rock. [3]

[10 marks]

4 The South Wales coalfield contains layers of coal beneath layers of limestone.

What does this tell you about the area in the distant past? Explain you answer. [4]

[4 marks]

5 Archaeologists rescued a rusty iron cannon from the sea bed.

Rust is made of iron oxide, so they turned the iron oxide back into iron by heating the cannon with hydrogen.

$$Fe_2O_3 + 3H_2 \rightarrow 2Fe + 3H_2O$$

a What happens to the mass of the gun as it is heated with hydrogen? Explain your answer. [2]

b i What mass of oxygen will combine with 112 g of iron to make Fe_2O_3?

(O = 16, Fe = 56) [2]

ii What mass of hydrogen is needed to produce 112 g of iron? [2]

c There is another type of iron oxide, Fe_3O_4, which reacts with hydrogen in the same way. Write a balanced chemical equation for this reaction. [3]

d Explain why hydrogen will convert iron oxide back to iron but it will not convert calcium oxide back to calcium. [2]

[11 marks]

6 It is possible to get 'self heating' cans of food.

One design has an inner can of food surrounded by an outer layer which contains water and quicklime. To heat the food you pull a tab which lets the water mix in with the quicklime.

The quicklime reacts with the water to make slaked lime, getting very hot.

$$CaO + H_2O \rightarrow Ca(OH)_2$$

a Use the equation to decide what the formula of quicklime must be. [1]

b Use the equation to decide what the formula of slaked lime must be. [1]

c 56 g of quicklime reacts with 18 g of water. What mass of slaked lime should this make? [1]

d The outer layer of the can needs slightly more water than expected.

Suggest a reason for this. [1]

[4 marks]

7 Large amounts of carbon dioxide are formed when the petrol burns in air.

The carbon dioxide in the atmosphere contributes to the greenhouse effect.

a Use ideas about radiation hitting the Earth and leaving the Earth to explain the greenhouse effect. [4]

b Carbon dioxide levels in a greenhouse containing plants change over the course of a 24 hour period.

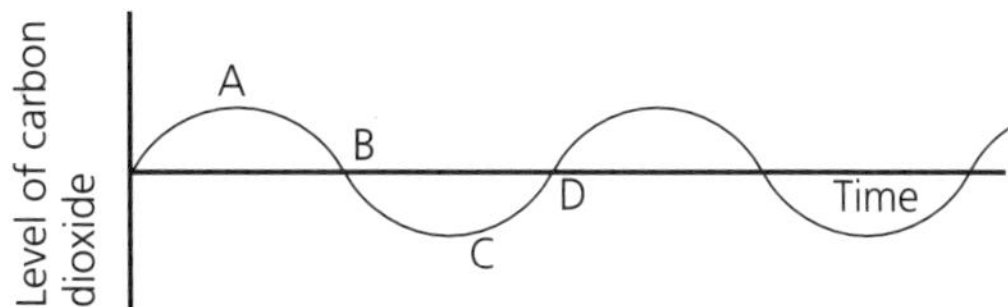

i Why does the level of carbon dioxide sometimes increase? [2]

ii Explain which letter represents afternoon. [3]

iii Explain which letter represents sunrise. [2]

c Photochemical smogs can also be created when petrol is burned.

i How is a photochemical smog caused? [2]

ii What effect does photochemical smog have on people? [1]

Crude oil is used to make fuels such as petrol.

d How is crude oil formed? [3]

[17 marks]

8 Some prospectors discovered rock containing metal ores. Here is some information about them.

Metal	Ore	Chemical name for ore	Information about metals
1	copper pyrites	copper sulphide	↓ increasing reactivity ↓ increasingly difficult to separate from ore
iron	iron ore	iron oxide	
aluminium	bauxite	aluminium 2	
sodium	rock salt	sodium chloride	

a i What should go in the space numbered 1? [1]

ii What should go in the space numbered 2? [1]

iii Which metal is the easiest to extract from its ore? [1]

b The first stage in extracting copper from copper ore is to heat the copper sulphide in air. The copper sulphide is converted to copper oxide and sulphur dioxide.

Which part of the air is used to do this? [1]

c Iron is extracted from iron ore by using carbon in a blast furnace.

Write a word equation for this reaction. [2]

d Carbon is not reactive enough to extract aluminium from its ore.

Suggest which other element or elements in the table cannot be extracted from their ores by carbon. [1]

[7 marks]

9 A student weighed two copper electrodes and put them into a beaker of copper sulphate. She connected the electrodes to a battery for an hour, then washed and re-weighed them.

a What would have happened to the mass of the negative electrode? [1]

b Explain why this happened. [2]

c What would have happened to the mass of the positive electrode? [2]

d Explain how this happened. [1]

[6 marks]

10 The directors of a chemical company decide to build a new factory.
Suggest **four** things that they should take into account as they decide where the factory should be built. [4]

[4 marks]

11 When petrol burns in air, small amounts of sulphur inside the petrol turn into a substance which causes acid rain.

a i What substance is formed when sulphur reacts with the oxygen in the air? [1]

ii Write a balanced chemical equation for this. [1]

iii This substance forms an acid in the rain water. What is the acid? [1]

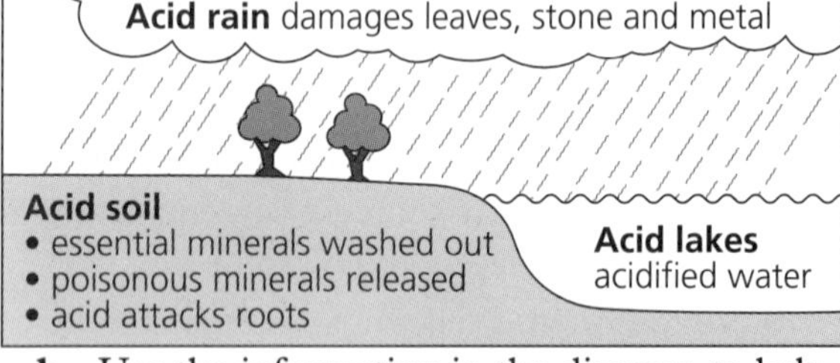

b Use the information in the diagram to help you explain how acid rain damages trees. [3]

[6 marks]

12 If you are stung by a bee you can put ammonia on the sting to stop it hurting. The ammonia works because it is pH of 8 and the bee sting is pH 6.

a What does pH measure? [1]

b What does pH 6 mean? [2]

c How does the ammonia stop the bee sting hurting? [1]

d How can you find the pH of the ammonia for yourself? [2]

[6 marks]

Patterns of behaviour

You will have met the ideas in this section when you worked on the units *Burning and bonding*, *Transporting chemicals*, *Mining and minerals*, *Construction materials*, *Controlling change*, *Food for thought*, *Burning and bonding*. Other units contain smaller amounts of material, such as *Keeping healthy* and *Waste not, want not*.
This section is divided into six spreads.

The Periodic Table

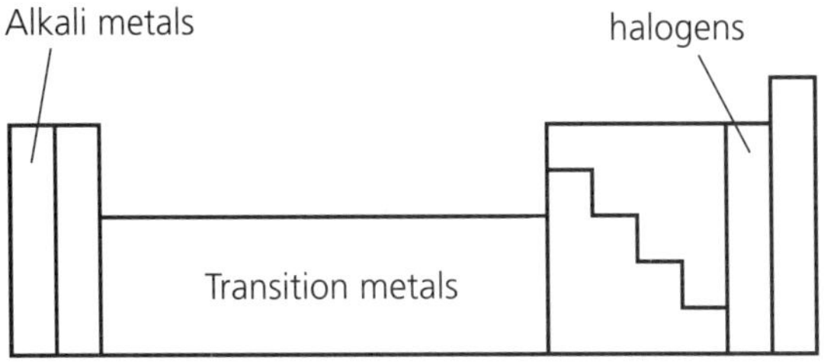

Alkali metals
halogens
Transition metals

What does the Periodic Table tell us?

Group I alkali metals
How do they react?
What do we use them for?
How do we make sodium hydroxide?

Group VII halogens
How do they react?
What do we use them for?
What is precipitation?

Transition metals
How are they special

Noble gases
How are they special

Rates of reaction

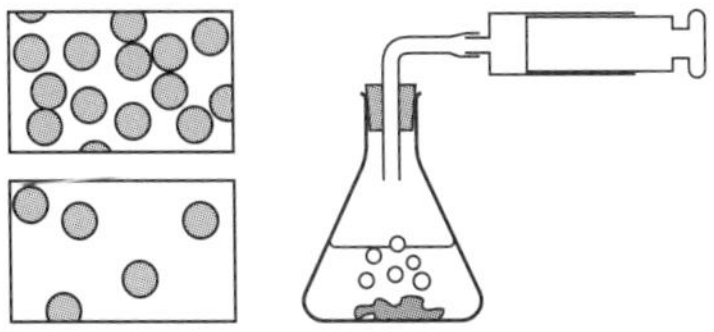

What makes the reactions go faster?

Enzymes and biotechnology

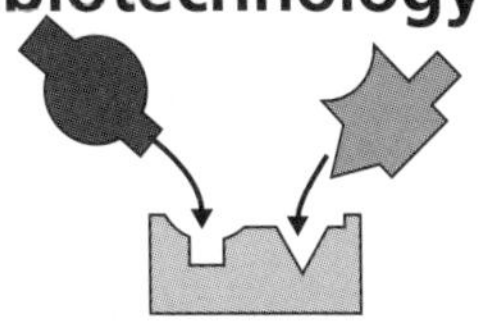

How do enzymes work?
How do we use them?

Reversible reactions

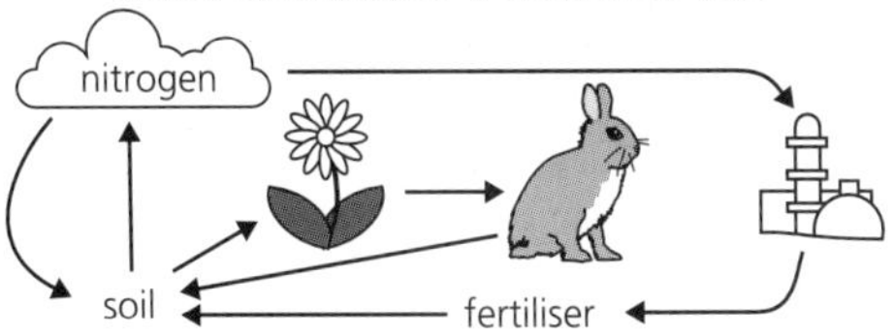

nitrogen
soil
fertiliser

How do we use reversible reactions?
How do we make ammonia?
How is nitrogen recycled?

$$N_2 + 3H_2 \rightleftharpoons 2NH_3$$

Warning symbols

How is the Hazchem code used?

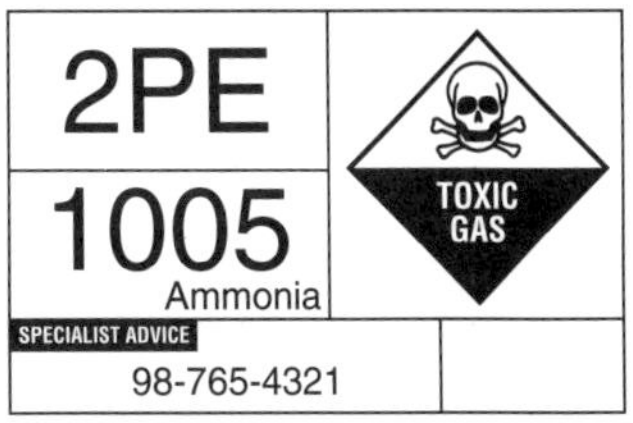

2PE
1005
Ammonia
SPECIALIST ADVICE
98-765-4321
TOXIC GAS

Energy

What do endothermic and exothermic mean?
How is energy linked to bond making and breaking?

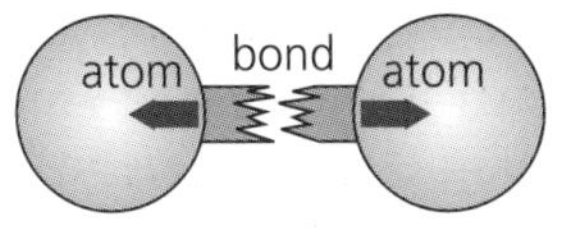

bond breaking takes in energy

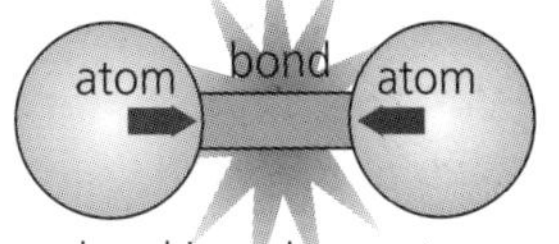

bond making gives out energy

The Periodic Table

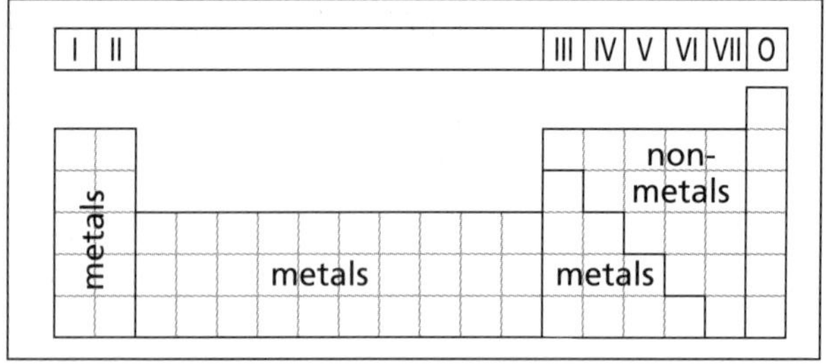

A Periodic Table will be printed on the back of your examination paper. The elements are in order of increasing number of protons in the nucleus (atomic numbers). The order goes from left to right along each row, starting with the top row. Each row is a **period**.

The columns of elements are called **groups**. The elements in a group are all similar. Hydrogen is the one element that is sometimes not put into a group.

Metals and non-metals

There are two sorts of elements, metals and non-metals. The zig-zag line shows the boundary between them. Metals are on the left-hand side of the table, non-metals are on the right.

Metals
- form positive ions
- form compounds with non-metals. The compounds are made of ions
- react with oxygen to form oxides which are basic. Basic oxides are ionic solids.

The most reactive metals are at the bottom left.

Most metals also
- react with water to form hydrogen
- react with acids to form hydrogen and a salt.

Non-metals
- often form acidic oxides
- form negative ions.

The most reactive non-metal is at the top of group VII – it is fluorine.

Groups

Group number	I	II	III	IV	V	VI	VII	0
Outer electrons	1	2	3	4	5	6	7	8

The elements in a group are very similar because they all have the same number of electrons in their outer shell. The number of electrons in the outer shell is the same as the group number.

- Metals form positive ions because they have only a few outer electrons, so they lose electrons.
- Non-metals form negative ions because they gain a few more electrons to gain a stable outer shell.

The number of electrons in the outer shell tells us the **combining power** of an atom. This means that if we know the combining power of an element in a group, other elements in the same group will have the same combining power.

Lithium is in group I and reacts with chlorine to make LiCl. Sodium and potassium are in the same group, so their chlorides are NaCl and KCl.

Oxygen is in group VI and reacts with hydrogen to make H_2O. Sulphur is in the same group as oxygen, so it makes H_2S with hydrogen.

Now do this

1 Lithium is in group I.

a How many outer electrons are in the outer shell of a lithium atom?

b What type of ion will it form?

2 Sulphur is in group VI.

a How many electrons are in the outer shell of a sulphur atom?

b What type of ion will it form?

3 The formula of aluminium chloride is $AlCl_3$. What is the formula of boron chloride?

Group I the alkali metals

The group I elements are called the alkali metals. You need to know about the first three: lithium, sodium and potassium.

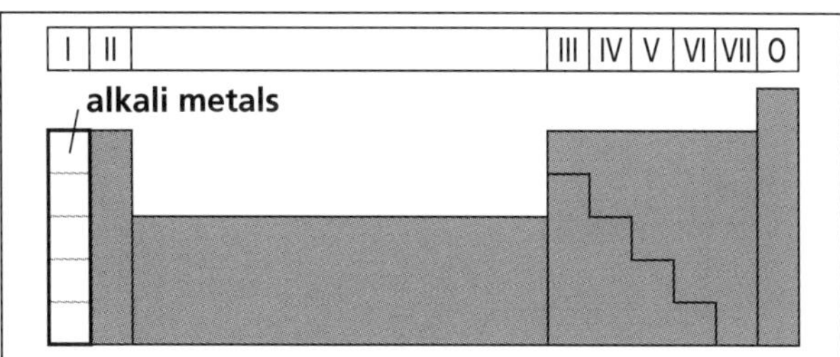

Element	Symbol	Relative atomic mass	Melting point
lithium	Li	7	180
sodium	Na	23	98
potassium	K	39	63
rubidium	Rb	85	39
caesium	Cs	133	29

As they are in group I they all have only one electron in the outer shell, so they are all very reactive. They get more reactive as you go down the group.

Reactions with water

All alkali metals react strongly with water. They force hydrogen gas out of the water and the metal turns into the metal hydroxide, which makes an alkaline solution.

lithium + water → lithium hydroxide + hydrogen
Li + $2H_2O$ → 2LiOH + H_2

The reaction gets more violent as you go down the group.

- Lithium reacts, but does not melt because it is the least reactive.
- Sodium melts and moves about the surface of the water as it reacts.
- Potassium melts, moves about the surface and bursts into flame.

Alkali metal compounds

Alkali metal compounds are very useful.

- Sodium chloride is table salt, it is used to make chlorine and sodium hydroxide.
- Sodium hydroxide (NaOH) is an alkali. It reacts with acids to make a salt and water. It is used in making soap, plastics and many other chemicals. It is made by electrolysing salt solution (brine) – salt is made of Na^+ and Cl^- ions; water splits into H^+ and OH^- ions. Hydrogen is formed at the cathode and chlorine is formed at the anode, leaving a solution of sodium hydroxide in the container.
- Sodium carbonate is another alkali, it reacts with acids to make carbon dioxide gas, a salt and water. It is used in soap powder and to make sodium hydroxide.

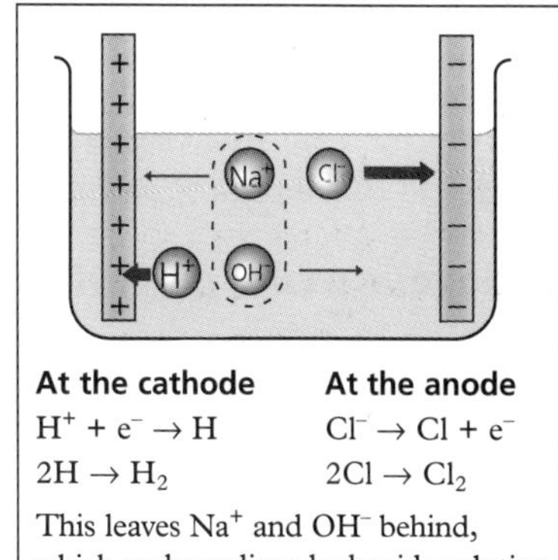

At the cathode
$H^+ + e^- \rightarrow H$
$2H \rightarrow H_2$

At the anode
$Cl^- \rightarrow Cl + e^-$
$2Cl \rightarrow Cl_2$

This leaves Na^+ and OH^- behind, which make sodium hydroxide solution.

Now do this

1. Write a word equation for the reaction of sodium with water.
2. What is made if you add sodium hydroxide to hydrochloric acid?
3. What is made if you add sodium carbonate to sulphuric acid?
4. During the electrolysis of brine
   - **a** What is produced at the anode?
   - **b** What is produced at the cathode?
   - **c** What **two** ions are left behind?

Group VII the halogens

The group VII elements are called the halogens. You need to know about chlorine, bromine and iodine.

Element	Symbol	Relative atomic mass	Normal state	Colour
fluorine	F	19	gas	
chlorine	Cl	35.5	gas	green
bromine	Br	80	liquid	orange
iodine	I	127	solid	black

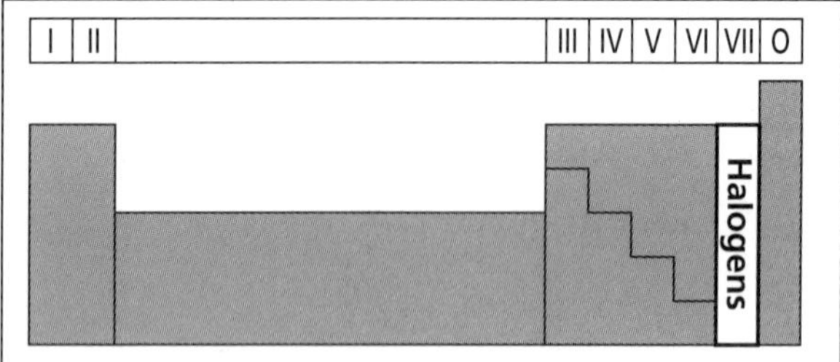

As they are in group VII they all have seven electrons in the outer shell, so they are very reactive non-metals. They get less reactive as you go down the group, but they will all react strongly with metals.

Chlorine is made by the electrolysis of brine, see page 91.

What are the halogens used for?

Halogens make silver halides for photography

If you mix sodium chloride solution with silver nitrate solution, a solid will appear in the test tube. Silver ions from the silver nitrate react with chloride ions from the sodium chloride to form silver chloride, which doesn't dissolve. The silver chloride is a **precipitate**.

silver ions + chloride ions → silver chloride
$Ag^+ + Cl^- \rightarrow AgCl$

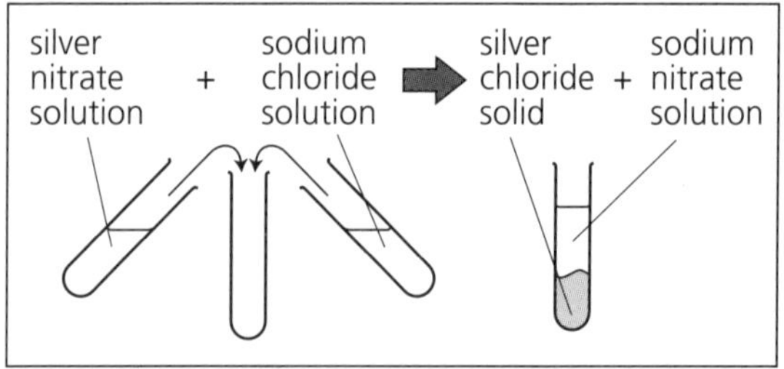

Sodium bromide will form a precipitate of silver bromide, sodium iodide will make silver iodide.

Silver compounds like this turn back into solid silver when you shine light on them because the light makes them react. The solid silver looks black, so we use silver halides to make photographic film.

Halogens make powerful germicides

Germicides are any substances which kill microbes. There are different types of germicide.

Disinfectants are very powerful killers of harmful microbes. They are too powerful to use on your own body, they are for killing microbes on work surfaces, in drains, etc. Bleach is a good disinfectant because it contains chlorine. Chlorine is used to sterilise drinking water because it is so good at killing microbes.

Antiseptics are milder than disinfectants, we use them to kill microbes on the outside of our bodies, such as cuts and grazes. Iodine is an antiseptic.

Now do this

1. What will the precipitate be if you add silver nitrate to sodium bromide solution?
2. Write a word equation for this reaction.
3. Rewrite the equation, showing what happens to the ions.
4. Name **three** chemicals which go black when light is shone on them.
5. Why do we add chlorine to drinking water?
6. How is chlorine made?

Transition metals and noble gases

The transition metals

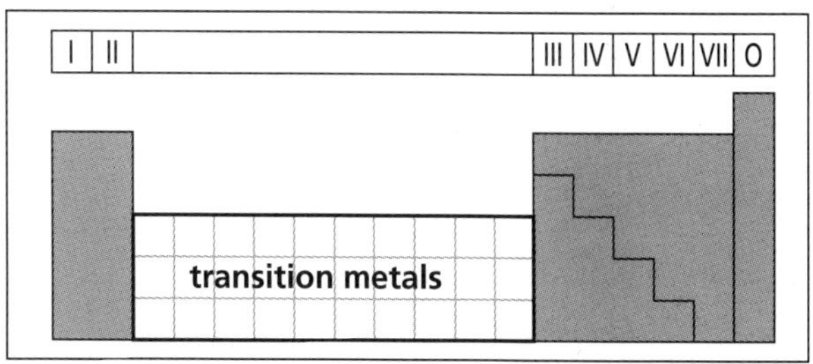

The transition metals are common metals such as iron and copper, silver and gold. They are all what we normally think of as metals – they conduct electricity and heat, they are shiny, hard, strong, dense and have high melting points.

Transition metals are not violently reactive like the alkali metals.

We can use iron to make things such as cars or bridges without them reacting too much. Iron objects corrode if oxygen and water are present, but we can control that. When iron corrodes we say that it rusts. There is more about rust prevention on page 81.

Other transition metals react even more slowly than iron. Copper and nickel are used to make coins because they don't corrode easily. Silver and gold corrode even less, so they are used for jewellery. The reactivity of these metals depends on their position in the reactivity series, see page 78.

Transition metals and their compounds can make good catalysts. Iron is the catalyst in the Haber process for making ammonia, see page 98.

Compounds of the transition metals

Most of the transition metal compounds are coloured. The colour is due to the metal ion inside the compound, so the colour tells you which transition element is present. Copper compounds are blue, iron compounds can be green or red-brown.

The noble gases

The noble gases are helium, neon, argon, krypton, xenon and radon. They are colourless gases and they have almost no reactions. This is because they all have a stable outer shell (usually eight electrons, except helium which has two).

This lack of reactivity means that the gases are used when an inert atmosphere is needed, such as for welding. Helium is also light, so it is used to fill airships and weather balloons. When an electric discharge passes through neon it creates coloured light, so neon is used inside some types of lamps.

Now do this

A metal

- **a** forms coloured compounds
- **b** conducts electricity
- **c** acts as a catalyst
- **d** reacts with acids.

1 Which **two** things show you that it is a metal?

2 Which **two** things show you that the metal is probably a transition metal?

3 What does a catalyst do?

Rates of reactions

Chemical reactions happen at different speeds. You can see some of them around you. Rusting is a slow chemical reaction. Burning is a fast chemical reaction, explosions are even faster! The speed of a reaction is called its **rate**.

Speeding up reactions

Reactions happen when reactant particles collide and are changed into products, so most ways of speeding up reactions make the particles collide more often.

1 Increase the **temperature**. This makes the reactant particles move faster so they hit each other more often. Even more important, they also hit each other harder, so more of the collisions have enough energy to cause chemical change. Marble chips react faster with acid if the acid is warm.

2 Increase the **concentration**. This only works with a solution! Increasing concentration makes the particles closer together, so they collide with the other reactant more often. Marble chips react faster with acid if the acid is more concentrated.

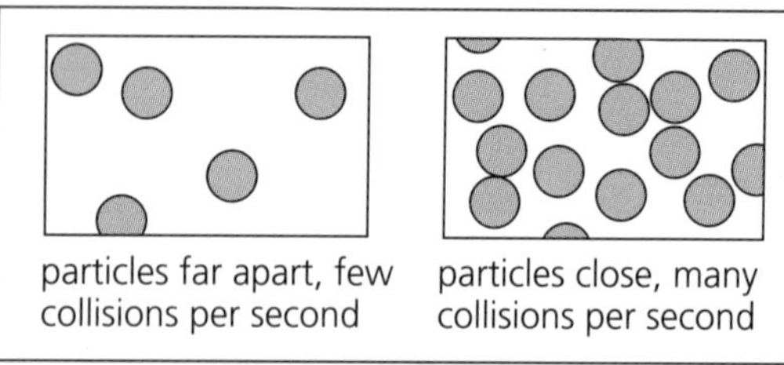

3 Increase the **surface area**. This gives more places for reaction to happen. If one of the reactants is a solid, break it down into smaller lumps. Marble chips react faster with acid if the marble chips are small.

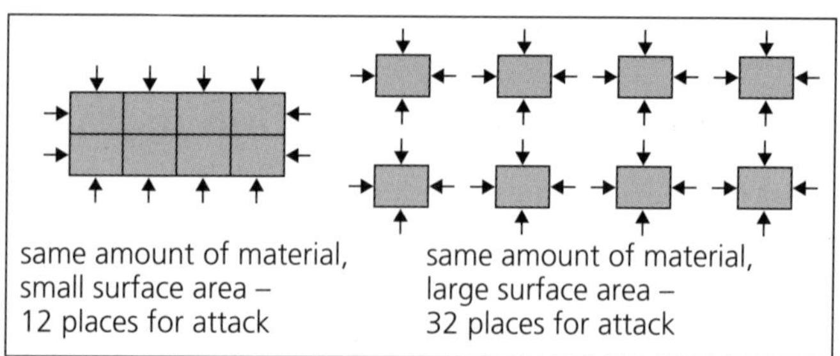

4 Use a **catalyst**. Catalysts speed up a reaction. They are only needed in small amounts and are not used up by the reaction, they can be re-used. Different reactions need different catalysts to speed them up.

For example, hydrogen peroxide slowly breaks down into water and oxygen.

hydrogen peroxide → water + oxygen

$$2H_2O_2 \rightarrow 2H_2O + O_2$$

To speed this up you can add manganese dioxide as a catalyst.

All the manganese dioxide is left in the beaker at the end, and it can be used again.

Examiner's tip

A catalyst takes part in the reaction, otherwise the reaction wouldn't happen. It can all be recovered at the end.

Catalytic converters

Many modern cars use catalytic converters. The catalyst helps the polluting gases in the exhaust to react with oxygen from the air. This changes the exhaust gases to less harmful gases.

Now do this

1 Give **three** ways of speeding up the reaction between acid solution and a solid carbonate.

2 Which ways will still work for a reaction between acid solution and a carbonate solution?

3 Limestone is used to neutralise acid soil. Why does powdered limestone work faster than limestone chips?

4 Here is the word equation for a reaction that uses a catalyst.

hydrogen + oxygen + platinum → water + platinum

a Which is the catalyst in this reaction?
b How can you tell?

How can you find the speed of a reaction?

The easiest way to find the speed (or rate) of a reaction is to measure how fast one of the products is made.

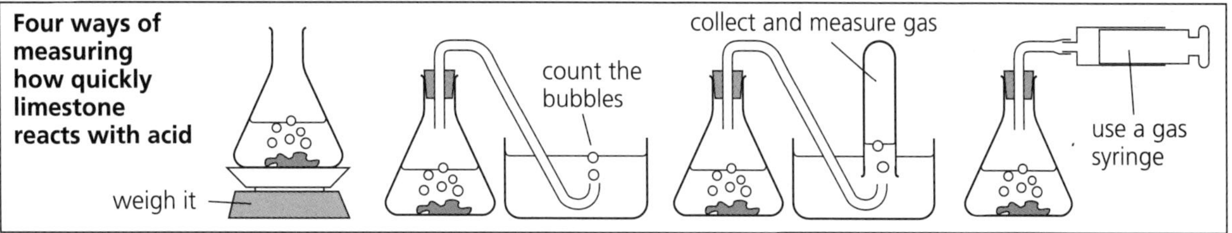

Reactions always start fast and then slow down as the reactant chemicals are used up. Reactions carry on until one of the reactants runs out.

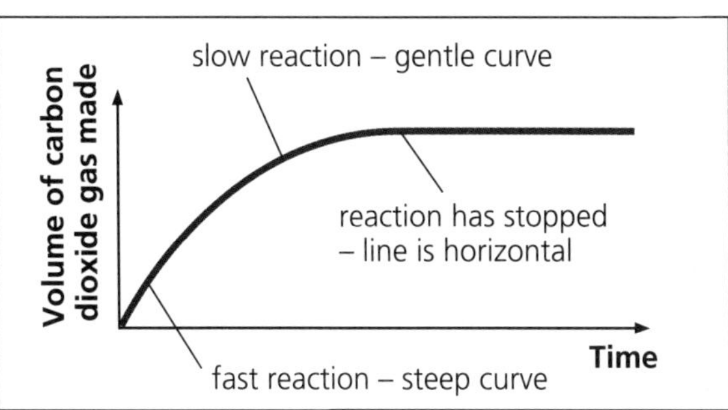

Now do this

5 This graph shows the way the mass of marble chips changes during a reaction with acid.

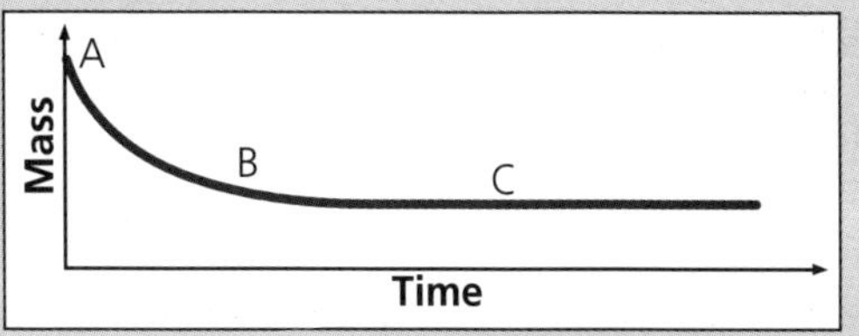

a Which letter shows where the reaction is fastest? Explain why.
b Which letter shows where the reaction has stopped?

Enzymes and biotechnology

Catalysts are important in a wide range of industrial processes. In some industries the catalysts used are **enzymes**. Enzymes are biological catalysts, they are produced inside living things and control the rate of reactions inside them.

Like other catalysts, specific enzymes are needed for specific reactions. Unlike other catalysts, enzymes are proteins. Proteins have a complex structure which is quickly damaged by changes in pH or by temperatures that are too high. If you heat the reactants in a reaction involving an enzyme the reaction will only get faster up to a certain temperature, then it will slow down or stop due to damage to the enzyme. The enzyme has been **denatured**. The shape of the enzyme has now changed enough for it to stop working.

'Lock and key'

Why will enzymes only help certain chemicals to react?

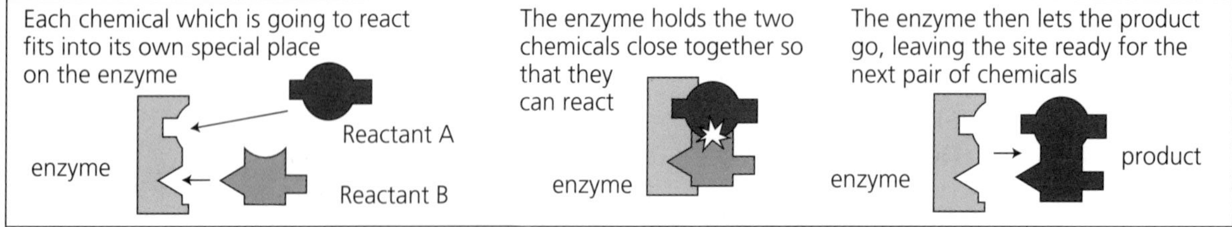

If the enzyme is denatured by changes in pH or temperature it no longer holds the reactants in the right places, so it stops working as a catalyst. Some drugs work by blocking the active sites on enzymes inside microbes. This stops the microbes functioning normally, so they die.

Using enzymes

Enzymes are important in the baking, brewing and dairy industries. Yeast is used in both baking and brewing because the yeast cells contain enzymes which convert sugar into carbon dioxide and alcohol.

The yeast is using the sugar to obtain energy, it is respiring. There is no air present, so this is **anaerobic respiration**.

sugar → alcohol + carbon dioxide

Baking

Sugar and yeast are added to bread dough so that the enzymes in the yeast can produce bubbles of carbon dioxide. The bubbles push up through the dough and make it rise. When it is cooked the dough solidifies round the bubbles, giving bread an open texture. The high temperature of the cooking kills the yeast and drives off the carbon dioxide and the alcohol.

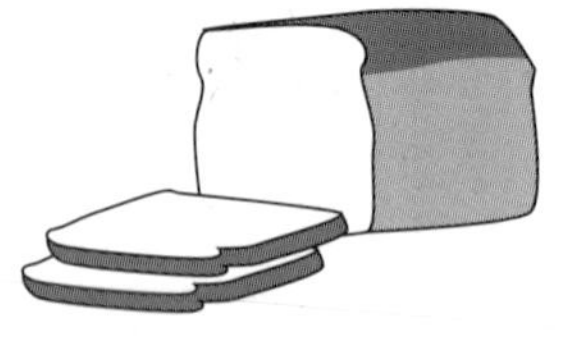

Brewing

Yeast is added to grape juice to make wine, and to barley grains to make beer. The enzymes in the yeast convert the sugars into alcohol during fermentation. Barley grains make beer, grape juice makes wine. The carbon dioxide bubbles out of the liquid.

Clear fruit juice

Apples contain a substance called pectin. The pectin makes apple juice look cloudy. Pectin molecules can be broken down by an enzyme, pectinase. Once the enzyme has broken down the pectin the juice becomes clear instead of cloudy.

Soft chocolate

The insides of chocolates with soft centres are solid when they are first made. The 'soft' centre contains crystals of solid sugar, a little water and the enzyme invertase. The enzyme breaks the sugar molecules into simpler sugars which will dissolve in the water. As these simpler sugars start to dissolve the mixture goes soft and runny.

Problems with enzymes

Some enzymes are a problem because they speed up the decay of fresh food. These enzymes might be part of the food itself, or they might be from microbes on the food. They can be controlled in the following ways:

- **Cooking** – this destroys the enzyme and stops the food decaying. The food must be covered once it is cooked, otherwise microbes from the air will fall back on to the food and fresh enzymes from the microbes will make the food decay again.
- **Refrigeration** – this does not destroy the enzymes, but the low temperature slows down any reactions so it keeps food fresh for a short time.
- **Freezing** – this does not destroy the enzymes, but it stops any reactions so it is a good way of keeping food fresh for a long time.

One example of the way in which enzymes can cause food to 'go off' is the way that fruit such as apples go brown and spoil once they have been cut open. In this case the reaction between the fruit and oxygen from the air is speeded up by an enzyme.

Apple browning does not happen if the apples are kept under water, or sprinkled with lemon juice, or if they are cooked. If the apple is kept under water the air cannot get to it. Cooking will denature the enzyme, as will even a weak acid such as lemon juice.

Now do this

1 When yeast ferments it converts sugar into two chemicals. What are they?

2 Apples go brown when you cut them open because of a reaction which is speeded up by an enzyme.
 a What does the apple react with when it goes brown?
 b Lemon juice stops the apple going brown – suggest why.
 c Cooked apples don't go brown – suggest why.
 d Apples cut underwater go brown more slowly – suggest why.

3 **a** Use your understanding of 'lock and key' mechanisms to explain why an enzyme will enable two chemicals to react.
 b If one of the chemicals is a slightly different shape, the enzyme no longer allows it to react. Why is this?

Reversible reactions

Some reactions will go in both directions.

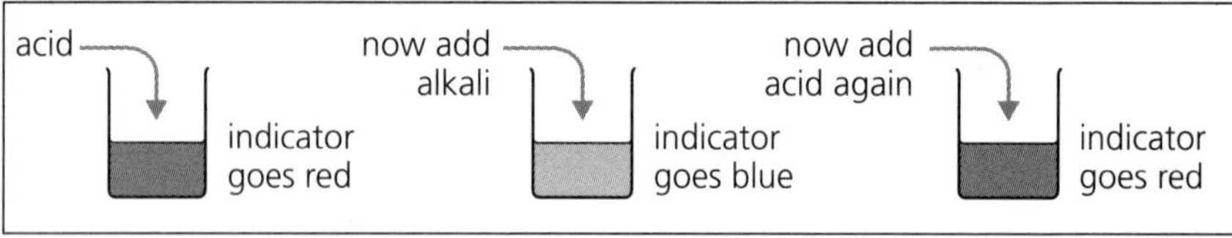

If you put acid with pH indicator, the indicator will turn red. If you now add alkali the indicator changes to blue. Add acid again, and it goes back to red.

You can do this as many times as you want. The reaction will go in either direction just as easily.

Usually it is very difficult to make a reaction go backwards but in this case it is very easy, we call this type of reaction a **reversible reaction**.

Making ammonia

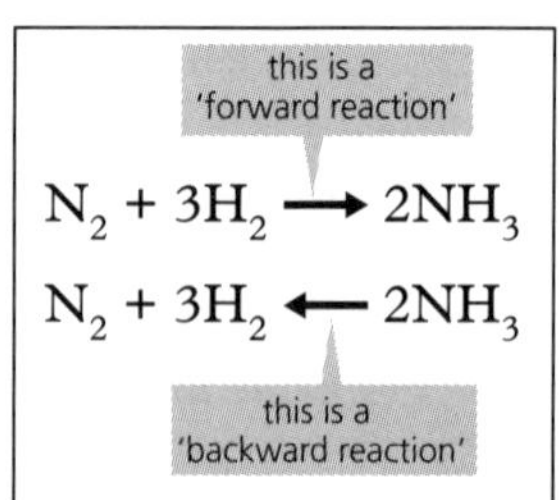

Ammonia is made from nitrogen and hydrogen.

When you react nitrogen and hydrogen a small amount of ammonia is produced. But it immediately starts to turn back to nitrogen and hydrogen. The reaction goes in both directions at the same time. This backward reaction made it impossible to make ammonia industrially by mixing nitrogen and hydrogen.

Eventually the forward reaction goes at the same speed as the backward reaction. From this point onwards there will not be any change in the amount of chemicals.

$$N_2 + 3H_2 \rightleftharpoons 2NH_3$$

How to change the yield of a reversible reaction – the Haber Process

The amount of the product that is made from a reaction is called the **yield**.
We can change the yield in a reversible reaction by changing the temperature of the reaction, or the pressure, or the concentrations, or all of these.
Fritz Haber used this idea to solve the problem of the backward reaction of ammonia.

1 He used high pressure to make the forward reaction go faster – this increased the yield of ammonia.
2 As soon as any ammonia was made he cooled it into a liquid so that he could remove it. This stopped ammonia turning back into nitrogen and hydrogen.
3 He used a fairly high temperature and an iron catalyst to speed up the reaction. (The temperature couldn't be too high or it would make the ammonia break down as fast as it was made.)
4 He re-cycled any unreacted nitrogen and hydrogen to make more ammonia.

This is called the Haber Process.
Millions of tons of ammonia are produced every year so that we can make fertiliser.
The ammonia is made from the easily obtained **raw materials**, natural gas and air. Natural gas is the raw material used to make hydrogen, air gives us the nitrogen. As this reaction makes ammonia and nothing else, there are no **by-products**.

Now do this

1 What is a reversible reaction?

2 What is produced if you put an iron catalyst with ammonia?

Making fertiliser from ammonia

Ammonia solution is alkaline and when you neutralise it with an acid it forms an ammonium salt. There is more about this on page 66.

The nitrogen cycle

Nitrogen compounds are essential for life – nitrogen is an essential element in proteins. The air contains 80% nitrogen but nitrogen is a very unreactive gas, so it is difficult to turn it into nitrogen compounds. Bacteria in the roots of clover, pea or bean plants are able to convert nitrogen from the air into nitrogen compounds that the plants then use. Animals then get their protein by eating plants. Protein which is left in the remains of animal and plants is converted into other nitrogen compounds by nitrifying bacteria from the soil. These compounds are then re-used by plants, or they are turned back into nitrogen gas by more bacteria in the soil.

Crops in farmers' fields remove nitrogen compounds from the soil faster than the bacteria in plant roots can replace them. Fertilisers can be used to add extra nitrogen compounds to the soil and so increase crop growth. If too much fertiliser is used, the extra will be washed out of the soil into streams and rivers, causing eutrophication. For more about eutrophication see page 46 (biology section).

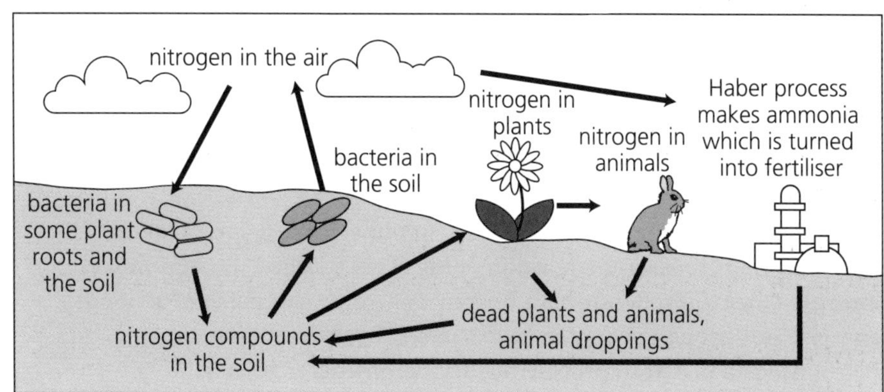

Sulphuric acid

Sulphuric acid is another compound which can be used to make some types of fertiliser. It is also made by a reversible reaction.

Sulphuric acid, H_2SO_4, is made by three stages:

1 Burn sulphur in oxygen from the air to make sulphur dioxide.

sulphur + oxygen → sulphur dioxide
$S + O_2 \rightarrow SO_2$

2 React the sulphur dioxide with more oxygen to make sulphur trioxide.

sulphur dioxide + oxygen ↔ sulphur trioxide
$2SO_2 + O_2 \leftrightarrow 2SO_3$

This stage is a reversible reaction, it goes in both directions. A catalyst is used to speed it up.

3 React the sulphur trioxide with water to make sulphuric acid:

sulphur trioxide + water → sulphuric acid
$SO_3 + H_2O \rightarrow H_2SO_4$

Now do this

3 What helps a plant get its nitrogen from the air?

4 Where do animals get their nitrogen from?

5 What converts nitrogen compounds back into nitrogen gas?

6 Sulphuric acid is made from three chemicals and a catalyst.
What are the **three** chemicals that are needed?

Energy

Exothermic and endothermic reactions

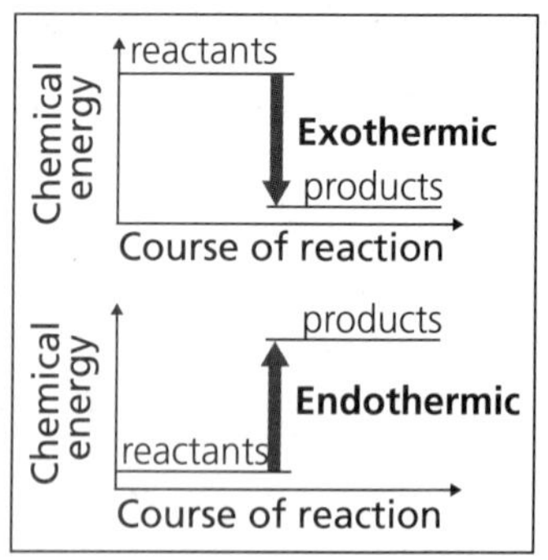

Most chemical reactions transfer energy. Reactions which get hot are **exothermic**, they are giving out energy. The chemicals end up with less energy because they give some of it out as heat.

Reactions which get colder are called **endothermic**, they take in energy from the surroundings. The chemicals turn heat from the surroundings into energy inside the chemicals.

Bond making and breaking

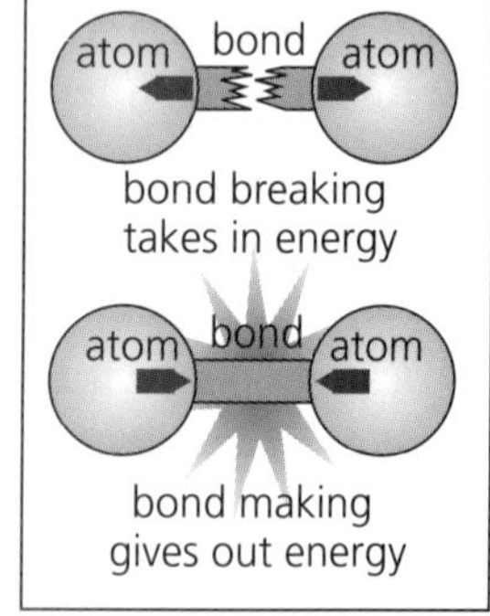

When compounds react the first thing that they do is to split into atoms, then the atoms join together to make different compounds. To split a chemical apart, its bonds have to be broken. When the atoms join together, new bonds are made.

Energy has to be put *in* to *break* the bonds, this is an endothermic process. Energy is given *out* when bonds are *made*, this is an exothermic process.

If more energy is taken in than given out, the whole reaction is endothermic. If more energy is given out than is taken in, the whole reaction is exothermic.

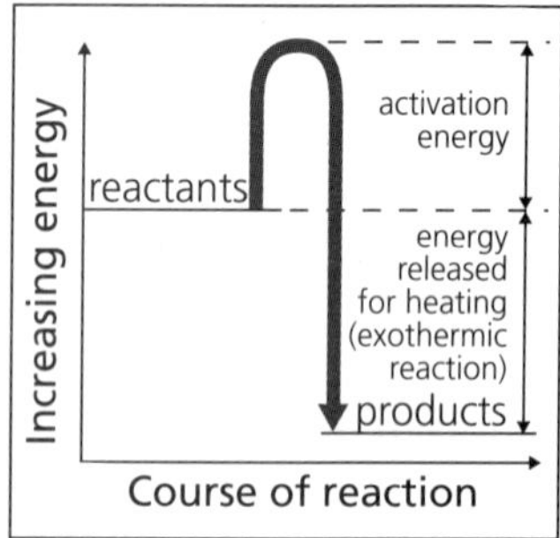

Most chemical reactions need an extra amount of energy to break the first few bonds to start the reaction going. This is called the **activation energy**. Once a few bonds have broken the atoms can make new bonds and give out enough energy to keep the rest of the reaction going. Petrol needs a match to provide the activation energy to start it burning. The energy graph for burning petrol is shown here.

Some reactions get their activation energy when light hits the chemicals. Photography is one example of this, photosynthesis is another.

Sometimes we deliberately put energy into a chemical just to smash some of the bonds. Limestone is heated to break it down into smaller fragments called quicklime, and also into carbon dioxide. This is called **thermal decomposition**.

limestone	=	**quicklime**	+	**carbon dioxide**
$CaCO_3$	=	**CaO**	+	**CO_2**

Energy and reversible reactions

Reversible reactions go in both directions. They are exothermic in one direction and endothermic in the other.

The forward reaction in the Haber process is exothermic.

nitrogen + hydrogen = ammonia *exothermic*

This means that the backward reaction will be endothermic.

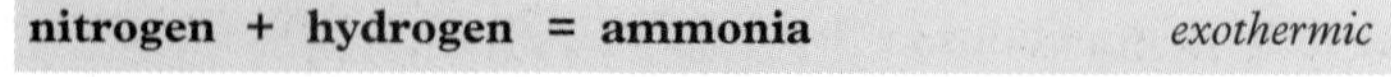

ammonia = nitrogen + hydrogen *endothermic*

??? Now do this

1 If you put a lighted splint into a mixture of hydrogen and oxygen, the mixture will explode. It is an exothermic reaction.

a Use ideas of bond making and breaking to explain why it is exothermic.

b Why does it need a lighted splint to start it going?

Warning symbols

Containers of harmful chemicals should always carry a warning diamond.

You should know these four warning symbols.

The Hazchem code

Lorries and trains which transport dangerous chemicals have a Hazard Warning sign on the outside.

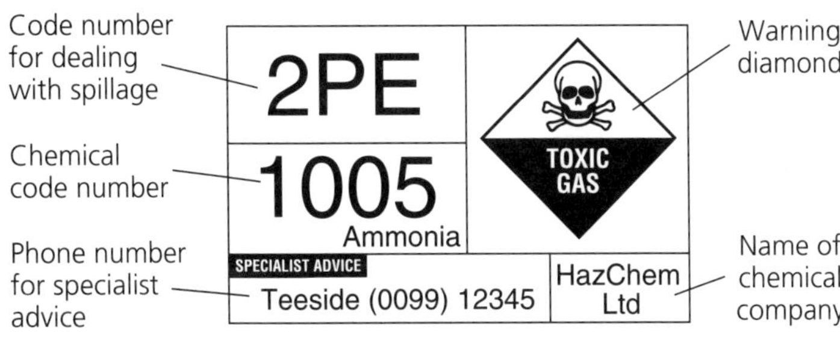

P	V	full	dilute
R			
S	V	BA*	
T			
W	V	full	contain
X			
Y	V	BA*	
Z			
E	consider evacuation		

1 JETS 2 FOG 3 FOAM 4 DRY AGENT
*BA means breathing apparatus.

The way firemen deal with spillages depends on the properties of the chemicals, such as toxicity, reactions with air or water and flammability. Firemen have a code table to tell them what the hazard code means.

Imagine that a tanker crashes and spills some of its chemical on the road.

When the firemen get to the accident they see the code '3WE' on the tanker, so they look it up in their code book.

The number '3' shows what to do if there is fire, in this case use foam.

The first letter 'W' shows them which boxes in the code table to look at.
'W' is level with boxes that say FULL and CONTAIN, so firemen must wear full protective clothing, and any spilt chemical must be contained and collected.

'W' is also level with a 'V' box. The 'V' warns them that the chemical reacts violently.

The 'E' at the end shows that the area should be evacuated.

If the code on the tanker was 1T, this would tell the firemen to use jets of water to put out any fire. There is no 'V', so the chemical does not react violently. Full protective clothing is not essential, the BA shows that only breathing apparatus and gloves need to be used. DILUTE tells the firemen that any spilt chemical can be washed away into the drains.

Now do this

1. Ammonia has the code 2PE.
   Think of **four** things that firemen should do if there is an ammonia spillage.
2. The firemen's code book gives an extra piece of information about the chemical which is not shown on the lorry. What is it?

Exam questions

1 When the nuclear power station at Chernobyl released radioactive dust containing strontium compounds into the air, some of the dust fell on the Lake District in Britain. Sheep ate the dust that settled on the grass and produced radioactive milk. Sheep normally use calcium compounds from the grass to make milk, but this time they were using strontium compounds as well.

a i Strontium is element number 38. Find strontium in the Periodic Table.
What group is strontium in? [1]

ii Strontium is a metal. How can you tell by looking at the Periodic Table? [1]

iii How many electrons does strontium have in its outer shell? [1]

iv Write the symbol for a strontium ion [1]

b Use the Periodic Table to explain why sheep are likely to take in strontium as well as calcium. [2]

c A tiny lump of the strontium element was dropped into water so that it could react.

$$\mathbf{Sr + 2H_2O \rightarrow Sr(OH)_2 + H_2}$$

i Why do you think that a *tiny* lump was used? [1]

ii Use the position of strontium in the Periodic Table to explain why. [1]

iii Name each of the **two** chemicals produced. [2]

iv After the experiment a pH meter was put into the water.
Suggest a number for the reading on the pH meter. [2]

[12 marks]

2 We think that wine was first produced by accident when wild yeasts landed on some crushed grapes and made them ferment.

a i What are the **three** important conditions for fermentation to go well? [3]

ii What are the sugars in the grapes converted to during fermentation? [1]

b Yeast will not make grapes ferment if the grapes are too acidic. Explain why. [2]

c Yeast is also used in breadmaking.
What does yeast produce to make the bread rise? [1]

d If bread is left in a cold place the yeast will only work very slowly.
What will happen to the speed that the yeast works at as the temperature increases? Explain your answer. [4]

[11 marks]

3 A student wanted to see how fast magnesium reacts with hydrochloric acid.
She used the same amount of acid and the same mass of magnesium for each experiment.

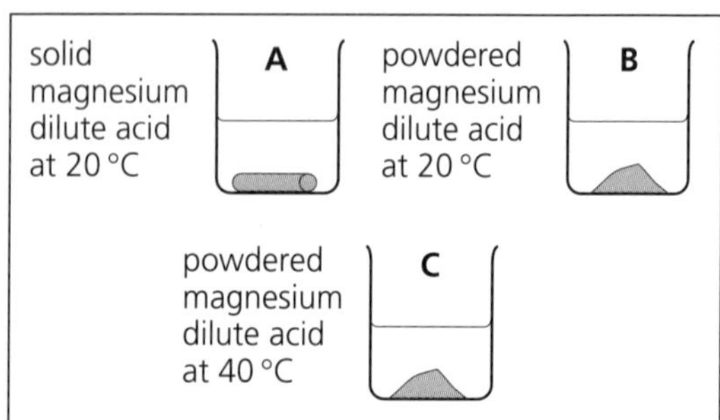

a Use the idea of particles to explain why the reaction in beaker B was faster than A. [2]

b Use the idea of particles to explain why the reaction in beaker C was faster than B. [2]

c Suggest **two** other ways of speeding reactions up. [2]

[6 marks]

4 A tanker crashes on a busy road and spills some of the chemical that it is carrying. Fortunately, nothing catches fire. Firemen are called to deal with the spillage.

This is the Hazchem sign on the tanker.

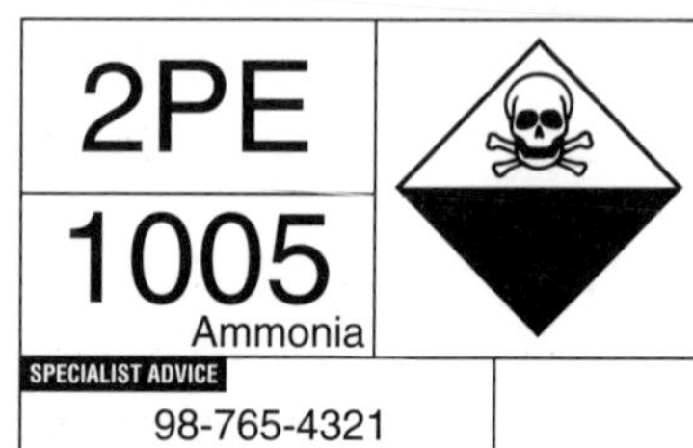

Using the information in the officer's code book (see page 101):

a What is the name of the chemical that has been spilt? [1]

b The Hazchem sign starts with the number 2, yet the firemen don't use fog or spray. Why not? [1]

c What should the firemen do with the chemical spilt on the road? [1]

d What should the firemen wear while dealing with the spill? [1]

e The police cleared everyone else from the area.

What bit of the Hazchem code warned them to do that? [1]

[5 **marks**]

5 The film used in cameras can be made of white crystals of silver chloride (AgCl) stuck to a layer of plastic. Silver chloride doesn't dissolve in water. It is made by mixing two colourless solutions, silver nitrate solution ($AgNO_3$) and sodium chloride (NaCl) solution.

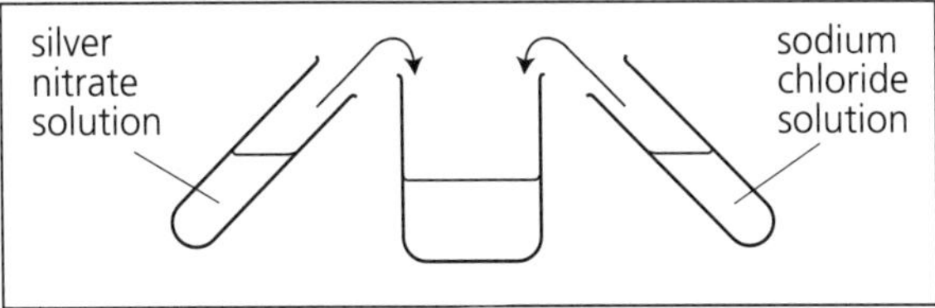

a What would you *see* as the two chemicals were mixed? [2]

b Another chemical is made as well as silver chloride. What is it? [2]

c Write a balanced chemical equation for this reaction [1]

d Other silver compounds will also respond to light.

i What other chemical could you try that is very similar to silver chloride? [1]

ii Explain why you suggested that chemical. [1]

[7 **marks**]

6 Many fertilisers contain ammonium compounds. Ammonia is made by passing nitrogen and hydrogen over a hot iron catalyst. This is a reversible reaction.

nitrogen + hydrogen ⇌ ammonia

a What do we mean if a reaction is reversible? [1]

b Where do we get the nitrogen from to make the ammonia? [1]

c Nitrogen on its own is no good as a fertiliser. Why not? [1]

Ammonia is sometimes dissolved in water and put straight on to fields, but it can harm the plants and also pollutes rivers in rainy weather.

d i Suggest **one** property of ammonia which might harm plants. [1]

ii Why would rainy weather make the rivers polluted? [2]

e Fertiliser is usually made from compounds such as ammonium nitrate.

What would react with ammonia to make ammonium nitrate? [2]

Plants will grow without fertiliser because nitrogen from the air forms nitrogen compounds in the soil all the time.

f i What takes the nitrogen from the air and converts it into useful compounds? [2]

ii What are the nitrogen compounds converted into inside the plant? [1]

[11 **marks**]

7 Divers explored the wreck of an old sailing ship that they found buried in the wet mud at the bottom of the sea. Once they had cleared the mud away they found a pile of iron musket balls and a pile of iron cannon balls. The balls were only a little bit rusty, even though they had been under water for such a long time.

a The balls had not rusted much because something was missing in the wet mud of the sea bed. What was it? [1]

b The pile of musket balls had rusted faster than the cannon balls. Suggest why. [1]

c The cannon balls were treated to turn the rust back into iron. The scientists measured how well the cannon balls conducted electricity to see how much treatment was needed.

How well would a new cannon ball conduct compared to a very rusty one?

Explain your answer. [2]

d When aluminium objects corrode they form a white powder. Find aluminium in the Periodic Table and suggest why the powder is not coloured. [2]

[6 marks]

8 Air bags in cars inflate during a collision in order to reduce the damage to the occupants.

Some air bags contain a canister of a very unstable compound called sodium azide. An electric wire inside the canister heats up slightly, which is enough to start the sodium azide decomposing in an exothermic reaction.

$$2NaN_3 \rightarrow 2Na + 3N_2$$

a Suggest why it is an advantage for the sodium azide to be very unstable. [1]

b During the reaction some bonds are broken and some are made.

i Suggest which bonds might be broken. [1]

ii Suggest which bonds might be made. [1]

iii Use ideas of bond breaking and making to explain why the reaction is exothermic. [3]

c The electric wire only provides a very small amount of heat energy.

Explain why this is enough to make the reaction happen. [2]

d Complete the diagram to show how the energy inside the chemicals changes during the course of the reaction. [2]

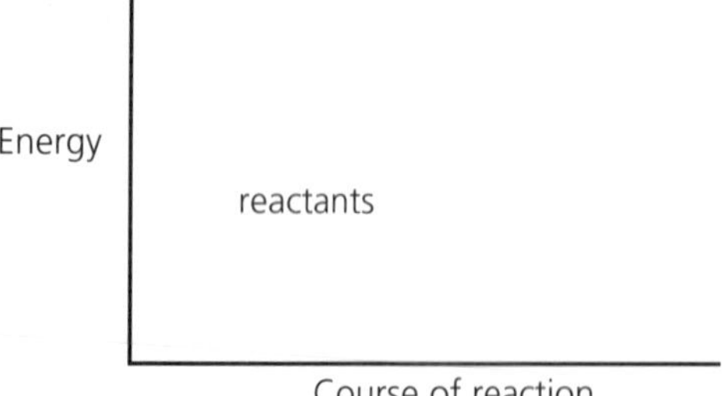

[10 marks]

9 Chlorine is made by passing an electric current through a cell containing sodium chloride solution. The solution contains Na^+ and Cl^- ions. During the electrolysis chlorine is produced at one electrode and oxygen is produced at the other.

a At which electrode is the chlorine produced? [1]

b Use your knowledge of ions and electrons to explain how chlorine is produced at that electrode. [3]

c The water in the cell also forms ions. Write an equation to show which ions are formed by the water. [2]

d At the start of the electrolysis the cell contains sodium chloride solution.

What solution is present in the cell at the end? [1]

[7 marks]

Electricity and magnetism

You will have met the ideas in this section when you worked on the units *Electricity in the home*, *Energy matters*, *Energy today and tomorrow* and *Sound reproduction*. This section is divided into eight spreads.

Electrical current

How much current is flowing round?
What happens to current in series and parallel circuits?

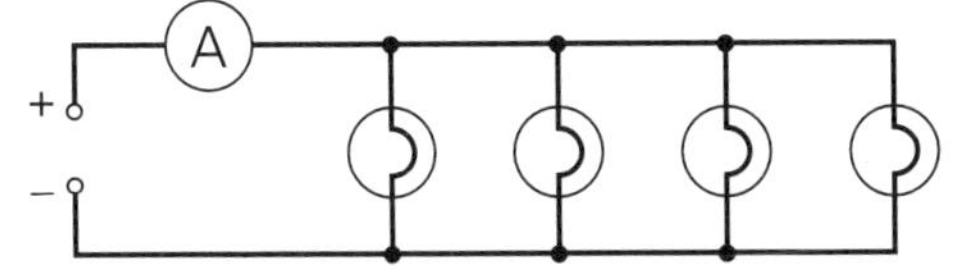

Voltage and resistance

Where does current get its energy from?
What is the effect of resistance?

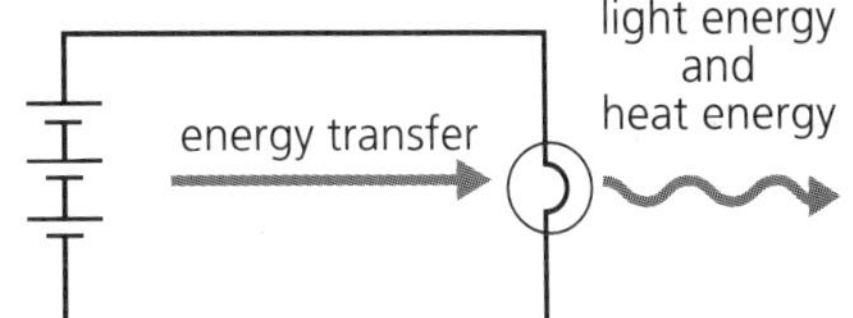

Static electricity

What causes static electricity?
Can it be useful?

Magnetism

Like poles repel.
Unlike poles attract.
What is the effect of a magnetic field on an electric current?
How do motors and loudspeakers work?

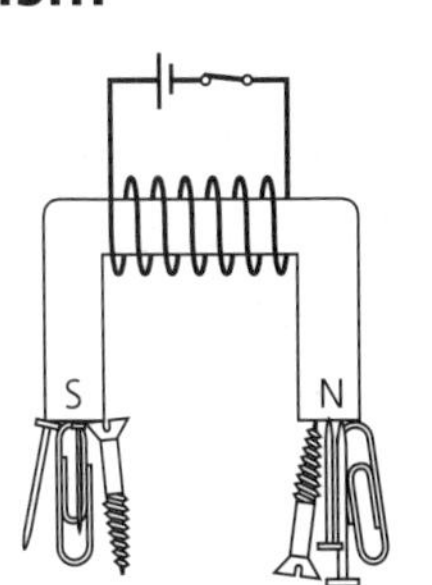

Electrical safety

How should you wire a plug?
How do you know what fuse to use?

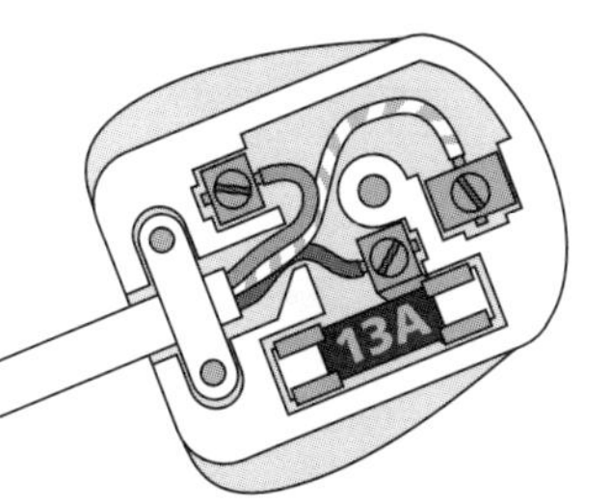

Electromagnets in action

Using electromagnets in tape recording and microphones.
How do we generate electricity?

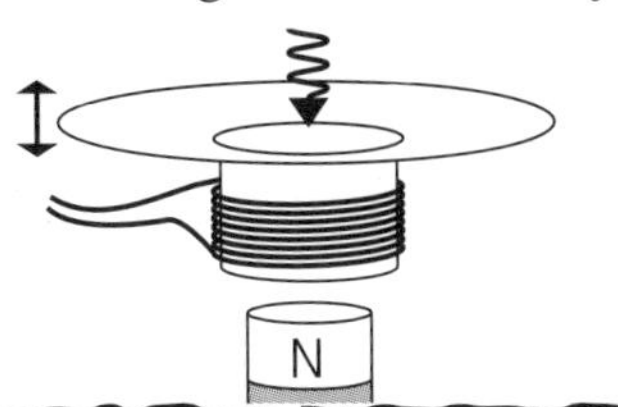

Electrical power and cost

Generating and transmitting electricity.
Generators and transformers.
What are watts?

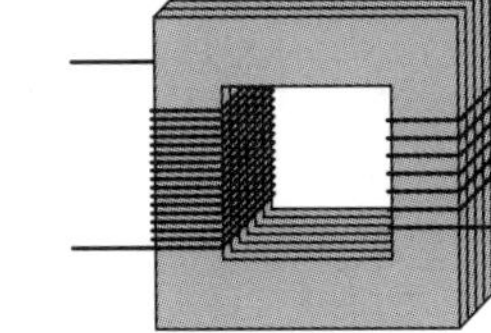

Electricity on a large scale

How are large quantities of electricity made?

How do we get electricity safely into our homes?

Electrical current

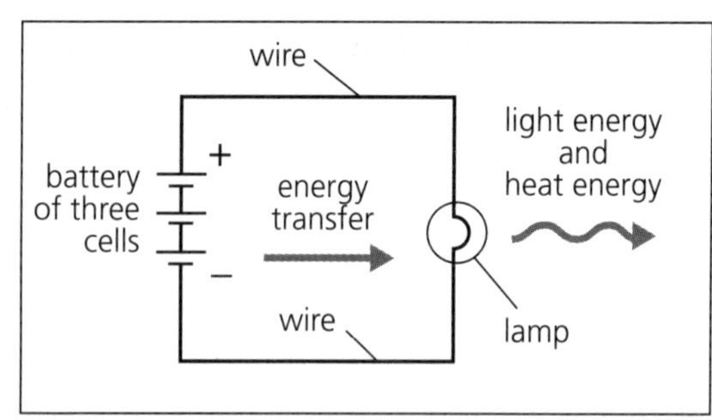

Here is the circuit diagram for a lamp connected to a battery by a pair of wires.

Chemical energy in a battery makes electrons in the metal wires of the circuit flow from the negative terminal (–) to the positive one (+). A flow of electrons or **charge** is called a **current**. There is only a current if the circuit is complete and unbroken.

$$\text{current} = \frac{\text{charge}}{\text{time}} \qquad I = \frac{Q}{t}$$

Symbol	Meaning	Units of measurement
I	current	ampere or A
Q	charge	coulomb or C
t	time	second or s

Worked example

Q A current of 250 mA flows in a lamp for 2 minutes. How much charge passes through the lamp?

A $I = 250\text{ mA} = 0.25\text{ A}$
$Q = ?$
$t = 2\text{ minutes} = 120\text{ s}$

$I = \frac{Q}{t}$

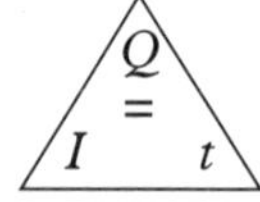

$Q = It \qquad ? = 0.25 \times 120 = 30\text{ C}$

Now do this

1 Calculate the charge which flows through a 500 mA lamp in 30 s.

2 If 1200 C of charge passes through a motor in a minute, what is the current in it?

Series and parallel

There are two basic types of circuit. In a **series** circuit the electrons have to pass through all of the components. So the current is the same all the way round a series circuit.

In a **parallel** circuit the flowing electrons have to be shared by some of the components. So the current is shared in a parallel circuit.

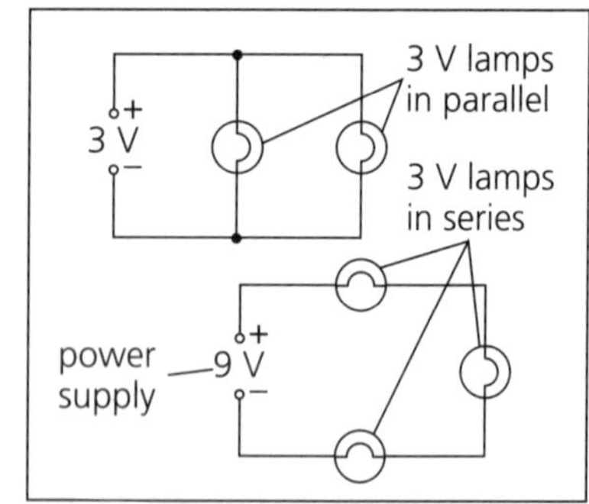

Switches

Switches are used to control the flow of electrical energy in a circuit. When the switch is open charge cannot flow through it because the circuit is broken. There can only be a current in a switch when it is closed.

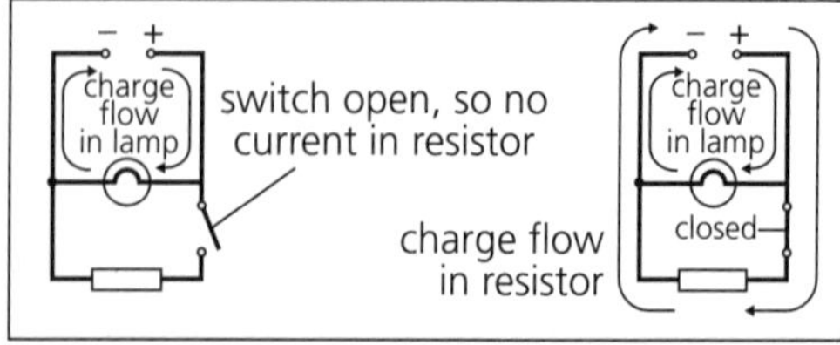

Now do this

3 Complete this table with the words ON and OFF.

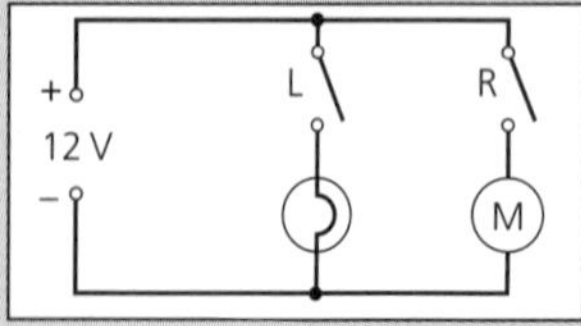

Switch L	Switch R	Bulb	Motor
open	open		
open	closed		
closed	open		
closed	closed		

Measuring current

Current is measured in **amps** (or **A**). It is the same all the way round a series circuit, even if there are several components. The amount of current in a component is measured with an **ammeter**. The meter is connected in series with the components.

In a parallel circuit the current from the electricity supply is shared between the components. The total current is the sum of the currents in the components.

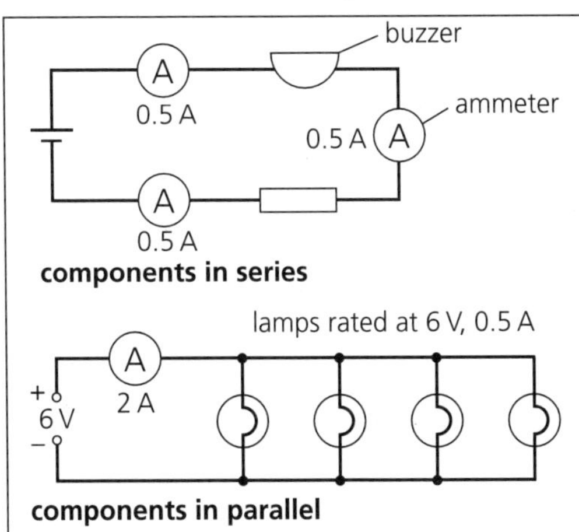

Now do this

4 Draw a diagram to show how to measure the current in a lamp being run off a 6 V battery.

5 Fill in the readings of the ammeters in this circuit.

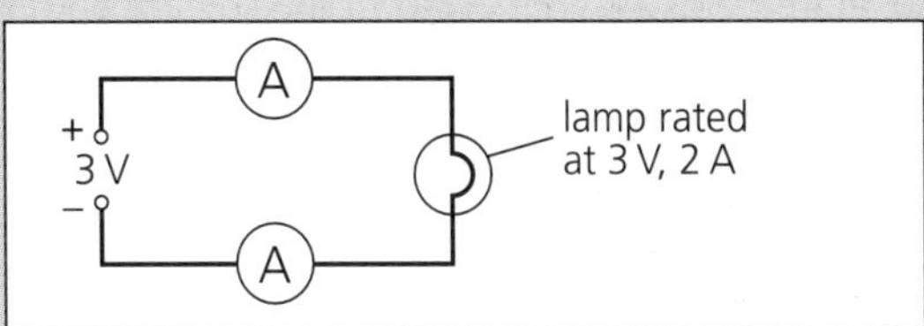

6 One lamp draws a current of 0.25 A when connected to a supply. How much current will be drawn by 8 lamps connected in parallel to the same supply?

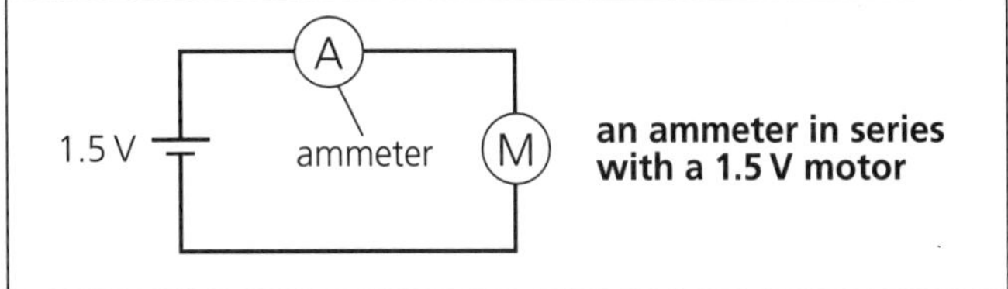

an ammeter in series with a 1.5 V motor

Types of current

There are two types of current. When the current has the same direction all the time it is called **direct current (dc)**. Batteries and solar cells supply dc.

When the direction of the current keeps changing it is called **alternating current (ac)**. Mains electricity is ac. Dynamos and generators make ac.

A cathode ray oscilloscope (or CRO) can be used to show the difference between ac and dc supplies.

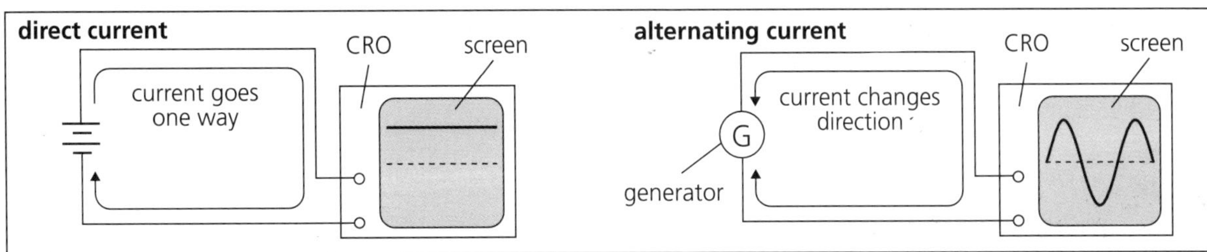

Now do this

7 What types of current do each of the following use?

a A torch? **b** A washing machine?

c An electrical heater? **d** A personal stereo?

Voltage and resistance

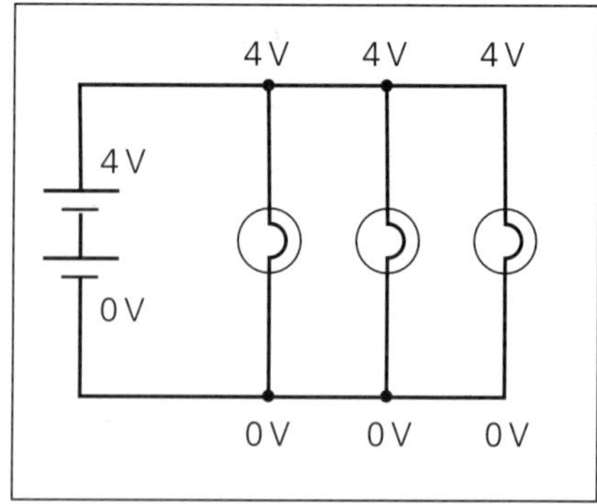

In an electric circuit, a battery (or other power supply) provides the energy to keep electric charge flowing. The amount of energy supplied to each **coulomb** of charge is called the **voltage**.

Electrical components are designed to work at a particular voltage and should only be connected to the correct power supply.

When components are connected in parallel, they each receive the full voltage.

When components are connected in series the voltage is shared between them. The current is the same in each component, but the energy from the power supply is shared between them.

The voltage across a component is measured by connecting a voltmeter in parallel with it. Voltage is measured in **volts** (or **V**).

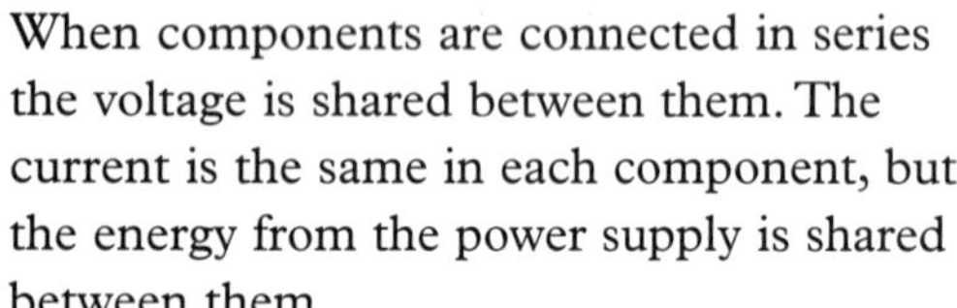

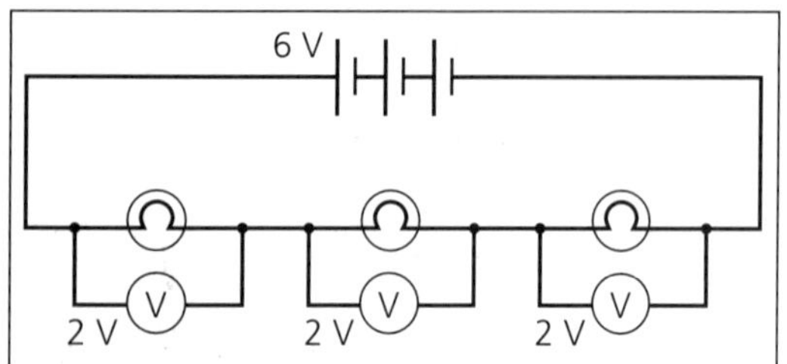

Now do this

1. A circuit contains components connected to a 12 V power supply. Should the components be in series or parallel if they are:
   - **a** A 12 V bulb and a 12 V motor?
   - **b** Four 3 V bulbs?
   - **c** Two 6 V bulbs and a 12 V heater?
2. There is a voltage drop of 12 V across a lamp. How much energy is delivered to the lamp when 8 C of charge flows through it?
3. A resistor and a motor are connected in series with a 12 V battery. Draw a circuit diagram to show how the voltage across the motor can be measured.

Resistance

All electrical components resist the flow of electrons through them. They try to slow down the flow. This is called **resistance**. Resistance makes the components heat up.

The bigger the resistance in a circuit, the smaller the current. You can work out resistance with this formula.

$$\textbf{resistance} = \frac{\textbf{voltage}}{\textbf{current}} \qquad R = \frac{V}{I}$$

Components can have the same voltage but different currents. If a 3 V motor has a smaller resistance than a 3 V bulb, then it has a larger current. As the voltage of a component increases, so does the current.

Symbol	Meaning	Units of measurement
R	resistance	ohms or Ω
V	voltage	volts or V
I	current	amperes or A

Worked example

Q There is a current of 0.2 A in a resistor connected to a 3.0 V battery. Calculate the resistance.

A $R = ?$
$V = 3.0\,\text{V}$ $\quad R = \frac{V}{I} \quad ? = \frac{3.0}{0.2} = 15\,\Omega$
$I = 0.2\,\text{A}$

A variable resistor is sometimes called a **rheostat**. It can be used to control the current in a circuit. As its resistance is increased, the current decreases. Rheostats can be used to control the speed of a motor or the brightness of a bulb.

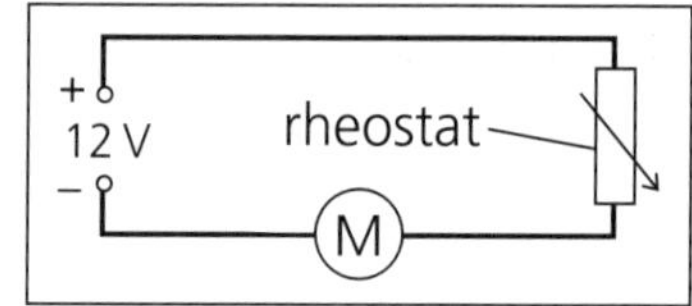

Now do this

4 Which of these circuits has the highest resistance?

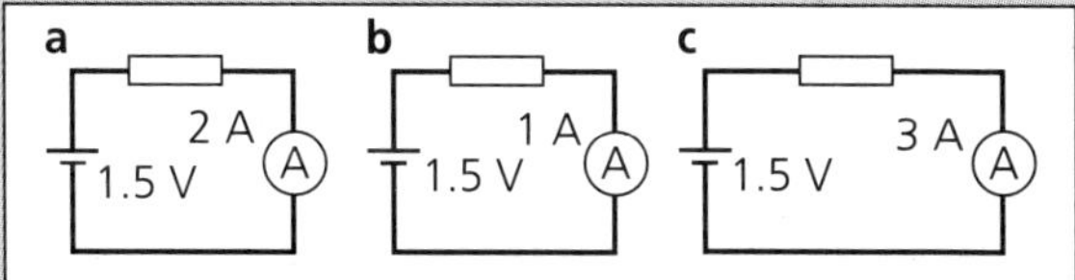

5 Write down the formula for electrical resistance. Explain the symbols and give their units.

6 A resistor has a current of 0.5 A when the voltage across it is 24 V. Calculate its resistance.

7 Show how a rheostat can be used to adjust the brightness of a lamp connected to a battery.

8 What is the current in a 3 Ω resistor when the voltage across it is 12 V?

9 What is the voltage across a 25 Ω resistor when there is a current of 4 A in it?

When resistors are connected in series their resistance adds up. So 4 Ω in series with 6 Ω has an overall resistance of 10 Ω.

Temperature and light sensitive components

Things which contain a lot of free electrons have a low resistance. The number of free electrons in a metal is fixed, but can be changed in a semiconductor. The electrons in thermistors and LDRs can be freed by giving them extra energy. Increased light reduces the resistance of a light-dependant resistor (LDR). Similarly, increased temperature reduces the resistance of a thermistor.

LDRs are used in circuits which respond to light levels. Thermistors are used in temperature controlled circuits.

Now do this

10 Explain how the resistance of thermistors and LDRs depends on their environment.

Voltage-current curves

These graphs show how the current in a wire resistor and a lamp depend on the voltage across them. Neither of these components have a polarity, so the graphs look exactly the same if the voltage is reversed.

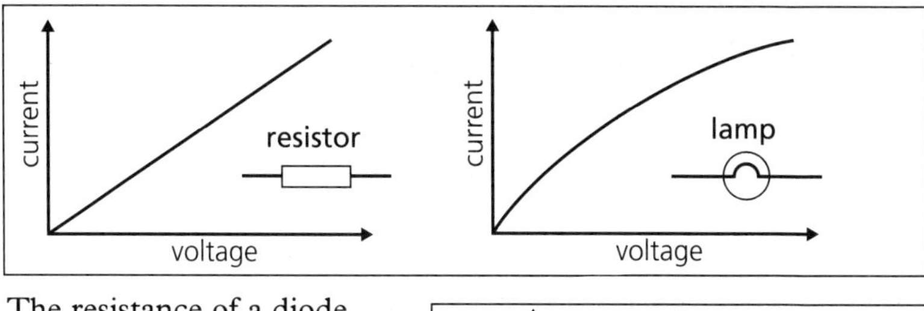

The resistance of a diode depends on the voltage across it. The current rises steeply when the anode voltage rises above the cathode voltage.

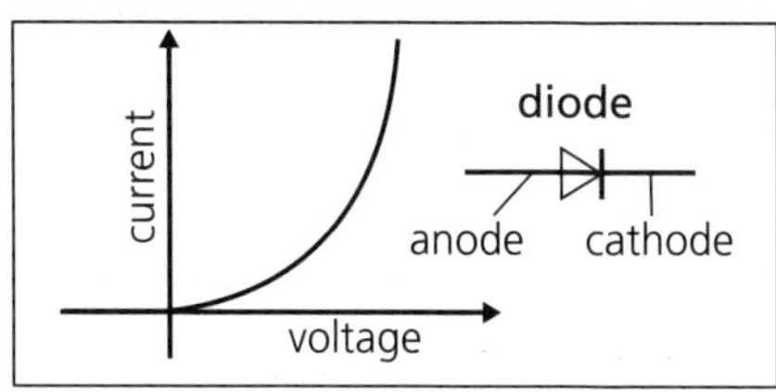

Now do this

11 Sketch graphs to show how the current depends on the voltage for
a a wire resistor;
b a lamp. Explain the different shapes.

12 Sketch a voltage-current graph for a diode.

Electrical power

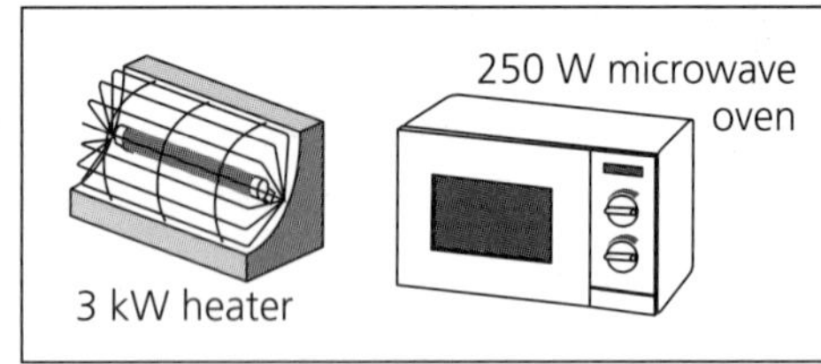

We need to know the **power** of our electrical appliances. Electrical heaters have high power ratings and are therefore expensive to run. Motors and lights have lower power ratings and therefore cost less to run.

The power of an electrical component is calculated with this formula.

power = current × voltage or $P = IV$

Symbol	Meaning	Units of measurement
P	power	joules/s or watts (W)
V	voltage	volts or V
I	current	amps or A

Worked example

Q There is a current of 2 A in an electric drill connected to 230 V. Calculate the power of the drill.

A $P = ?$ $P = IV$ $P = 2 \times 230 = 460\ \text{W}$

$V = 230\ \text{V}$

$I = 2\ \text{A}$

The energy transferred to a component can be measured with a **joulemeter**. The reading on the meter tells you how much energy (in joules J) has been transferred from the power supply to the component.

Now do this

1. Write down the symbols and units for power, voltage and current. Give the formula which connects them.
2. There is a current of 5 A in a lamp connected to a 12 V battery. Calculate the power of the lamp.
3. Draw a circuit diagram to show how an ammeter and a voltmeter should be connected to measure the power of a motor.
4. A 100 W lamp is connected to a 250 V supply. Calculate the current in the lamp.

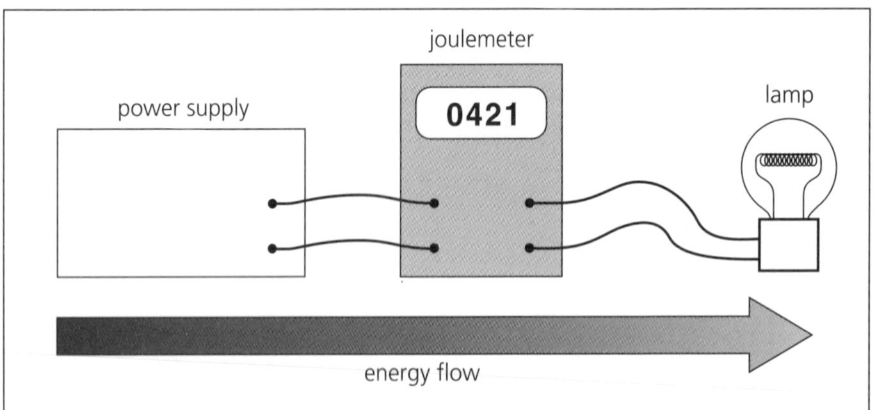

Now do this

5. The reading of a joulemeter changes from 421 J to 2821 J in a minute when a lamp is connected to it. Calculate the power of the lamp.

Working out the cost

Every electrical appliance has a voltage rating and a power rating. The voltage rating is usually 230 V. The power is measured in watts (W) or kilowatts (kW).

1 kW = 1000 W

The power rating of an appliance can be used to calculate how much electrical energy it will use. You multiply it by the number of hours the appliance is switched on.

One kilowatt-hour (kWh) of energy is called a **unit of electricity**. It costs about 10 pence.

energy (kilowatt-hour) = power (kilowatt) × time (hour)

Worked example

Q A bulb has a power of 200 W. If a unit of electricity costs 8 p, calculate the cost of running the bulb for a week.

A power in kilowatts = $\frac{200}{1000}$ = 0.2 kW
time in hours = 24 × 7 = 168 hr
units used = kilowatts x hours = 0.2 × 168 = 33.6 kWh
cost = units × 8 = 33.6 × 8 = 269 p

Off-peak electricity at night costs less. This encourages people to use more electricity at night when the demand is low, and less in the day when the demand is high.

Now do this

6 A TV is rated at 230 V, 150 W. If a unit of electricity costs 9 p, calculate how much it costs to run the TV for 5 hours.

7 If an off-peak unit of electricity costs 6 p, calculate how much it costs to run a 2.5 kW water heater for 4 hours at night.

8 Suppose a unit of electricity costs 8 p. How much money do you waste by leaving a 100 W bulb on for ten minutes?

9 An electric cooker has four 1 kW heating rings, a 1.5 kW grill and a 2 kW oven. Calculate how much it costs to use all the cooker elements for half an hour. A unit of electricity costs 10 p.

Electrical safety

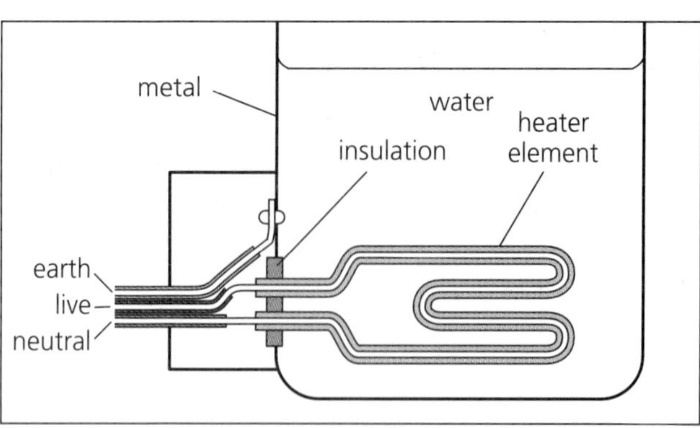

Safe wiring

Electrical appliances are connected to the 230 V mains supply by a pair of metal wires. They are called **live** and **neutral**. If the appliance has a metal outside case, there will be a third **earth** wire as well. This makes the appliance safe.

The earth wire should always be connected to the metal outside of an appliance. Then if the live wire comes loose and touches the outside, the current flows safely away through the earth wire.

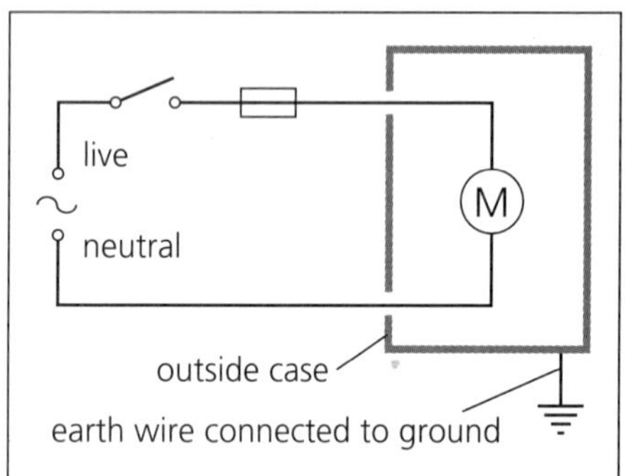

Appliances which are **double insulated** do not need an earth wire. If the live wire comes loose, it can't touch any metal which is on the outside of the appliance.

Each wire has a different coloured covering (insulation). The coloured insulation is important:

- to stop people being electrocuted by the live wire
- to keep the wires apart to stop current taking a short cut and not running through the appliance
- so that electricians can tell the wires apart

Wire	Insulation colour
live	brown
neutral	blue
earth	green and yellow

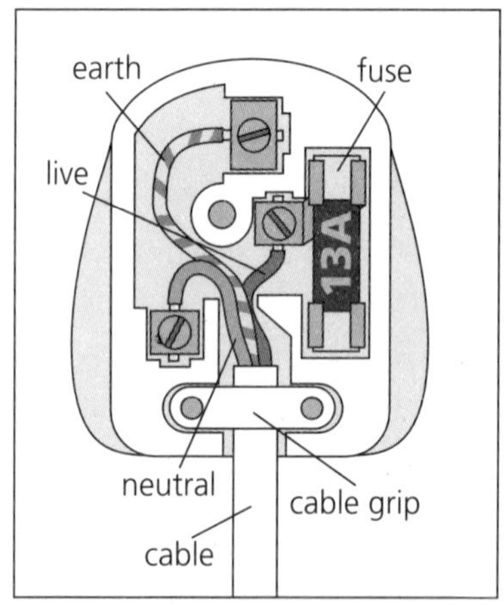

Wiring a plug

Now do this

1 Name the **three** wires connecting an electrical heater to the mains supply.
2 What colour is the insulation of each wire? Why is the insulation needed?

Fuses

There should be a **fuse** in series with an electrical appliance connected to the mains supply. This switches off the current if it gets too high.

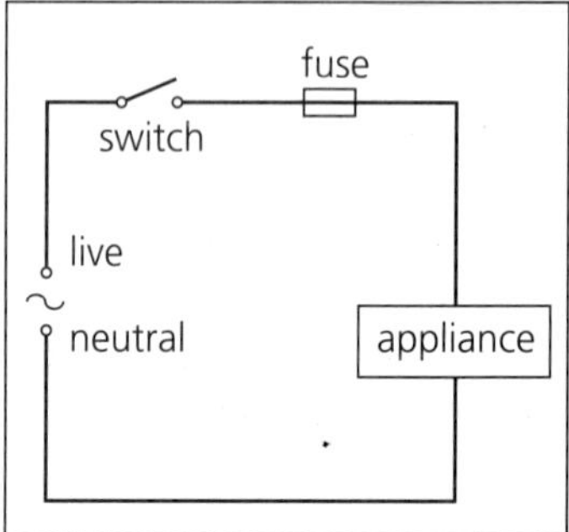

Large currents in a wire can cause it to get hot and damage its insulation. The fuse is the thinnest wire in the circuit, so it melts (blows) first, before the other wires are damaged. People now use **circuit breakers** more and more. These can be reset more easily than fuses, which have to be replaced.

Now do this

3 Explain why the wire in the heating element of a water heater is much thinner than the wire in the cable connecting the heater to the mains supply.

4 State the function of each of the three wires connecting an appliance to the mains electricity supply.

5 Explain how a fuse or circuit breaker protects the insulation of mains wires.

What size of fuse?

It is important to match the current rating of the fuse with the power of the appliance. Otherwise the fuse will blow too soon or too late.

$$\textbf{current in amps (A)} = \frac{\textbf{power in watts (W)}}{\textbf{voltage in volts (V)}} \qquad I = \frac{P}{V}$$

Worked example

Q A microwave oven is rated at 1 kW. Which of these fuses should be used for a 230 V supply: 13 A, 5 A or 2 A ?

A $I = ?$

$P = 1\text{ kW} = 1000\text{ W} \qquad I = \frac{P}{V} = \frac{1000}{230} = \mathbf{4.3\ A}$

$V = 230\text{ V}$

So the correct fuse rating is 5 A.

Now do this

6 Which fuse (13 A, 5 A or 2 A) should be used for a 2 kW heater connected to a 230 V supply?

7 Explain how a fuse can protect people from electric shock.

8 Where should the fuse and switch be connected?

9 What type of appliance does not need an earth wire?

10 Where should the earth wire be connected to an appliance? Why?

Ring mains

Electrical appliances are connected in parallel to the mains power supply. This means that they each get the full 230 V from the power supply. To save on installation costs, the live, neutral and earth wires form a ring around the building.

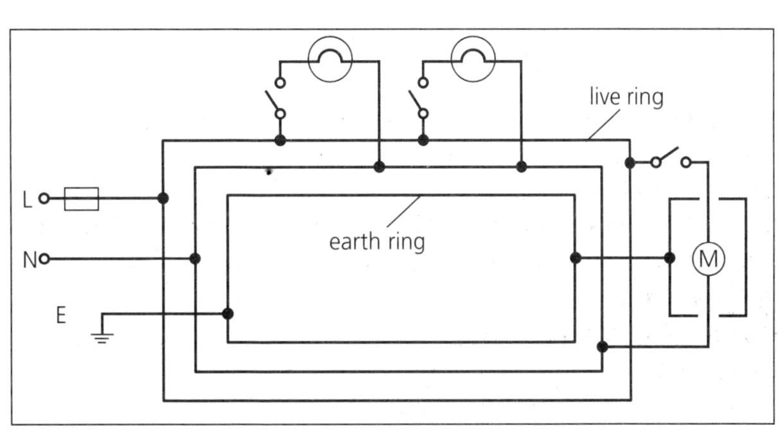

Static electricity

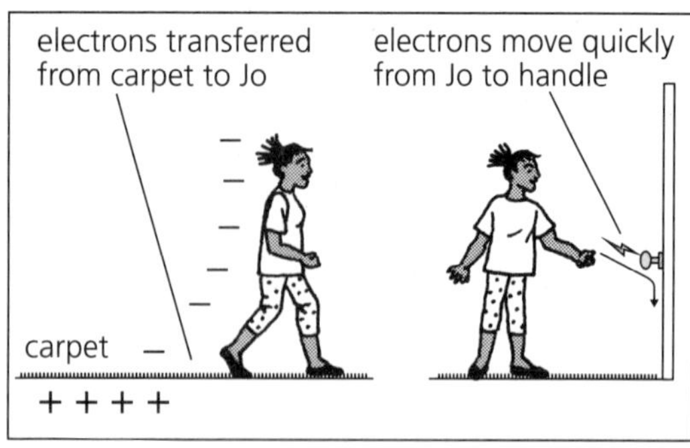

Jo walks across the room. Her feet rub against the carpet, knocking tiny particles (**electrons**) off it. As the number of electrons on her builds up, Jo becomes charged with **static electricity**.

When Jo reaches the door she touches the metal handle. All the electrons that she knocked off the carpet flow rapidly through her into the metal handle. She loses the charge but gets an electric shock at the same time.

Materials which allow electrons to move through them are **conductors**. Materials that electrons cannot move through are called **insulators**. Metals and water are conductors. Most other materials (such as glass, wood and plastic) are insulators. Static electricity only builds up on insulators as the charge cannot flow away through the material.

Now do this

1 What can move through conductors but not through insulators?

2 Name **two** materials which are conductors.

3 Name **two** materials which are insulators.

Positive and negative charge

There are two sorts of charge, **positive** and **negative**. Electrons have a negative charge, so the material which collects them is negatively charged. The material which loses the electrons has lost some of its negative charge, so it is positively charged.

The sort of charge picked up by objects when they are rubbed against each other depends on the two materials involved.

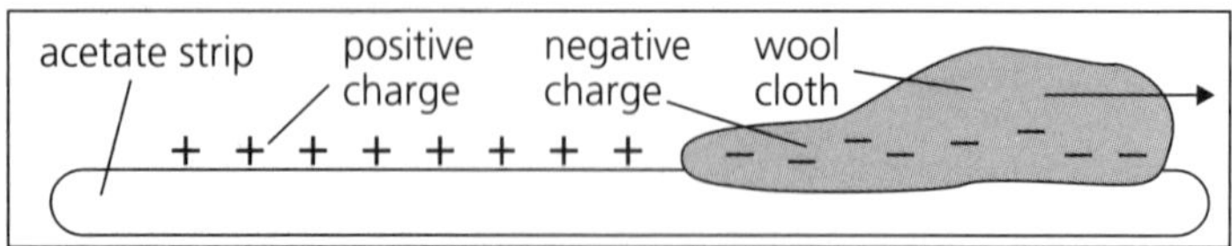

For example, polythene becomes negative when rubbed with wool. The wool becomes positive. Acetate becomes positive when rubbed with wool. The wool becomes negative.

Now do this

4 Copy and complete these sentences.

Fur becomes positive when rubbed on glass. This is because electrons are transferred from the __________ to the __________ during the rubbing. Electrons have a __________ charge. Objects which have lost electrons have a __________ charge.

5 When glass is rubbed with silk, electrons are transferred from glass to silk. What are the charges of the glass and the silk after rubbing?

Electric current

Electrons are charged. So a flow of electrons is a flow of charge, or an **electric current**. In an electrical circuit the electrons flow through the metal wires from the negative terminal of the power supply to the positive terminal. This is opposite to the direction of conventional current, which is supposed to be a flow of charge from positive to negative.

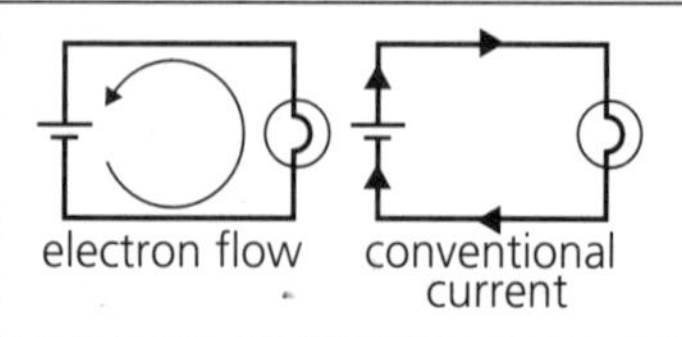

Now do this

6 Explain the difference between electron current and conventional current in a circuit.

Attracting and repelling

- Objects with positive or negative charge attract objects with no charge.
- Objects with the same charge always repel each other.
- Objects with different charges always attract each other.

Now do this

7 A rod is negatively charged. What charge on another rod would repel it? What charge would another rod need to be attracted?

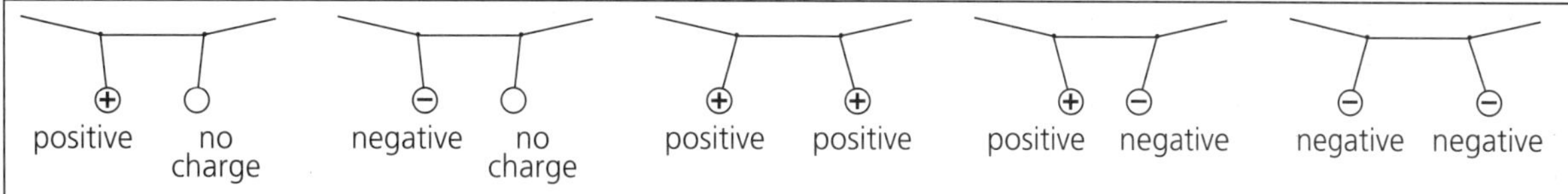

Electrostatic dangers

It is easy to make static electric charges. It happens all the time. If enough charge builds up on an object, it will suddenly discharge into a nearby object, making a **spark**.

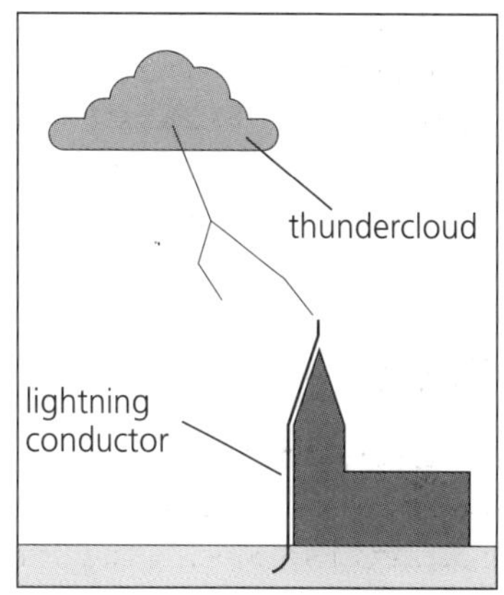

Clouds can become charged in thunderstorms. The enormous spark caused when the clouds discharge to the ground is called **lightning**. Pointed metal strips called lightning conductors at the top of buildings can conduct the current safely to earth.

Factories sometimes release flammable gas or dust into the atmosphere. It is important to stop electrostatic charging from happening in these environments. A single spark could set off a disastrous explosion.

Discharging safely

Cars often charge up when they move rapidly through dry air. The rubber tyres can stop a car from being safely discharged to earth. A metal strip between the metal car body and the ground will do this. You sometimes see a strip trailing from the back of a car.

Now do this

8 Airplanes have to be earthed with a metal strap before they are refuelled. Explain why.

9 Why do people get electric shocks as they get out of cars? How can this be prevented?

Electrostatic uses

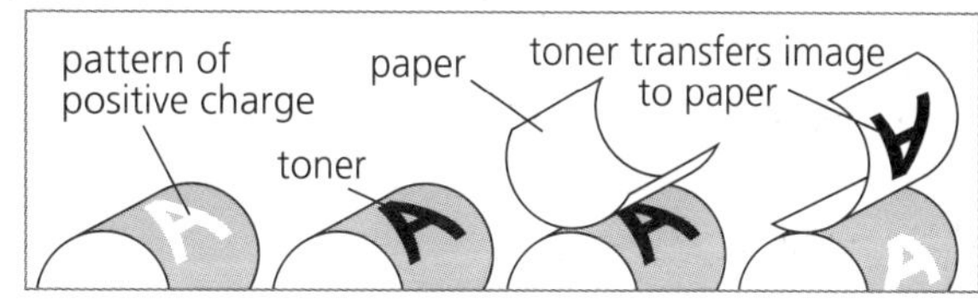

Photocopiers and laser printers use static electricity. Reflected light from a document is used to coat an insulating surface with a pattern of positive charge. This attracts tiny particles of negatively charged toner. The pattern of toner is then transferred to paper which has been strongly positively charged. The toner is fixed to the paper by heating to create the final copy.

Spray painting

Droplets of paint spray can be charged. They then repel each other, to give a fine mist which is strongly attracted to any uncharged metal objects nearby. The result is a very even coat of paint on the object, even round the back.

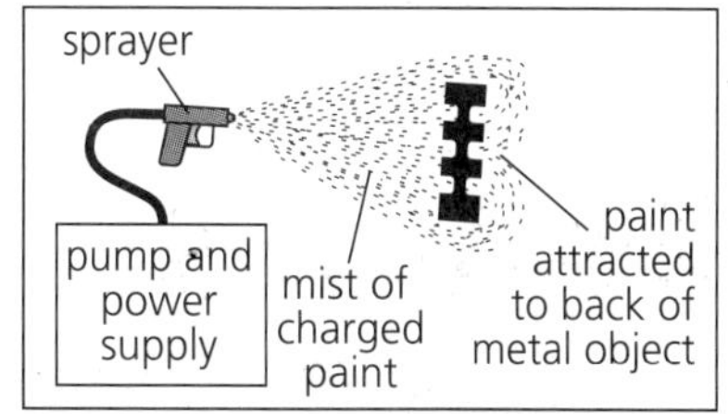

Magnetism

Magnets attract iron and steel which has not been magnetised. They do not attract other metals except cobalt and nickel.

The end of a magnet is called its **pole**. One pole is called south (S) and the other end is north (N). Either pole of a magnet will attract unmagnetised iron.

Poles which are the same repel each other. Poles which are different always attract each other.

Now do this

1 Here are some pairs of objects. For each pair, do they repel, attract or ignore each other?

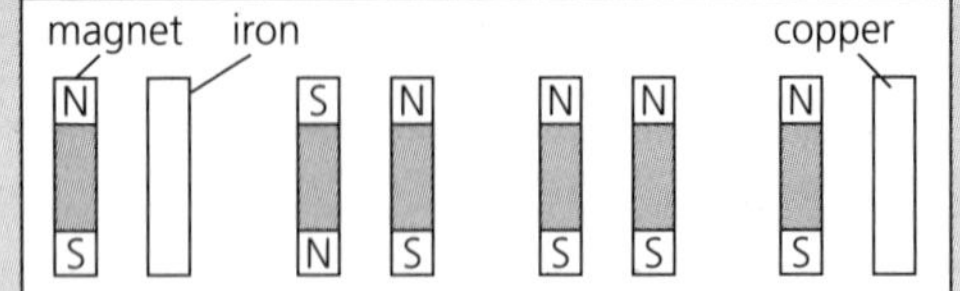

Magnetic fields

Here is the magnetic field around a bar magnet. Each field line has an arrow on it. The field lines tell you which way the needle of a compass points. The field lines come out of the north pole of the magnet and return at the south pole of the magnet.

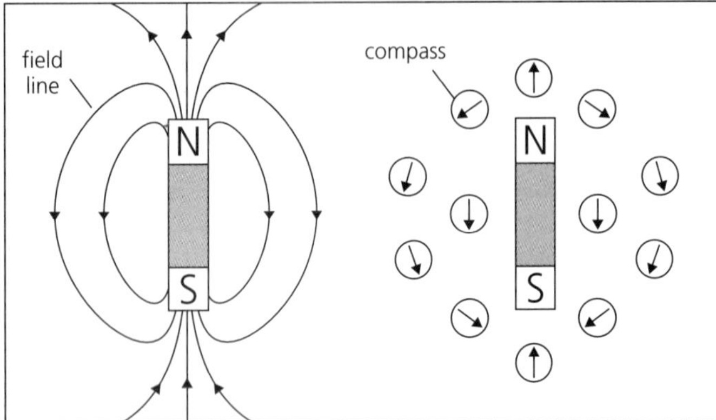

Now do this

2 Name the **four** materials which are attracted to magnets.

3 Name the pole at T on this magnet.

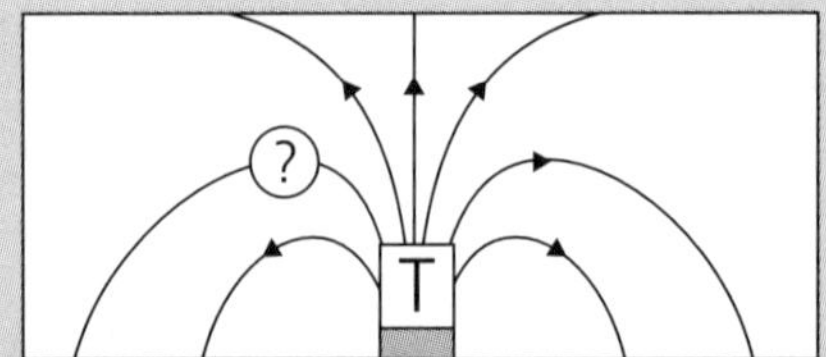

4 Which way will the compass needle point?

Current and magnets

There is a force on a conductor (such as copper) which carries an electric current in a magnetic field.

The force is at right angles to both the current and the field. The direction of the force can be reversed by reversing the direction of either the current or the field.

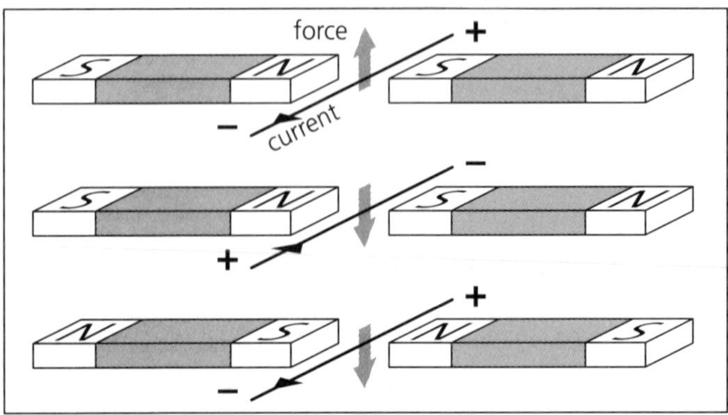

Motors

An electric motor contains a coil of copper wire inside a magnet. The coil is free to rotate on its axis. It sits in a magnetic field from a permanent magnet or an electromagnet.

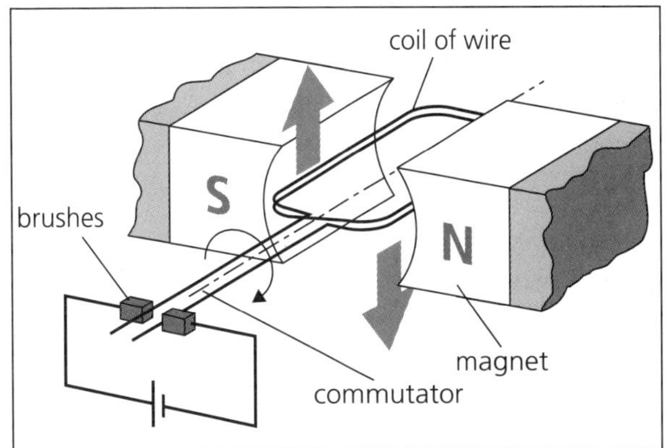

Electric current in the coil interacts with the magnetic field to create a pair of forces. These act in opposite directions, forcing the coil to turn round.

The current enters and leaves the coil via the commutator and brushes. These act as a switch which ensures that the forces on the coil always turn it in the same direction.

Now do this

5 Electric motors contain copper and steel. Explain what each material is used for.

6 Draw a diagram to show the forces on the coil of an electric motor.

7 Explain the function of the commutator in an electric motor.

8 Suggest **three** alterations to an electric motor which will increase its speed.

Loudspeakers

A loudspeaker converts electrical energy in a coil of wire into sound energy. The coil is connected to a **cone**. Alternating current in the coil interacts with the magnet's field to make the cone vibrate.

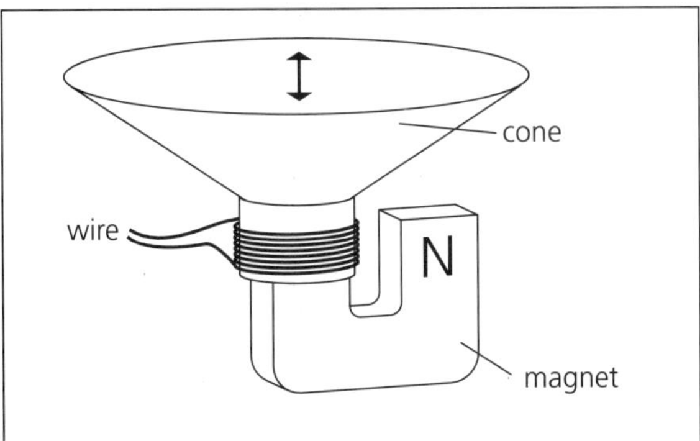

Now do this

9 State the energy transfers in a loudspeaker.

10 Copy and complete these sentences.

A loudspeaker has a cone connected to a __________ of copper wire. There is a __________ inside the coil. An __________ current in the coil makes the cone __________, creating a __________.

Electromagnets in action

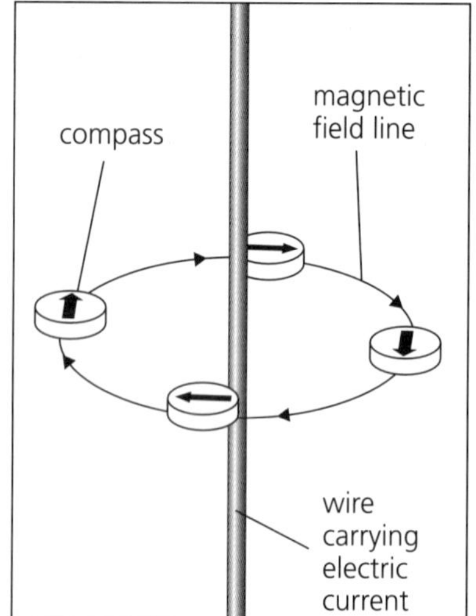

Electric current in a wire affects compasses placed nearby. The current makes a magnetic field.

There is a magnetic field around a coil of insulated wire carrying an electric current. This makes an **electromagnet**.

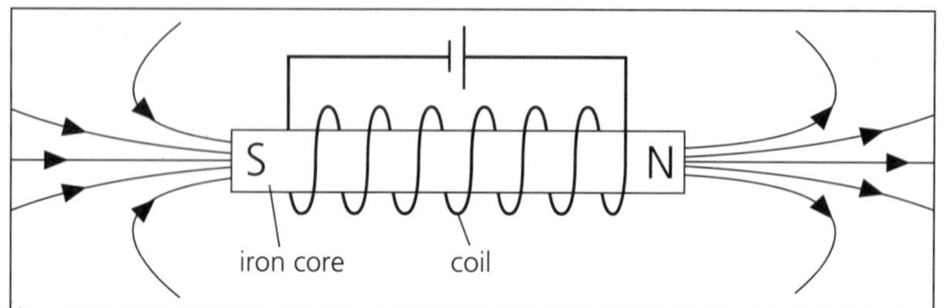

A U-shaped electromagnet is useful for picking up objects made from iron. It only attracts them when the current in the coil is switched on. The U-shaped core is made of **soft iron** to increase the strength of the coil's magnetism. It loses its magnetism when the current is switched off.

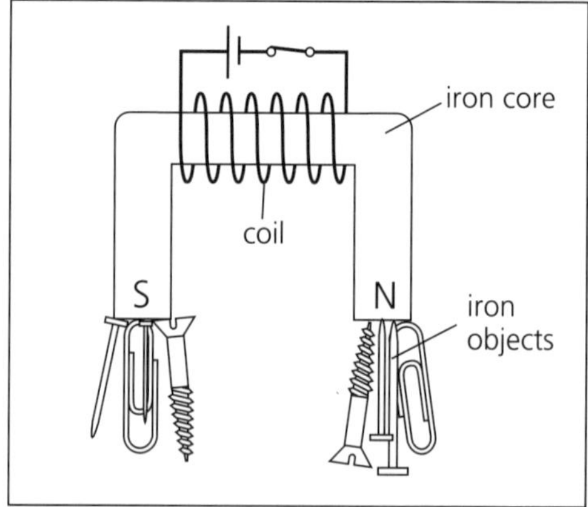

A steel core also increases the magnetism of a coil, but it stays magnetic when the current is switched off.

An electromagnet becomes stronger if:

- more coils of wire are put on it
- the current in it is increased
- an iron core is placed inside it.

Now do this

1 Sketch the magnetic field lines around a coil of wire which carries an electric current.

2 State **three** things which can be done to increase the strength of an electromagnet.

Electromagnetic induction

Electricity can be generated (or **induced**) by changing the magnetic field in a coil of wire. The voltage changes sign (between positive and negative) if the change of field is reversed.

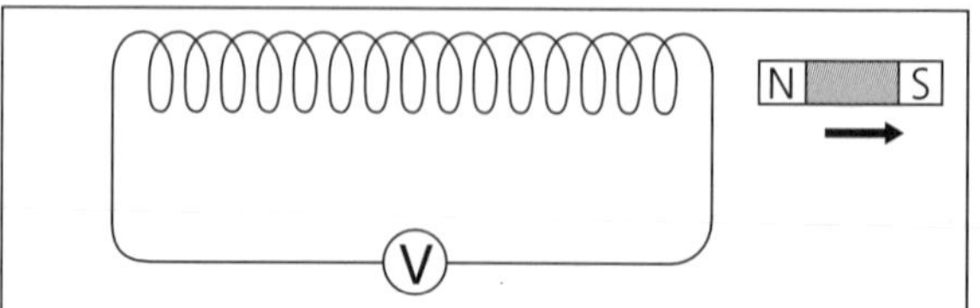

The size of the induced voltage can be increased by:

- speeding up the change of magnetic field
- increasing the strength of the field
- increasing the number of coils of wire.

Now do this

3 The voltmeter reads +0.1 V as the magnet is inserted into the coil. What will it read when the magnet is

a left in the coil

b removed from the coil?

Electricity is generated on a large scale by a **generator**. This uses large spinning coils of copper wire inside the fields of large magnets. The alternating current in the coil is brought out of the generator by brushes pressing on slip rings.

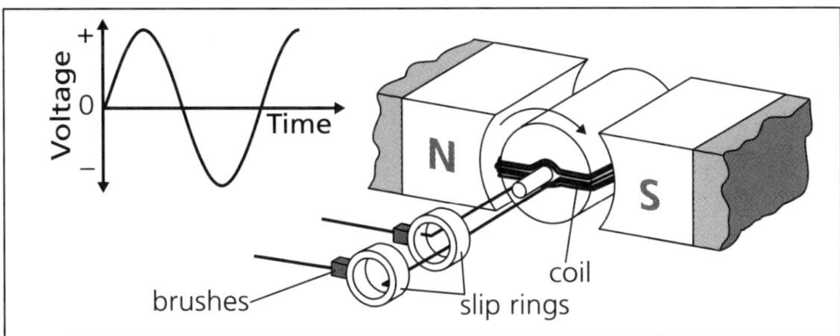

Now do this

4 A generator always contains lots of steel and copper. Suggest what each material is used for.

5 Look at the voltage-time graph for a coil spinning in a magnetic field. How does the graph change if the coil spins round twice as fast?

Microphones

A microphone uses the energy in a sound wave to create an alternating current in a coil of wire.

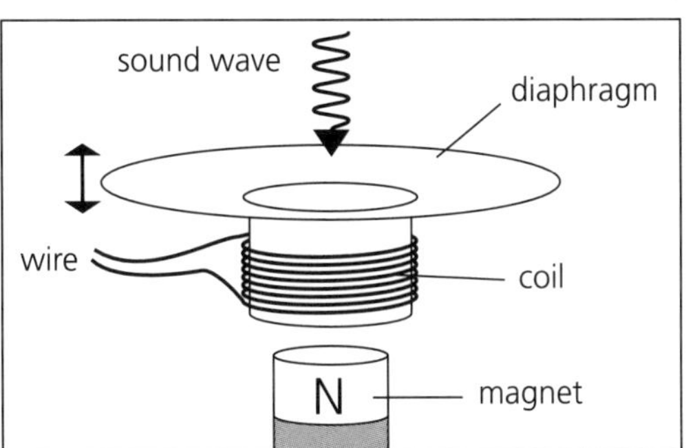

Now do this

6 Copy and complete these sentences.

A microphone converts ____________ energy into ____________ energy. The sound vibrates the ____________, moving it in and out of the field of a ____________. This induces an ____________ current in the coil.

Magnetic recording

Electromagnets can be used to store information about sound on magnetic tape. The tape passes steadily in front of the **recording head** (an electromagnet with the poles on either side of a small gap). The recording put on the tape is made of sections with different directions and strengths of magnetism. These depend on the strength and direction of the current in the coil.

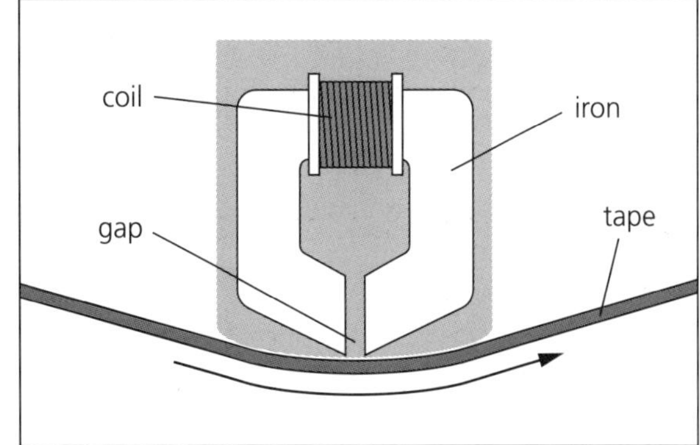

The pattern of magnetism laid down along the tape is a record of the sound wave being stored. This information can be read off the tape by passing it close to a **pickup coil**. The changes of magnetism on the tape induce an alternating voltage across the coil. That voltage can be amplified and fed into a loudspeaker to reproduce the sound wave.

The information stored on a magnetic tape can be destroyed (wiped) by placing it in a strong magnetic field. Always keep your tapes away from magnets!

Now do this

7 Explain how an electromagnet can be used to store information about sound on magnetic tape. How is information used to recreate the sound wave?

Electricity on a large scale

Generating electricity

Electricity is made on a large scale in power stations by boiling water to make high pressure steam. The steam passes through a **turbine**, making it spin round. The turbine is connected to the shaft of a generator. As it spins round, the magnetic field inside the coils of wire changes, generating electricity.

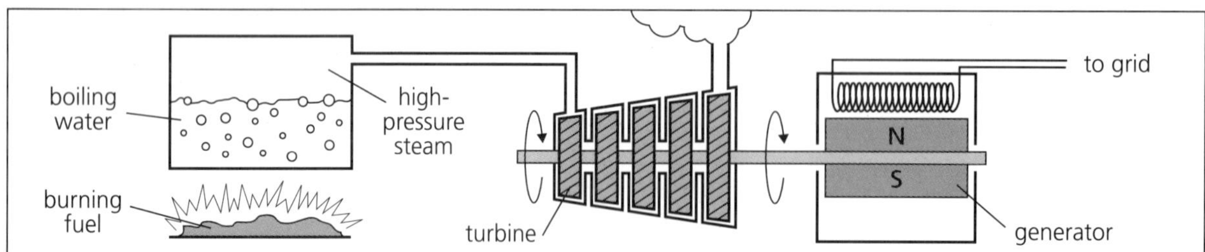

The steam is made by heating water by burning fuels such as coal or oil, or by the heat from nuclear reactions. There are several energy transfers along the way.

1 Chemical energy in the fuel becomes heat energy as it is burnt.
2 The heat energy becomes strain energy in steam from boiled water.
3 The steam is passed through a turbine to give it kinetic energy.
4 The turbine turns the generator, transferring kinetic energy to electrical energy.

Here is an energy flow diagram for a typical gas-fired electricity power station.

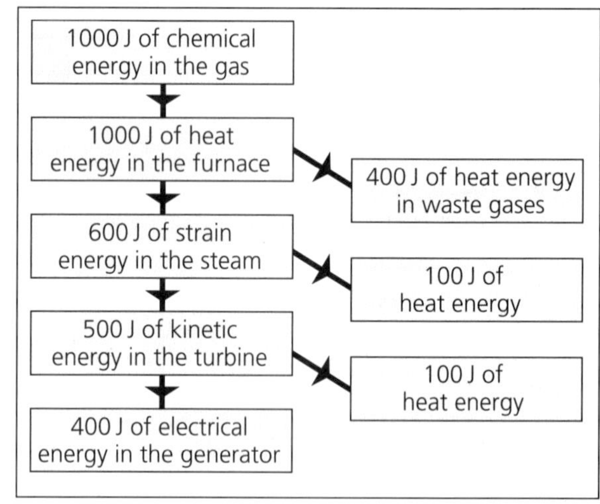

Each time the energy is transferred, some heat energy is lost. Overall, 1000 J of chemical energy in the gas becomes 400 J of electrical energy in the wires coming out of the generator. The remaining 600 J becomes heat energy at various places.

The **efficiency** of the whole process can be calculated with a formula.

$$\textbf{efficiency} = \frac{\textbf{useful output}}{\textbf{input}} \times \textbf{100}$$

input = 1000 J

output = 400 J $\quad$ efficiency $= \frac{1000}{400} \times 100 = 40\ \%$

efficiency = ?

The final value for the efficiency is quoted as a percentage. This is why it is sometimes called **percentage efficiency** (or % efficiency).

Now do this

1 Describe the stages in which electricity is generated from oil.
2 Draw an energy flow diagram for a power station.
3 Write down the formula for calculating efficiency.
4 200 J of chemical energy in coal becomes 50 J of electrical energy in a power station. Calculate the efficiency of the power station.

Transmitting electricity

Electricity is carried from power stations around the country by the **National Grid**. This is a network of cables. It means that electricity can be distributed anywhere in the country, depending on where it is needed.

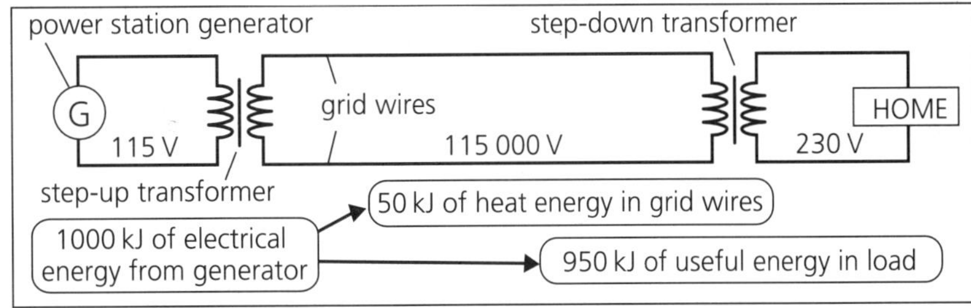

The electric current in the network creates heat energy because of the resistance of the wires. This is a waste of energy. Less heat energy is wasted by keeping the current in the grid at a very high voltage. **Step up transformers** raise the voltage of the electricity between the power station and the grid.

The voltage used for transmission is lethally high for users at the other end of the cable. It has to be converted back into a much lower voltage for use. A **step down transformer** lowers the voltage of the ac as it leaves the grid.

Now do this

5 What is the National Grid? What does it do?

6 Why is the grid run at a high voltage?

7 There are always transformers at each end of high voltage transmission wires. What do the transformers do?

Transformers

A **transformer** is a loop of soft iron with two insulated coils wound around it. Alternating current in the **primary coil** continually changes the magnetism of the iron. This change of magnetism induces a voltage in the **secondary coil**.

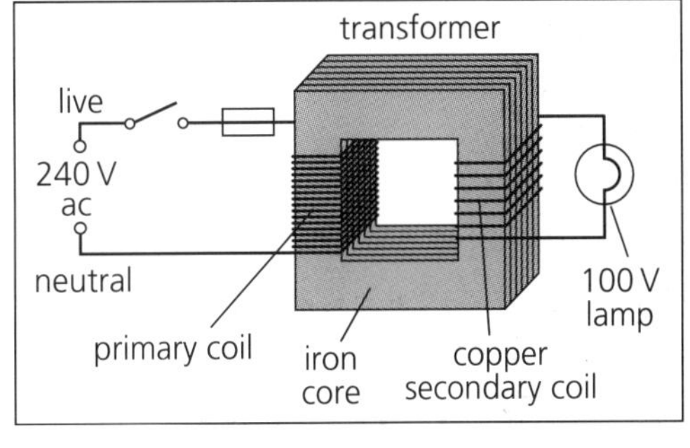

Very little electricity gets converted to heat energy on the way through a transformer. Soft iron is used so that the loop can be magnetised and demagnetised easily.

This formula can be used to calculate the voltage at the secondary coil.

$$\frac{\textbf{primary voltage}}{\textbf{secondary voltage}} = \frac{\textbf{primary turns}}{\textbf{secondary turns}} \qquad \frac{V_p}{V_s} = \frac{n_p}{n_s}$$

Worked example

Q A transformer steps down 230 V to 12 V. If it has 60 turns of wire in its secondary coil, how many turns does it need in the primary coil?

A $\frac{V_p}{V_s} = \frac{n_p}{n_s}$ so $\frac{230}{12} = \frac{?}{60}$

therefore $? = 60 \times \frac{230}{12} = 1150$

Now do this

8 Draw a labelled diagram of a transformer.

9 Explain why transformers operate on ac, not dc.

10 The primary and secondary coils of a transformer have 920 and 48 turns of wire. If the primary is connected to a 230 V ac supply, what voltage appears at the secondary?

Exam questions

1 Julie has five electrical appliances in her room. Look at the table.

Appliance	Power (kW)
hair dryer	1.2
lamp	0.1
heater	2.0
TV	0.2
computer	0.4

a Each appliance is switched on for an hour. Which one will cost the most to run? Why? [1]

b Julie turns on her computer for three hours.

i Calculate how many units of electricity this uses, in kilowatt-hours. [2]

ii Each unit of electricity costs 8 p. Calculate how much it costs for Julie to run her computer. [1]

c The heater is connected to the mains supply by three wires.

i Copy and complete these sentences.

Electrical energy flows to the heater from the mains along the __________. wire. The __________ wire completes the electrical circuit. The __________ wire prevents Julie from electrocution. [3]

ii There is a fuse in one of the wires. Which one? What is the function of the fuse? [2]

iii The mains supply is 230 V. Do a calculation to show that a 5 A fuse would not be suitable. [2]

[11 marks]

2 Look at the diagram.

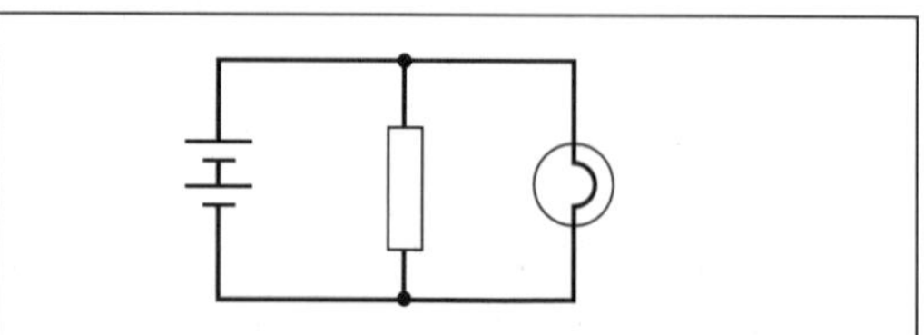

a Redraw the diagram with an ammeter and a voltmeter to measure the current and voltage of the lamp. [2]

b State the energy transfers which take place in the lamp and the resistor. Where does the energy come from? [5]

c The meter readings for the lamp are 0.5 A and 2.5 V. Calculate:

i the resistance of the lamp, [3]

ii the power of the lamp. [3]

d The resistor is 10 Ω.

i Calculate the current in the resistor. [3]

ii How big is the current in the cells? [1]

[17 marks]

3 a Look at the circuit diagram.

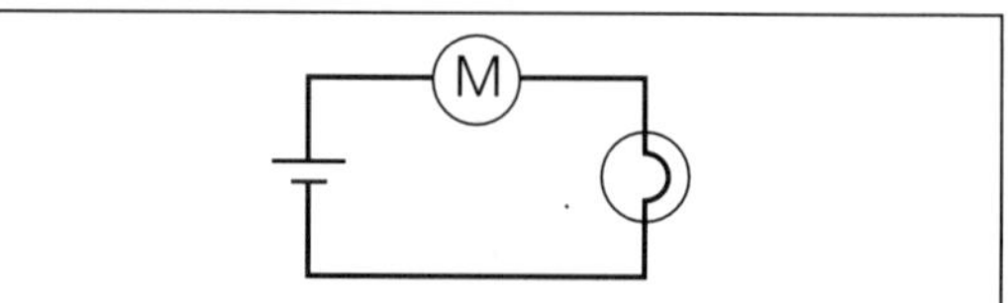

The lamp and the motor are both working. You want the lamp to be brighter. State and explain **two** things you could do. [2]

b A lamp and a variable resistor are connected to a cell.

The variable resistor controls the brightness of the lamp.

i Draw a circuit diagram. [1]

ii Explain how the brightness is controlled. [2]

[5 marks]

4 Look at the circuits. All of the cells and resistors are the same.

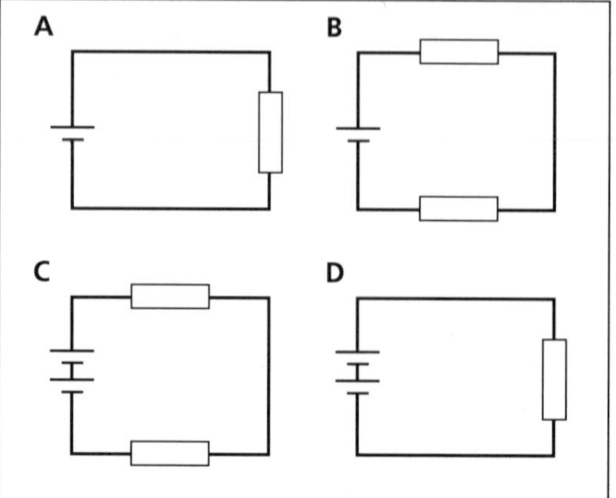

a Which circuit has the greatest current? Why? [2]

b Which circuit has the hottest resistors? Why? [2]

[4 marks]

5 Ann charges up a strip of plastic.

a Write down what Ann could do to charge the plastic. Explain the charging process in terms of electron transfer. [3]

The plastic becomes negative.

It repels a plastic ball.

b State the charge on the ball. Give a reason. [2]

[5 marks]

6 It is safe practice to connect an airplane to the ground with a metal strap before attempting to refuel it.

a Use the idea of electron transfer to explain why an airplane can become charged as it flies through the air. [2]

b State and explain the possible danger of refuelling an airplane which is charged. [2]

c Explain how the metal strap makes the refuelling safe. [2]

[6 marks]

7 Look at the diagram of the electromagnet.

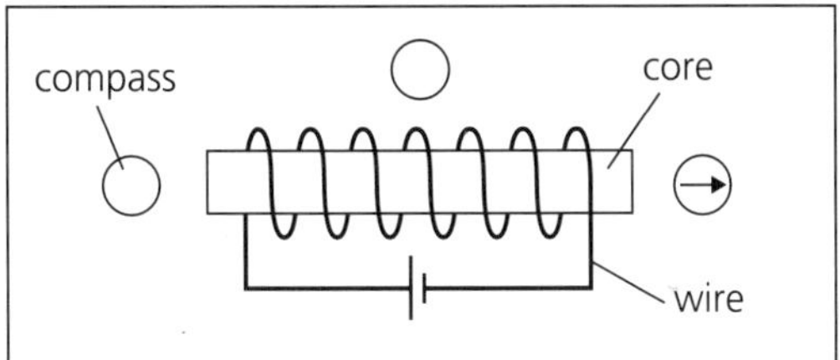

a What is the best material to use for the core? Why? [2]

b Write down **two** things you could do to change the strength of the electromagnet. [2]

c There are three compasses near the electromagnet.

The needle has been drawn for one compass.

i Draw in the other two needles. [2]

ii Write down what you could do to make the needles face in the opposite direction. [1]

[7 marks]

8 **a** Draw a diagram of a transformer. Label the coils and the core. Suggest, with reasons, suitable materials for them. [7]

b Describe the energy transfers which take place in a transformer. [3]

c The primary coil has 690 turns and is connected to the 230 V mains supply. The secondary coil has 69 turns and is connected to a 46 W lamp.

i Calculate the voltage across the lamp. [3]

ii Calculate the current in the secondary coil. [3]

iii Explain why the power supplied by the mains is 46 W. [1]

iv Calculate the current in the primary coil. [2]

v Suggest why the wires in the primary coil can be much thinner than the wires in the secondary coil. [1]

[20 marks]

9 With the help of a labelled diagram, explain how a microphone converts sound into an alternating voltage. [6]

[6 marks]

10 A power station burns coal to make electricity.

a Describe the energy transfers which take place in the power station as the chemical energy of the coal becomes electrical energy in the wires leading from it. [4]

b The station uses 250 MJ of chemical energy in the coal to make 75 MJ of electrical energy. Calculate the efficiency of the power station. [2]

c Useless heat energy appears at various places in the power station. Suggest three places. [3]

d The power station is connected to the national grid by a transformer.

i What is the national grid? [1]

ii Explain the function of the transformer. [3]

[13 marks]

11 A motor is connected to a cell. The motor shaft turns round.

a What changes could you make to the circuit to make the shaft

i turn round the other way

ii rotate more slowly? [2]

b The motor contains copper and steel. Explain what each of these materials is used for in the motor. [4]

c The motor and a lamp are to be run from a single cell, with switches to turn them on and off independently.
Draw a suitable circuit. [3]

[9 marks]

12 Here is a simple relay. The armature is made of soft iron.

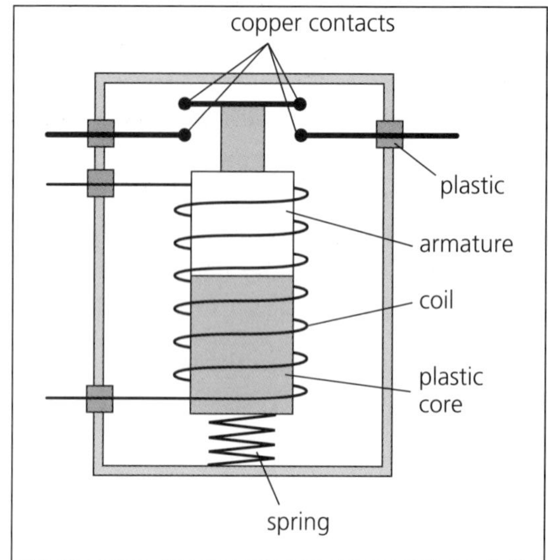

a Explain why the copper contacts touch when a cell is connected across the coil. [4]

b What happens to the contacts when the cell is removed? Give an explanation for your answer. [2]

[6 marks]

Forces and motion

You will have met the ideas in this section when you worked on the units *Moving on*, *Earth in space*, *Sports science*, *Burning and bonding* and *Atmosphere*. This section is divided into four spreads.

Measuring motion

How can you calculate speed?
Why are speed and velocity different?

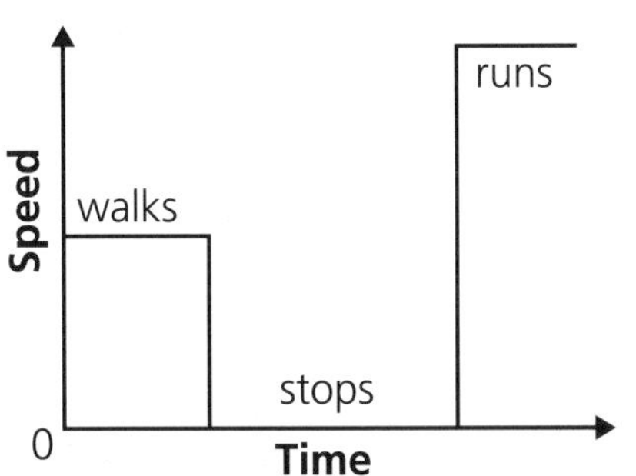

Speeding up and slowing down

What is acceleration?
How do forces affect speed?

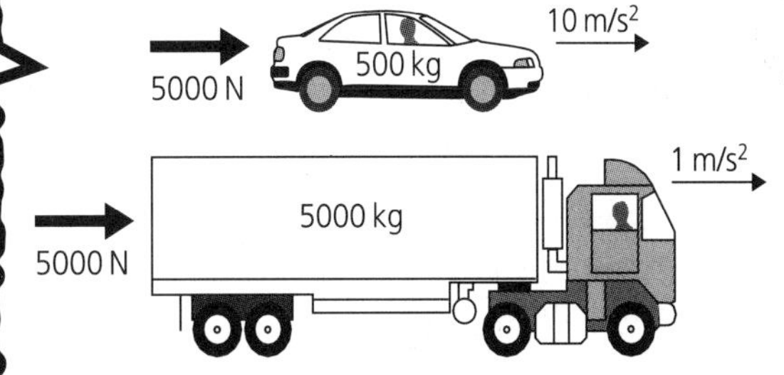

Stopping safely

How can we survive an accident?

Plastic v elastic?

Under pressure

What is pressure? $P = \frac{F}{A}$
How can we use pressure to make cars stop?
What is atmospheric pressure?

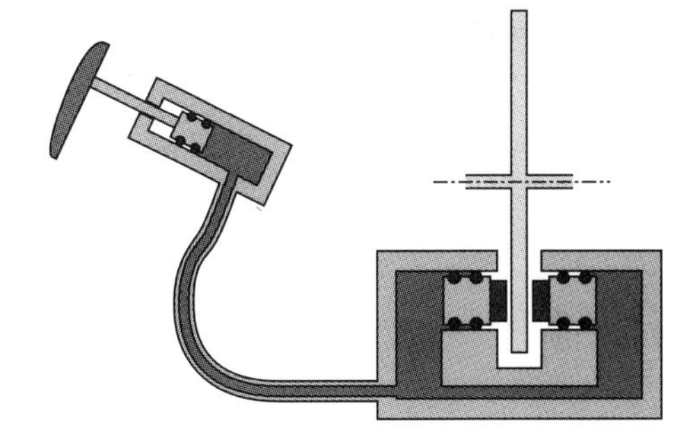

Measuring motion

Joe's car has a top speed of 35 metres per second (m/s). This means that it can move forwards 35 metres in each second. Or 70 metres in two seconds.

The following formula can be used to calculate a speed if you know the distance and the time.

$$\textbf{speed in metres per second (m/s)} = \frac{\textbf{distance moved in metres (m)}}{\textbf{time taken in seconds (s)}}$$

Symbol	Meaning	Units of measurement
v	speed	metres per second or m/s
s	distance	metres or m
t	time	seconds or s

Examiner's tip

You must know this one by heart. Always put the distance and time into the correct units before using the formula.

(v is for velocity, a word which can mean speed. s is for space, another word for distance. Don't get confused.)

Now do this

1 Write down the symbols and units for speed, distance and time.

2 Write down the formula for speed using symbols.

Worked example

Q A car at 30 m.p.h. travels 1.2 km in a minute. Calculate its speed in metres per second.

A v = ? m/s
s = 1.2 km = 1200 m
t = 1 minute = 60 s

$$v = \frac{s}{t} = \frac{1200}{60} = 20 \text{ m/s}$$

Now do this

3 A car travels 400 m in 20 s. Calculate its speed.

4 Sound can travel 2.8 km in 8 s. How fast does it move?

5 Bill can walk 0.5 km in 5 minutes. How fast can he walk?

6 The legal top speed for a car is 110 km per hour. What is this in m/s?

Worked example

Q How far will a car with a speed of 15 m/s go in 10 minutes?

A v = 15 m/s
s = ?
t = 600 s

$$v = \frac{s}{t}$$

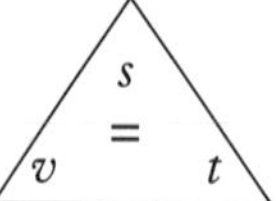

$s = vt$? = 15 × 600 = 9000 m

List the data … write the formula … draw the triangle … change the formula … insert the data.

Now do this

7 A plane has a speed of 50 m/s. How far will it go in a minute?

8 A cheetah runs at 20 m/s. How long will it take to run 100 m?

Velocity

The **velocity** of an object tells you the direction in which it is moving as well as how fast it moves. So Sam and Jo have the same speed (5 m/s), but have different velocities. Sam's velocity is 5 m/s to the right. Jo's velocity is 5 m/s to the left.

Distance-time graphs

Distance-time graphs are a very good way of describing motion.

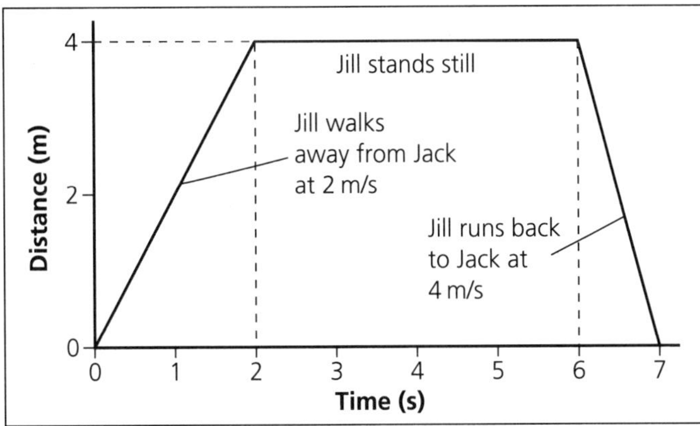

Velocity-time graphs

Here is a distance-time graph for Paul. He walks away slowly, stops for a while and then runs away quickly. This can also be shown in a velocity-time graph.

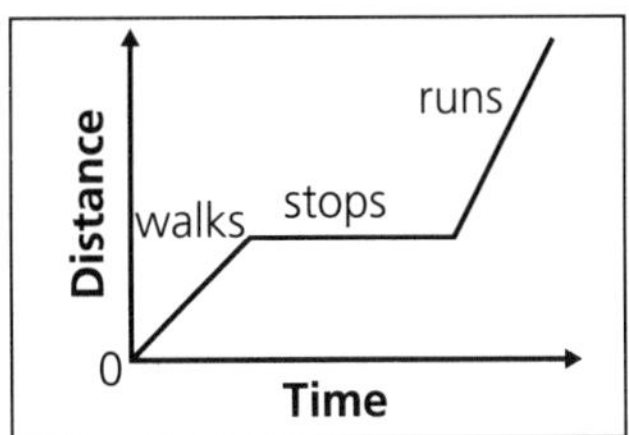

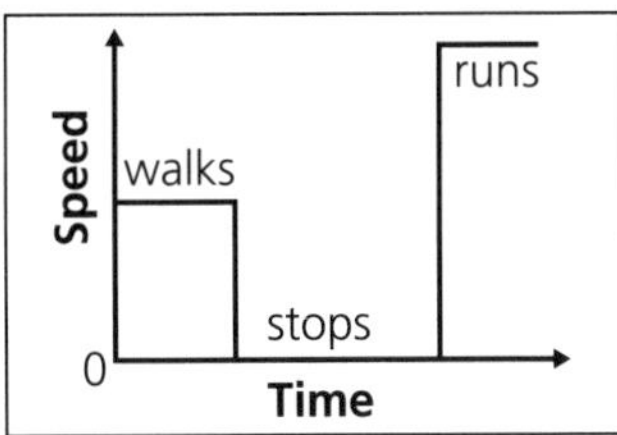

Now do this

9 Here are three different distance-time graphs. Match each one with the best sentence from this list.

a Starting off quickly and slowing to a halt.

b Moving at a steady speed.

c Moving away faster and faster.

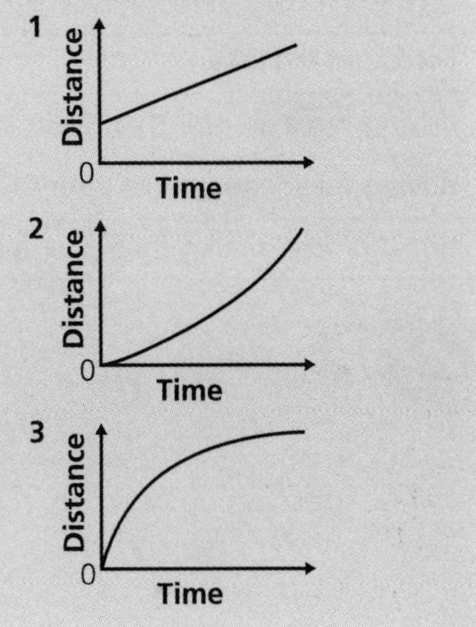

Acceleration

If you start to go faster on your bike or in a car you are **accelerating**. Your speed increases as time goes on.

Here is the velocity-time graph for a bike which is accelerating.

The velocity increases from 4 metres per second (m/s) to 10 m/s, a change of 6 m/s. It takes 3 seconds to do this. So the velocity changes by 2 m/s in each second. The bike accelerates at 2 m/s^2 (metres per second squared).

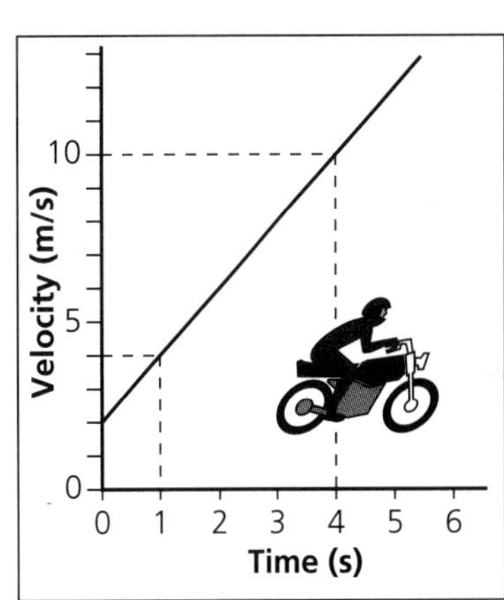

Here is the formula for calculating acceleration. You need to know it by heart.

$$\textbf{acceleration (m/s}^2\textbf{)} = \frac{\textbf{change of velocity (m/s)}}{\textbf{time taken (s)}}$$

Now do this

10 Write down the formula for calculating acceleration.

11 What are the units of velocity, time and acceleration?

Speeding up and slowing down

Forces

Jo pedals her bike along a level road. She applies a **driving force** in the direction that the bike is moving. The **counter forces** act in the opposite direction.

The counter forces come from:

- air resistance from the air in front of the bike
- contact between the tyres and the road
- friction from the moving parts of the bike rubbing against each other.

Forces on the bike	Motion of the bike
driving force greater than counter force	velocity increases
driving force equal to counter force	velocity does not change
driving force smaller than counter force	velocity decreases

When the driving forces and counter forces are the same they are **balanced**. The forces are **unbalanced** when one is larger than the other.

Now do this

1 Are each of these objects speeding up, slowing down or moving at a steady velocity?

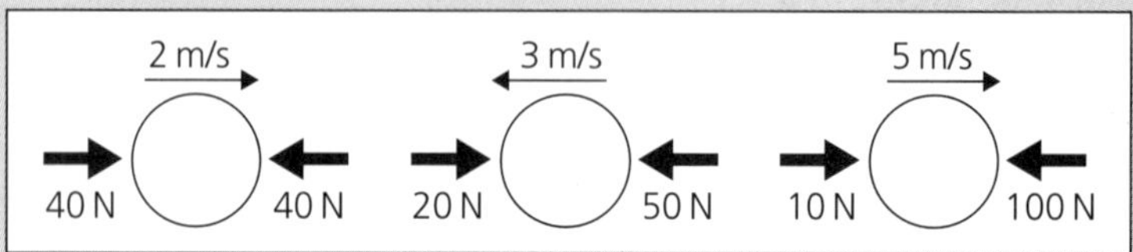

Free fall

The force of gravity on an object is called **weight**. The acceleration of an object in free fall without friction is called *g*. It is about $10\,m/s^2$ for all objects near the Earth.

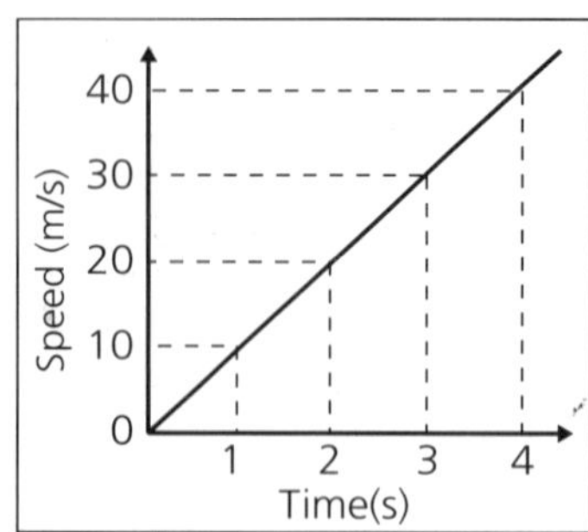

Now do this

2 A ball is dropped down a deep well. It is released from rest and hits the bottom after 3 s. If there is no friction with the air, calculate:

a the speed of the ball after 3 s
b the average speed of the ball during its flight
c the depth of the well.

Terminal velocity

Jo drops a ball over the edge of a high cliff. Gravity tugs the ball downwards. So the ball accelerates.

As the ball speeds up, the counter force (air resistance) increases until it is the same size as the driving force (weight). At this point the forces are balanced. The ball starts travelling at a steady speed called the **terminal velocity**. It stays at that speed until it hits the ground.

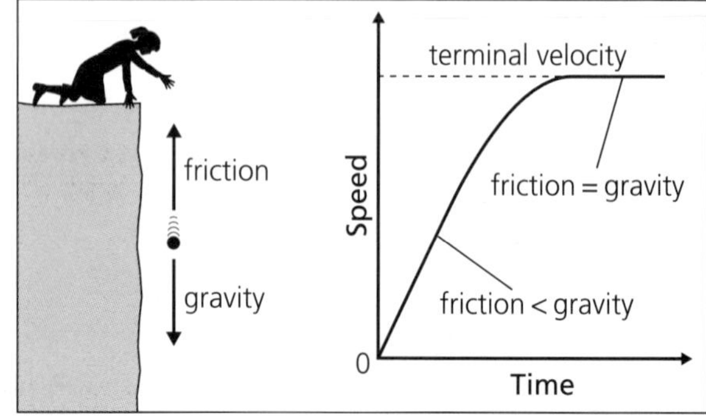

Now do this

3 Name the two forces acting on a falling object. In which direction do they act?

4 Copy and complete the following sentences:

When an object is released ____________ acts on it, so its ____________ increases.
The motion through the air produces a ____________ force which acts ____________.
The friction ____________ as the speed increases. At the terminal speed, the forces are ____________ and the speed ____________.

Rockets

The driving force on a rocket comes from the hot gas it flings out. Liquid fuel from one tank is burnt with liquid oxygen from another tank to make lots of hot gas. This gas is pushed downwards, away from the rocket. The exhaust gas pushes upwards on the rocket. If this driving force is greater than the weight of the rocket, the rocket will accelerate upwards.

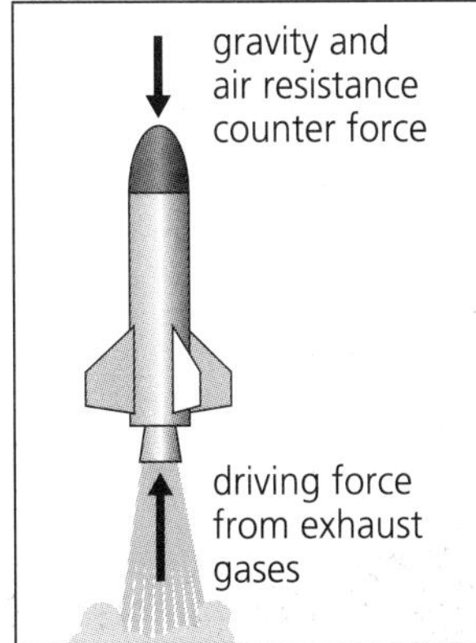

Now do this

5 Explain how a rocket accelerates upwards.

Mass and acceleration

Light objects accelerate more quickly than heavier ones when subjected to the same driving force. So a heavy lorry accelerates far more slowly than a small car when the same amount of force is applied to it.

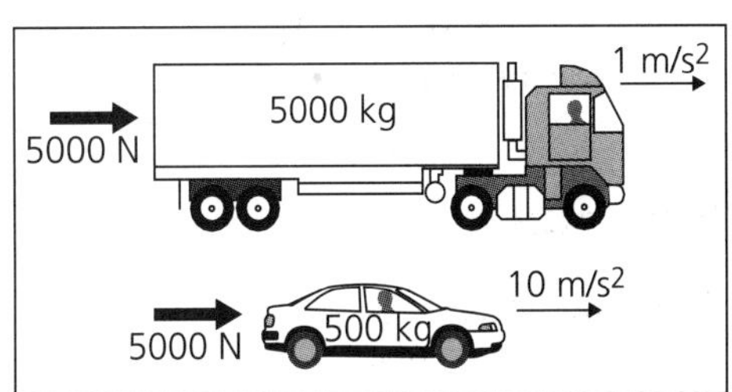

The acceleration of any object depends on the overall (resultant) force and the mass.

force = mass × acceleration $F = ma$

Symbol	Meaning	Units of measurement
F	force	newtons or N
m	mass	kilograms or kg
a	acceleration	metres per second squared or m/s^2

Worked example

Q A car has a mass of 800 kg. If the thrust is 600 N and the friction is 200 N, what is the acceleration of the car?

A $F = 600 - 200 = 400$ N
$m = 800$ kg
$a = ?$

$F = ma$

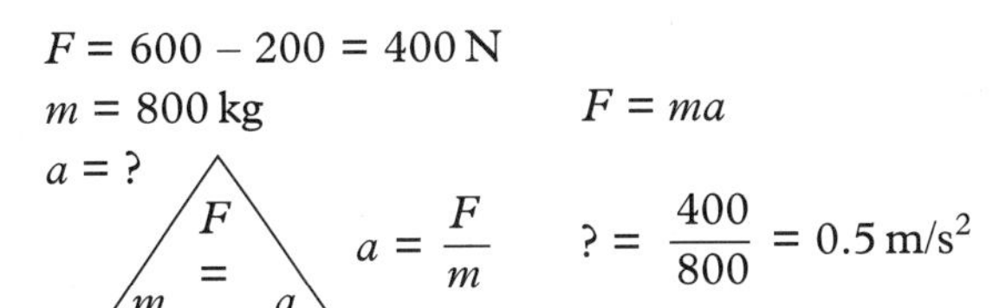

$a = \frac{F}{m}$ $? = \frac{400}{800} = 0.5\ m/s^2$

Now do this

6 A 1000 kg car accelerates at $-6\ m/s^2$ when the brakes are on. Calculate the force needed.

7 A rocket has a mass of 5000 kg and a weight of 50 000 N. It accelerates upwards at $3\ m/s^2$. Calculate the upwards thrust from its engines.

8 The thrust on a 600 kg car is 1500 N. Calculate its acceleration when the friction is 300 N.

Stopping safely

Sam is driving along a road at a steady speed. He sees a tree across the road ahead of him. He brakes and stops.

The **thinking distance** is how far the car travels between Sam noticing the tree and the brakes starting to slow down the car. The thinking distance will increase if:

- Sam is not concentrating
- he is tired
- he has been drinking alcohol.

The **braking distance** is how far the car travels once the brakes have started to work. This distance will increase if:

- the brakes are badly adjusted
- the road surface is wet
- the tyres are inflated incorrectly.

Now do this

1 Explain what thinking distance is. What increases it?

2 Explain what braking distance is. What increases it?

Car crashes

Sam crashes into the tree, but he survives this accident because:

- he is wearing a seatbelt
- his car has a crumple zone
- the airbag inflates.

Plastic and elastic

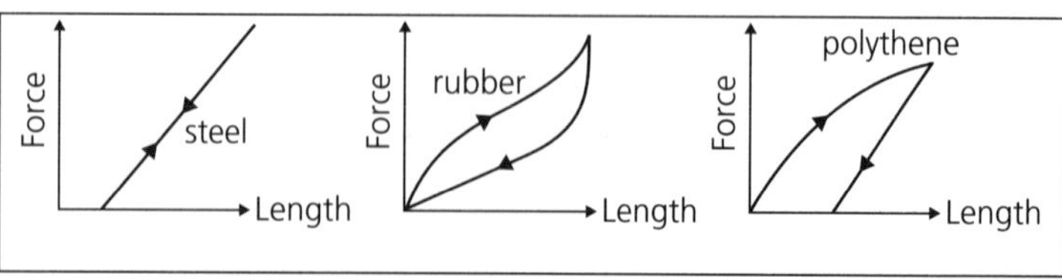

The metal in Sam's car is a **plastic** material. Its shape changes permanently if a large enough pressure is applied. So if he crashes, the kinetic energy of the car is used safely to squash the metal in the crumple zone, instead of squashing Sam.

Sam's seatbelt is made from an **elastic** material. Provided it hasn't been stretched too much, it will go back to its normal length when the stretching force is removed. If the force is large enough, the seatbelt will not return to its original shape, so it must be replaced after a bad crash.

Now do this

3 State **three** things in a car which protect the driver in a crash.

4 What is the difference between elastic and plastic materials?

Stopping gently

When Sam's car crashes, he is slowed down by a force. That force comes from his seatbelt and the airbag. Sam exerts a force of the same size, but opposite direction, on the seatbelt and airbag.

Sam will be injured during the crash if he is accelerated too rapidly. This can be avoided by stopping him over as long a time as possible. The time taken to stop Sam is increased by:

- the stretching of the seatbelt
- the squashing of the crumple zone.

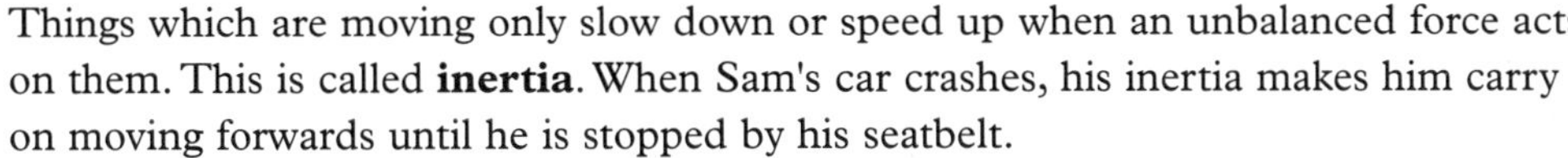

Things which are moving only slow down or speed up when an unbalanced force acts on them. This is called **inertia**. When Sam's car crashes, his inertia makes him carry on moving forwards until he is stopped by his seatbelt.

Hooke's Law

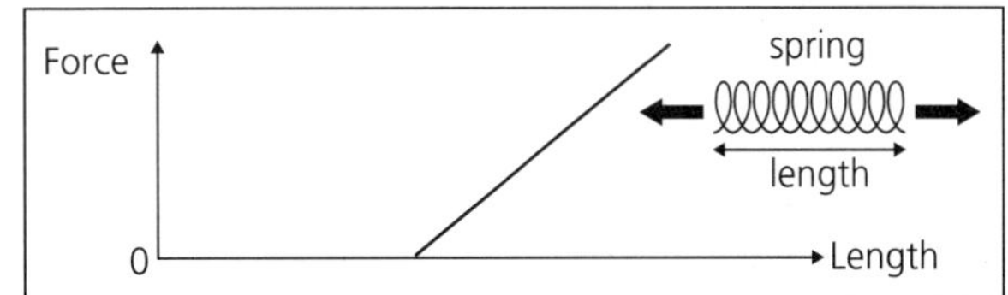

The force-length graph of many elastic materials (such as springs) is a straight line. Their extension is proportional to the force applied.

Worked example

Q A spring goes from 10 cm to 15 cm when a force of 20 N is applied. What is its length when 30 N is applied?

A 20 N gives an extension of 15 – 10 = 5 cm
1 N gives an extension of 5/20 = 0.25 cm
30 N gives an extension of 0.25 × 30 = 7.5 cm
So the length will be 10 + 7.5 = 17.5 cm.

Now do this

5 A 5 cm spring becomes 15 cm long when a force of 40 N is applied.

a How long is the spring for a force of 20 N?

b What force will give the spring a length of 20 cm?

Stability

Jo drives her tractor along the side of a hill. She has to be careful that the tractor does not fall over.

Her tractor is stable because it has a low centre of mass and a wide base. The tractor will not tilt over if the centre of mass remains above the base.

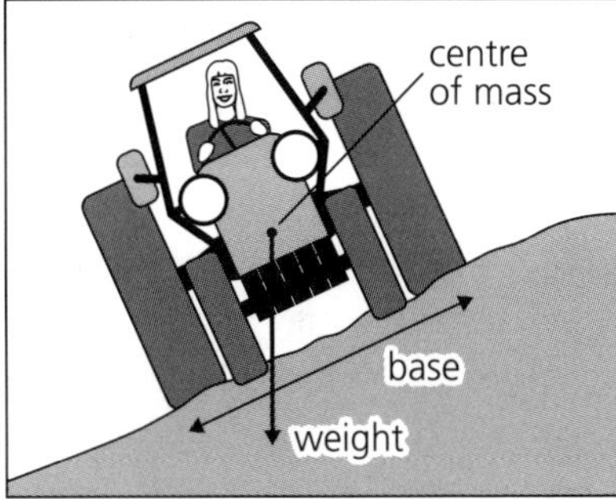

Now do this

6 The dot on each object shows its centre of mass. Which object is the most stable? Which is the least stable?

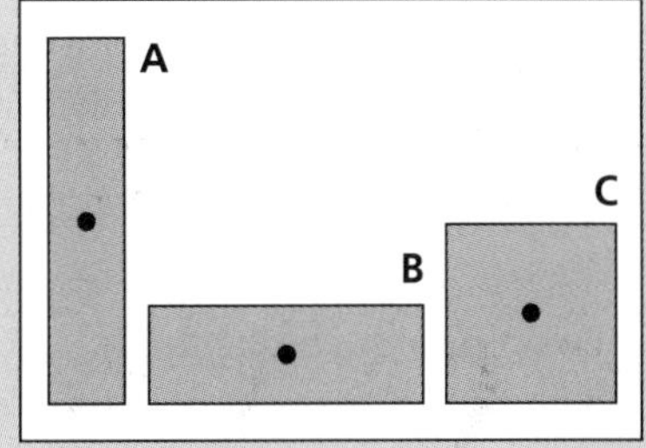

Under pressure

A force acting on a surface exerts a **pressure** on it. It can be calculated with this formula.

$$\text{pressure} = \frac{\text{force}}{\text{area}}$$

$$P = \frac{F}{A}$$

Symbol	Meaning	Units of measurement
P	pressure	pascals or Pa
F	force	newtons or N
A	area	metres squared or m^2

Examiner's tip

You must know this one by heart.

Worked example

Q A concrete block sits on the ground. The block weighs 5000 N. The base of the block is 0.5 m by 0.5 m. What is the pressure on the ground under the block?

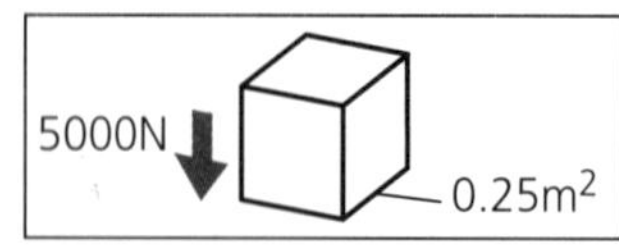

Q $P = ?$

$F = 5000\,\text{N}$

$A = 0.5\,\text{m} \times 0.5\,\text{m} = 0.25\,\text{m}^2$

$P = \frac{F}{A}$ $\quad ? = \frac{5000}{0.25} = 20\,000\,\text{Pa}$

Now do this

1 Write down the formula for calculating pressure.

2 What are the units of force, area and pressure?

3 The base of a 2000 N block is 0.2 m by 0.2 m. Calculate the pressure on the ground under the block.

4 A car weighs 10 000 N. If the total pressure of the car on the ground is 100 000 Pa, what is the area of contact between each of the four tyres and the ground?

Large forces on small areas can damage surfaces. Think about pushing on a drawing pin!

The pressure can be reduced by making the area of contact larger.

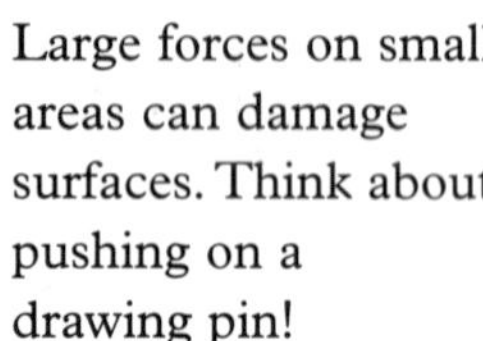

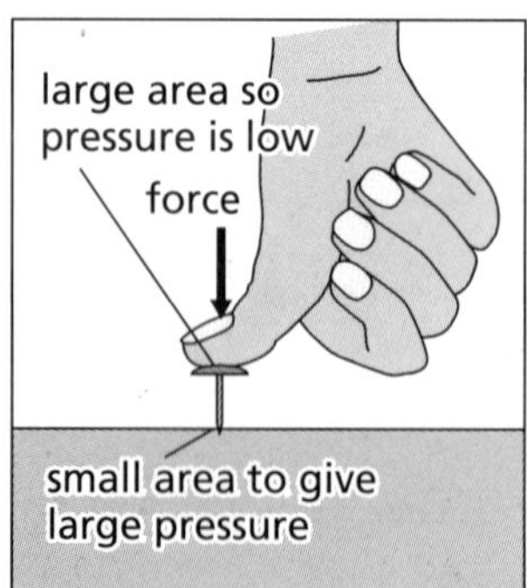

Now do this

5 Copy and complete these sentences.

A tractor has large tyres. This allows the ______________ of the tractor to be applied over a large ______________ giving a low ______________ on the ground. The wheels sink into the ground if the ______________ is too big.

Pressure in liquids

Pressure can be transmitted through liquids. They transmit pressure equally in all directions. This is used in car brakes:

1 The driver's foot presses on the brake pedal.
2 This pushes a piston (the **master** piston) down into the brake fluid.
3 The fluid presses on the **slave** pistons behind the brake pads.
4 The brake pads are forced against the wheel.

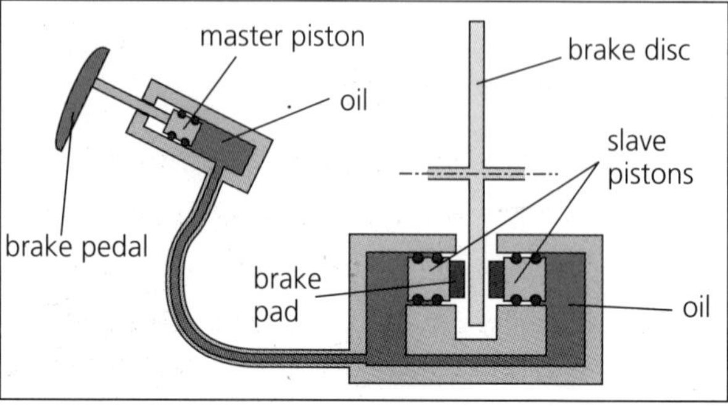

So when the brake pedal is pushed, the brake pads are forced against the brake disc.

Liquids transmit pressure because the particles in a liquid are close together, making it very hard to squash it into a smaller volume.

Worked example

Q A brake force of 50 N is applied to the master piston of area 0.001 m^2. This puts a pressure of $\frac{50}{0.001}$ = 50 000 Pa on the brake fluid. Calculate the force on the brake pads.

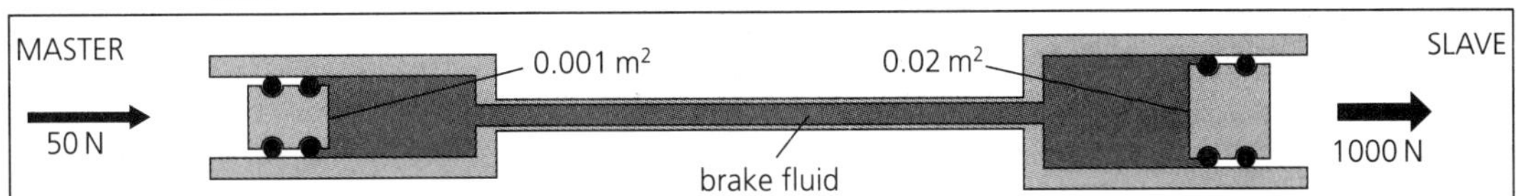

A The pressure at the slave piston will also be 50 000 Pa.

Its area is 0.02 m^2, so the force on the brake pads is 50 000 × 0.02 = 1000 N.

Now do this

6 A force of 100 N is applied to a master piston of area 0.004 m^2. The slave piston has an area of 0.1 m^2. Calculate the force on the slave piston.

Atmospheric pressure

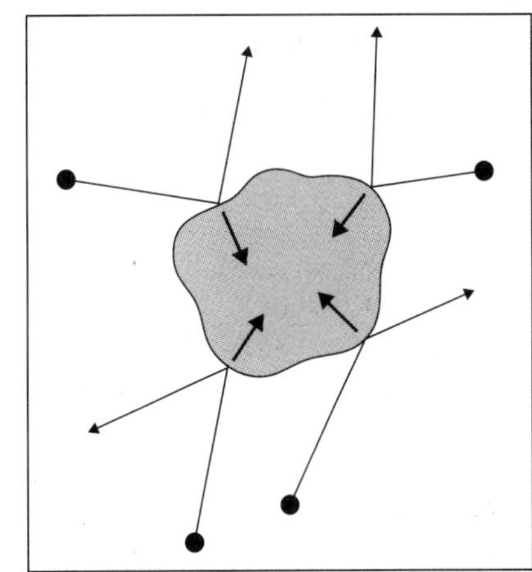

A cubic metre of air has a weight of about 10 N. The atmosphere is about 10 km high. So each square metre at sea level supports 100 000 N of atmosphere – the atmospheric pressure is 100 000 Pa.

Atmospheric pressure squashes in all directions, not just downwards. It gets smaller as you move up through the atmosphere to a higher altitude.

Air is a gas. Its particles are far apart and moving quickly. They bounce off a solid object placed in the gas. These collisions create the pressure on the object.

If the volume of a gas decreases, its pressure increases. This is because the particles are closer together, so they hit the walls more often. If the amount of gas is fixed and its temperature does not change, it obeys this rule

initial volume × initial pressure = final volume × final pressure

Now do this

7 What causes atmospheric pressure?

8 Explain how a gas can exert a pressure on a solid object.

9 What happens to the pressure of a gas if its volume is halved?

10 A balloon contains 0.2 m^3 of air at 100 kPa. What is the pressure of the air when the volume is reduced to 0.04 m^3?

Exam questions

1 Melissa cycles along the road.

Look at the graph.

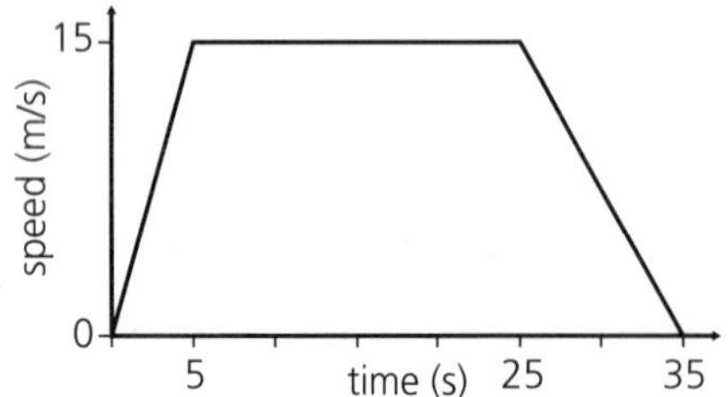

a Melissa starts off by accelerating.

i Calculate her acceleration. [3]

ii The overall force on Melissa during acceleration is 180 N. Calculate Melissa's mass. [3]

b What is Melissa's top speed? Calculate how far she travels at that speed. [4]

c Melissa stops pedalling after 25 s. Use the idea of unbalanced forces to explain why she stops moving at 35 s. [2]

d Melissa wears a cycle helmet. Use the idea of pressure to explain why the helmet will protect her if she falls off her bicycle. [3]

[15 marks]

2 The Highway Code states the distance required to stop an average car in good weather on a normal road.

Look at the information.

At 30 m/s

thinking distance	braking distance	overall stopping distance
20 m	85 m	105 m

a i Explain what is meant by thinking distance. [1]

ii Use the information to calculate the thinking time of a typical driver. [1]

iii State **two** things which could increase the thinking distance. [2]

b A car at 30 m/s takes 0.7 s to travel the thinking distance and another 5.6 s to travel the braking distance.

i How long does it take to travel the overall stopping distance? [1]

ii Sketch a graph to show how the speed of the car changes as it stops. [3]

iii Calculate the acceleration of the car as it stops. [3]

iv The mass of the car is 1000 kg. Calculate the braking force on the car. [3]

[14 marks]

3 A rectangular concrete building block weighs 500 N. The lengths of its sides are 0.1 m, 0.2 m and 0.4 m.

a The block is placed on the ground with the 0.2 m side vertical. Calculate the pressure of the block on the ground. [3]

b How should the block be placed to exert the smallest pressure on the ground? Calculate that pressure. [2]

[5 marks]

4 The acceleration of free fall in the absence of friction on Earth is $10\ m/s^2$.

a A 500 g ball is released from rest at the top of a cliff. It hits the ground 4 s later. Ignoring air resistance, calculate

i the final speed of the ball [2]

ii the average speed of the ball [1]

iii the height of the cliff. [2]

b Air resistance means that the ball reaches its terminal velocity before it hits the ground.

i Sketch a graph to show how the speed of the ball changes with time. Explain its shape. [2]

ii Add another curve to the graph for a ball with a greater mass but the same surface area. [1]

[8 marks]

Waves, space and radiation

You will have met the ideas in this section when you worked on the units *Communicating information, Sound reproduction, Earth in space, Seeing inside the body, Energy today and tomorrow* and *Restless Earth*. This section is divided into six spreads.

Properties of waves

What are waves?

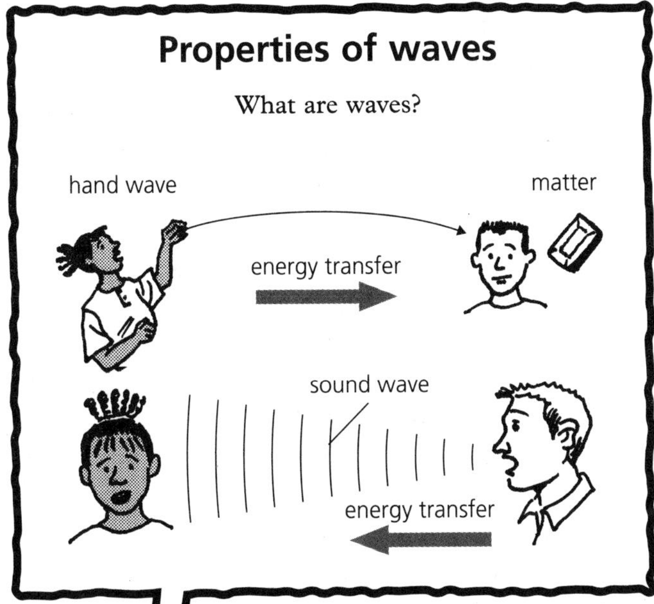

Ultrasound and electromagnetic spectrum

What are the uses of ultrasound?

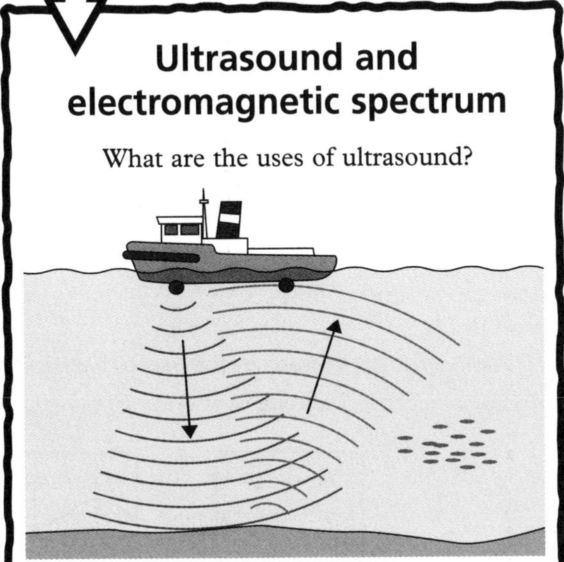

Reflection, refraction, diffraction

How do light and sound travel?

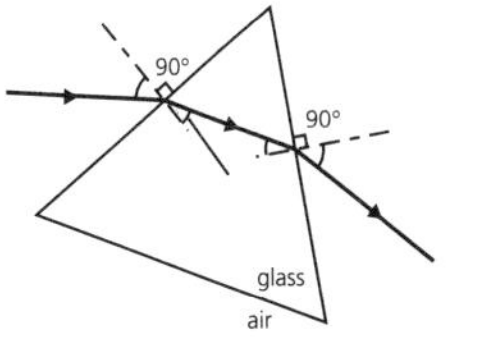

Optical instruments

How do periscopes, cameras, eyes, projectors and optical fibres work?

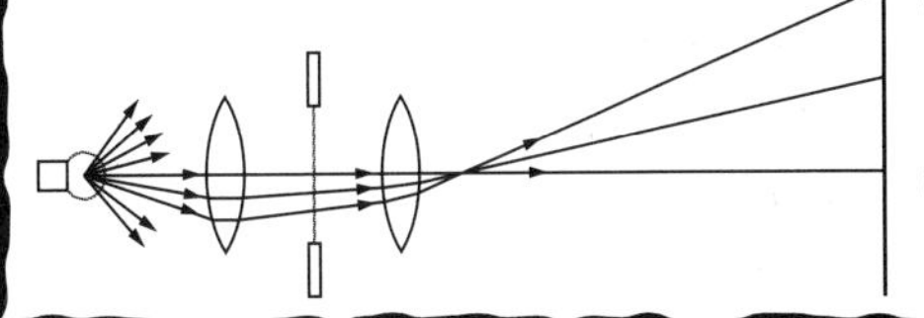

The solar system

What is the Earth's place in the solar system?

How does the Earth move to give us day, night and years?

Radioactivity

What is radioactivity?

How can we use it safely?

Properties of waves

hand wave
matter
energy transfer
sound wave
energy transfer

Jo throws a brick at Sam. The brick (made from matter) transfers some energy from Jo to Sam.

Sam shouts at Jo. He makes a **sound wave**. The wave transfers some energy to Jo by making the air between them **vibrate**. There is no transfer of matter from Sam to Jo.

Longitudinal waves

Sound is a **longitudinal wave**. It is caused by vibrations which **compress** and **rarify** the air, raising and lowering its pressure. The pattern of high and low pressure travels through the air as a wave, carrying energy away from the source of the vibrations.

You can see this most clearly in a spring. Each coil of the spring is squeezed and stretched in the same direction as the energy flow.

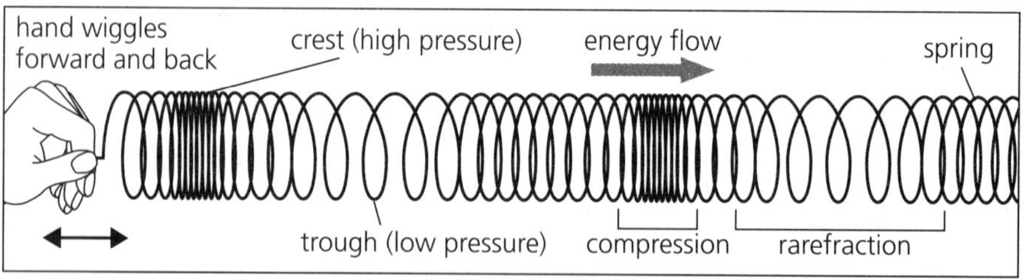

The **frequency** of the wave is the number of vibrations per second (measured in **hertz**, **Hz**). So if the source vibrates 1000 times in 5 s, the frequency is 1000/5 = 200 Hz.

The **wavelength** (measured in metres, m) of the wave is the distance from one compression (or expansion) to the next. So if there are 20 compressions in 60 m, the wavelength is 60/20 = 3 m.

Now do this

1 Calculate the frequency of a wave whose source makes 12000 vibrations in 6 s.

2 Calculate the wavelength of a wave which has 25 compressions in 100 m.

3 Copy and complete these sentences.

Sound is created by ______. The number of vibrations per second is the ______ of the wave, measured in ______. Sound is a ______ wave. It makes the air vibrate in the same direction as the ______.

Pitch and loudness

Pitch is a measure of how high or low a note sounds. The pitch of a sound wave depends on its frequency. As the frequency of a note is increased, the pitch goes up. In fact, the pitch of a note goes up by an octave each time that the frequency is doubled. This can be seen by studying sound waves with a microphone and an oscilloscope.

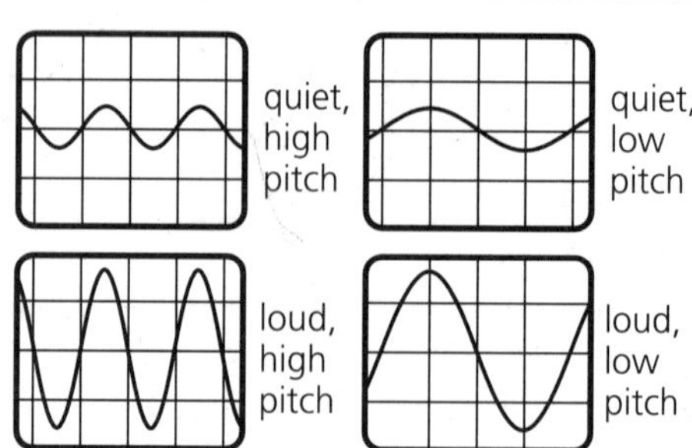

The loudness of a sound wave depends on its **amplitude**. Loud sounds have a larger amplitude than quiet ones. Loudness is measured in **decibels** (**dB**).

Music contains notes of different frequencies. Sound systems may distort music by amplifying some frequencies more than others.

Now do this

4 Copy and complete these sentences.

The ______ of a sound goes up as its frequency ______.

The loudness of a sound increases with increasing ______.

Loudness is measured in ______.

Transverse waves

Jo transmits a **transverse wave** to Sam along a stretched rope. As the wave travels from left to right, it makes each bit of the rope vibrate up and down.

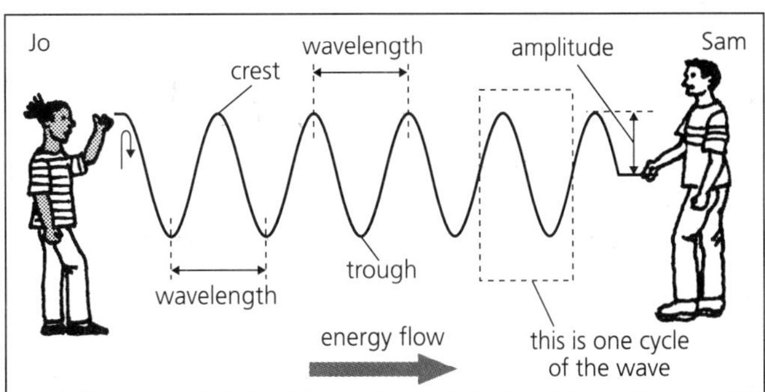

The **amplitude** of the wave is the height of the wave (measured from the centre of the wave). Amplitude is measured in metres (m).

The **wavelength** is the distance from one crest of the wave to the next crest, or from one trough to the next. It is measured in metres (m).

Now do this

50 cm

12 m

5 Calculate values for the number of cycles, the wavelength and the amplitude of this wave in a stretched rope.

6 Explain why you can tell that the wave is a transverse one.

The speed of waves

The speed of a wave is linked to its frequency and wavelength by this formula.

speed = frequency × wavelength or $v = fL$

Symbol	Meaning	Units of measurement
v	speed	metres per second or m/s
f	frequency	hertz or Hz
L	wavelength	metres or m

Now do this

7 State the formula linking speed, wavelength and frequency of a wave.

8 A water wave has a frequency of 6 Hz and a wavelength of 4 m. Calculate its speed.

9 A radio wave has a speed of 300 000 000 m/s. If it has a frequency of 6 000 000 Hz, what is its wavelength? If its wavelength is 500 m, what is its frequency?

Worked example

Q Sound has a speed in air of 300 m/s. Calculate the wavelength of a 1200 Hz sound wave in air.

A v = 300 m/s

f = 1200 Hz $\quad v = fL$

L = ? m

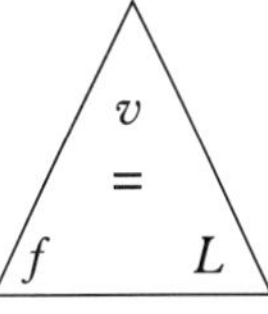

$L = \frac{v}{f} \quad ? = \frac{300}{1200} = 0.25\text{ m}$

Reflection and refraction

Reflection

Waves bounce off smooth hard surfaces. This is called **reflection**. Sound waves can be reflected in this way. The reflected sound is called an **echo**.

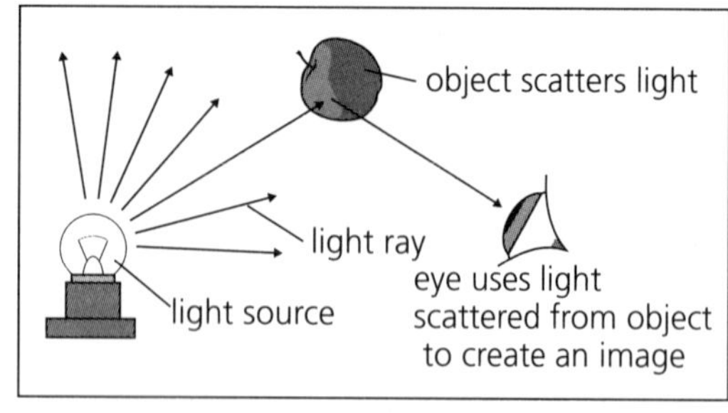

Examiner's tip

Always draw light rays with a ruler.

Light can be reflected too. Reflected light allows us to see things. Light waves travel in straight lines. These are drawn as **rays**.

When light rays reflect off a shiny surface, the **angle of reflection**, ***r***, is the same as the **angle of incidence**, ***i***. Both angles are measured from the **normal**. This is an imaginary line at right angles to the reflector at the point where the ray hits it.

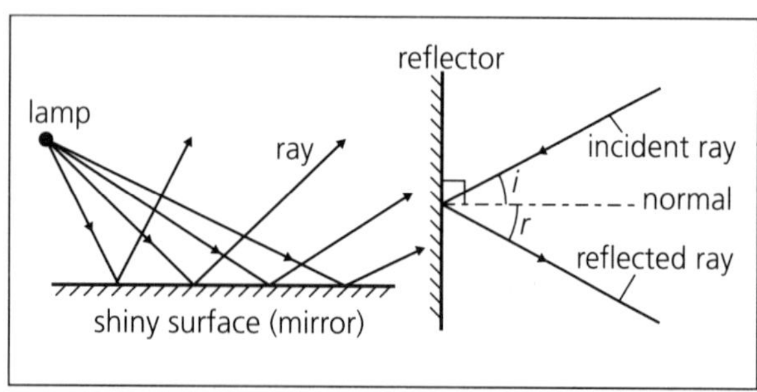

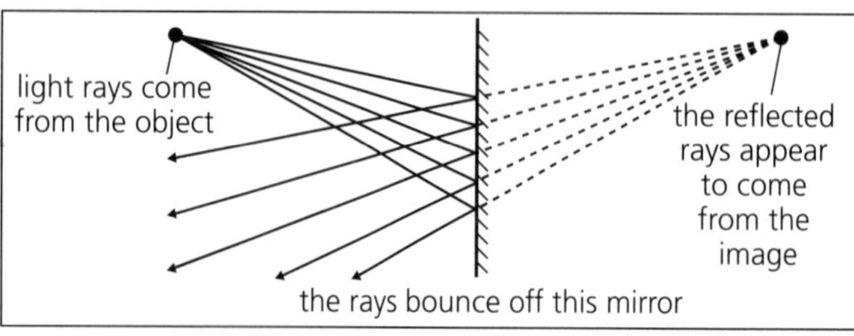

Light reflected from a flat mirror appears to come from behind the mirror. The distance from the image to the mirror is the same as the distance from the object to the mirror.

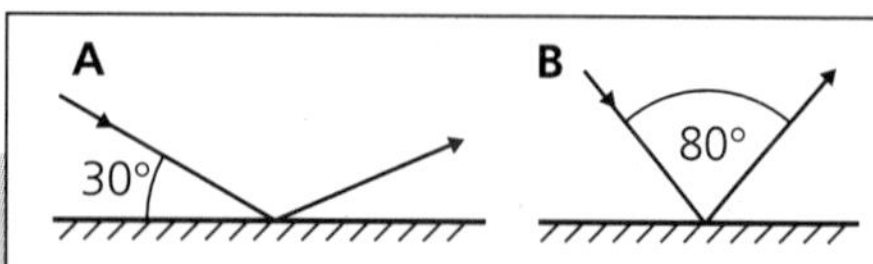

Now do this

1 What are the values for the angle of incidence and reflection for these rays of light?

2 A lamp is placed 50 cm in front of a flat mirror. Draw a diagram to show three rays reflected off the mirror. Exactly where will you see the image of the lamp in the mirror?

Refraction

When light goes from air into a transparent material it changes direction. It is **refracted**. This happens because the speed of light changes as it passes from one material into another.

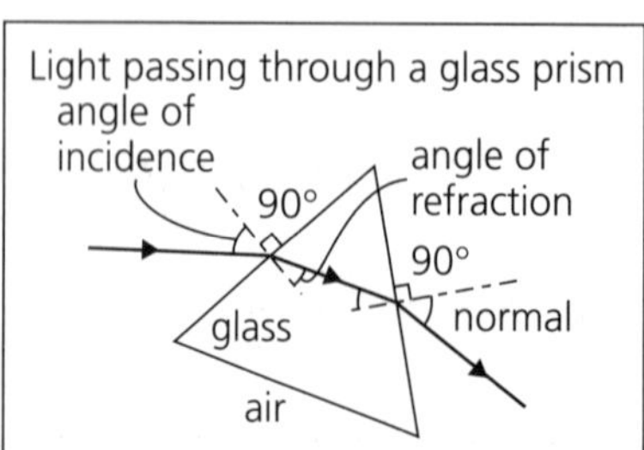

On the way into the material the **angle of refraction** is always smaller than the angle of incidence. Both angles are measured from the normal.

On the way out of the material the angle of refraction is always larger than the angle of incidence.

Now do this

3 How big are the values of the angles of incidence and refraction for this ray of light?

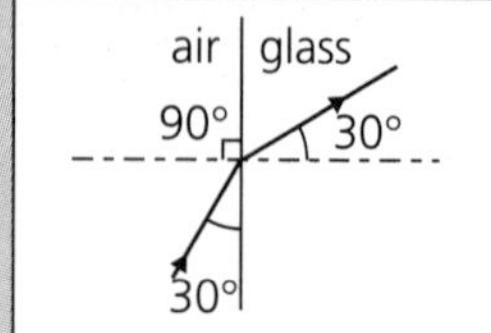

Water waves

Waves on the surface of water are represented with **wavefronts**. Each wavefront shows the position of a crest, so the distance between wavefronts is the wavelength.

Like sound waves and light waves, water waves are reflected when they hit barriers.

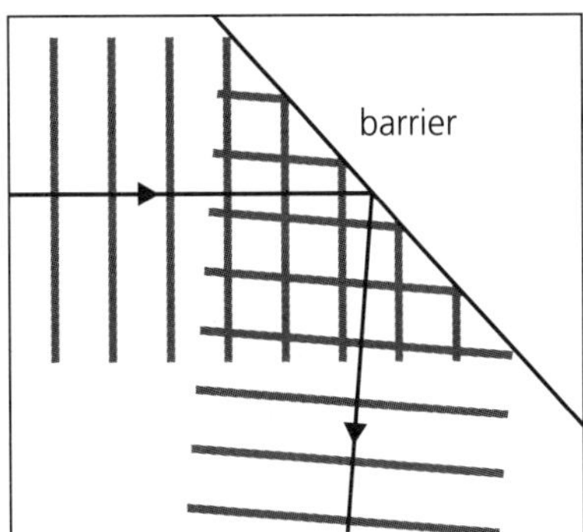

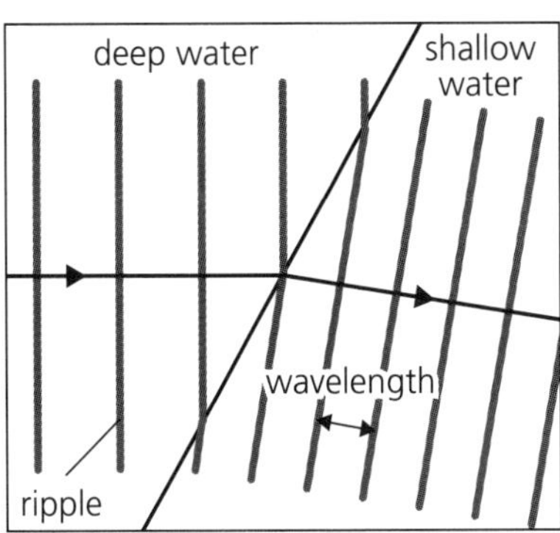

The speed of water waves depends on the depth of the water. The waves go faster in deep water. So water waves are refracted when they move from one depth to another.

Diffraction

When water waves pass through a gap they are **diffracted**. Plane waves which approach the gap emerge as circular waves if the gap is smaller than the wavelength. All waves (sound and light) are diffracted, but the gap has to be smaller than the wavelength for the effect to be noticeable.

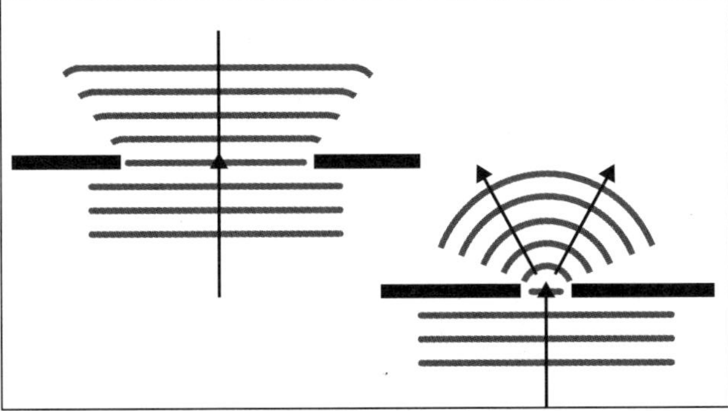

Now do this

4 Draw diagrams to show plane water waves being reflected from a straight barrier.

5 Draw a diagram to show water waves being refracted as they move from deep water to shallow water.

6 Draw a diagram to show water waves being diffracted as they pass through a small gap.

Optical instruments

Periscope

A periscope uses a pair of mirrors to create an image.

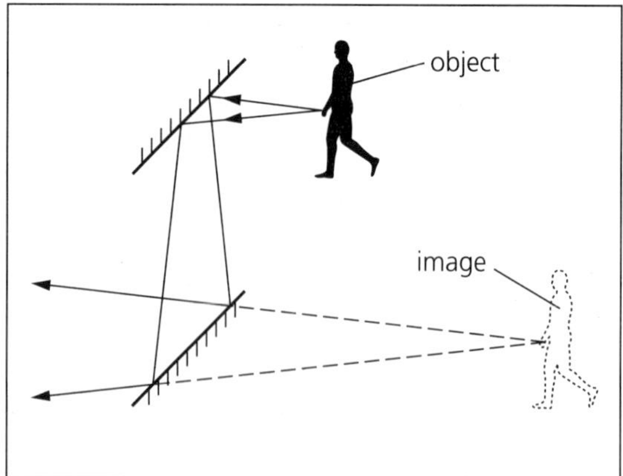

Now do this

1 With the aid of a diagram, explain how a periscope can be used to see over the top of a wall.

Lenses

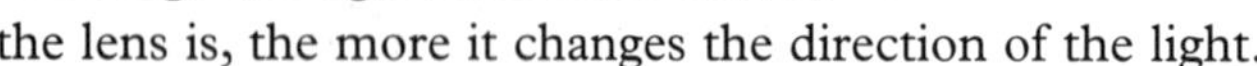

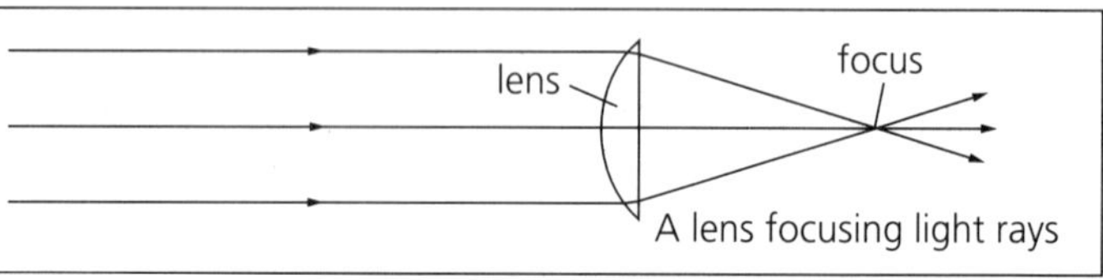

Convex lenses use refraction to make images. They collect parallel light rays and **focus** them down to a point. They **converge** the light. The more curved the lens is, the more it changes the direction of the light.

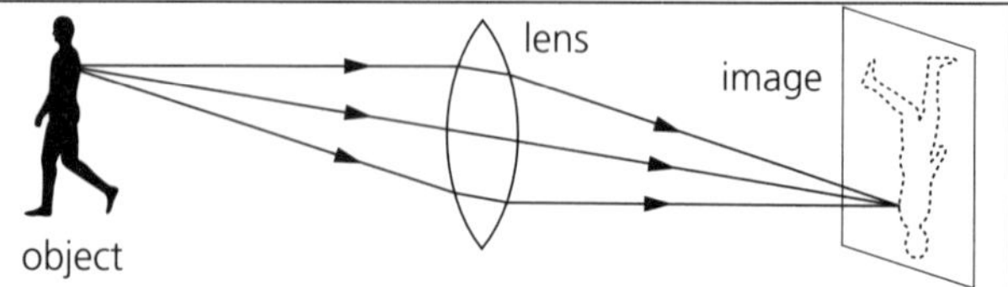

A convex lens can take the rays of light from an **object** and use them to form an **image** on a screen. The screen has to be in the right place for the image to be clear and sharp (in focus).

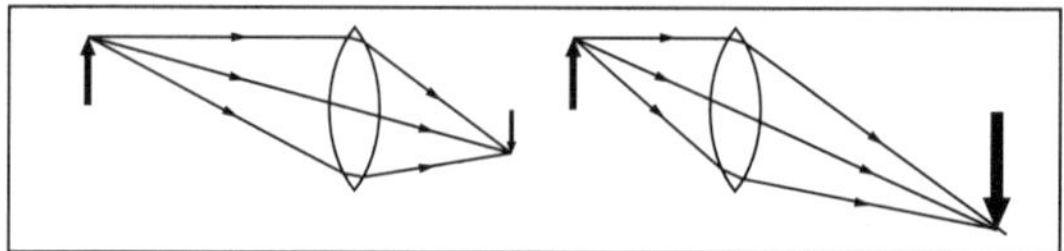

As the lens is moved towards the object, the screen has to be moved further away to keep the image in focus. The further the image is from the lens, the bigger it is.

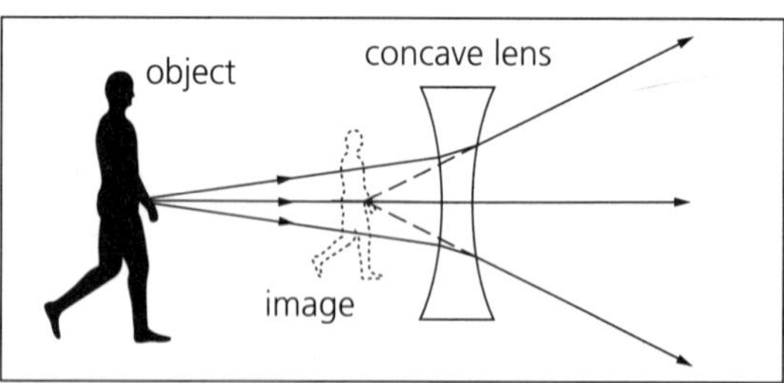

Concave lenses use refraction to diverge parallel rays. They cannot form images which can be focused on to a screen.

Cameras and eyes use convex lenses to form images of distant objects on light-sensitive surfaces. The images need to be much smaller than the objects, so the object-to-lens distance is large.

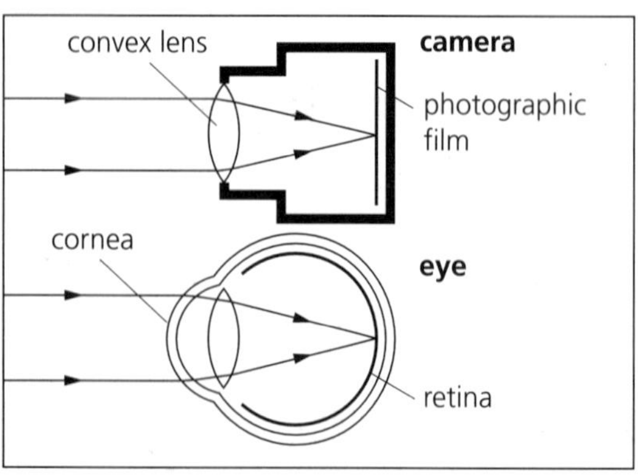

Now do this

2 Use diagrams to show what convex and concave lenses do to rays of parallel light. Which type can be used to put an image on a screen?

3 Show how a convex lens can form an image of an object on a screen.

4 Describe what happens to the size and position of the image when a convex lens is moved away from the object.

Projectors use convex lenses to place large images on a screen. The object-to-lens distance is therefore small.

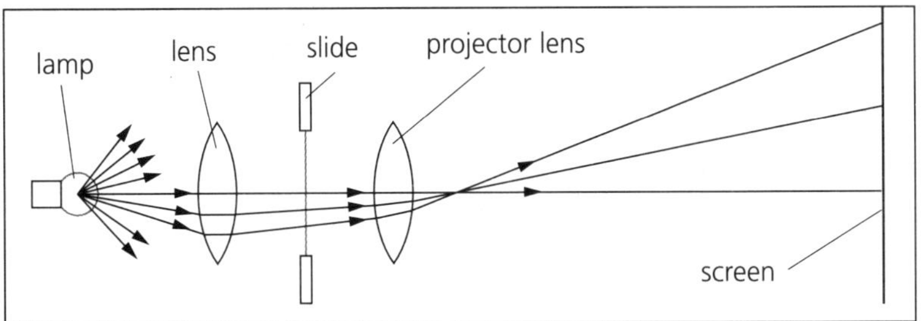

Now do this

5 Draw a diagram to show the formation of an image in
  a a camera
  b a projector.

Optical fibres

Light will always refract from air into a transparent material (such as glass or water). However, if the angle of incidence is greater than the **critical angle**, rays of light will not be able refract out. They are **totally internally reflected**.

This is used in optical fibres. Light which goes in at one end has to reflect off the edge of the fibre until it gets to the other end.

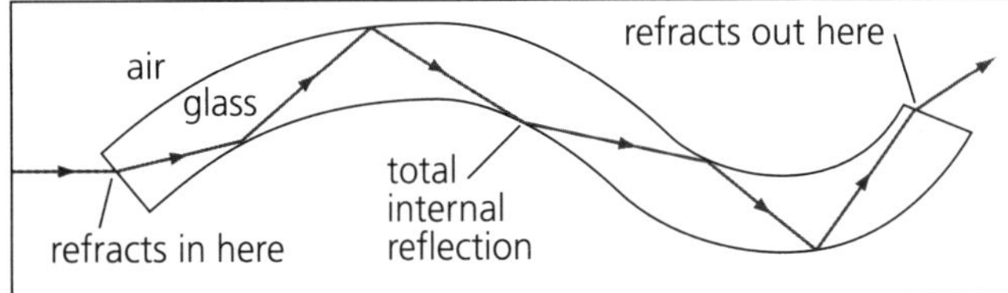

Now do this

6 Draw a diagram to show what is meant by total internal reflection.

7 Glass has a critical angle of 42°. What does this mean?

Carrying sounds

Optical fibres are very good at carrying short pulses of light over very long distances. By converting sound into a series of short pulses of light, optical fibres can be used to carry the signals from microphones in telephones.

Microphones convert sound into an **analogue** signal. This is a voltage whose value changes smoothly with time. An optical fibre carries pulses of light which are either on or off. This is called a **digital** signal.

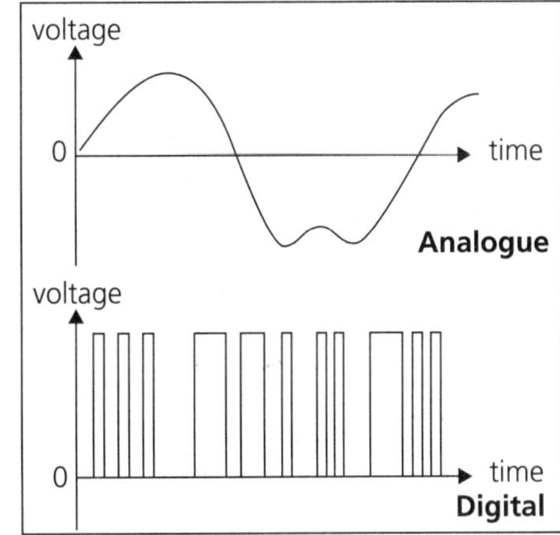

Digital signals are better than analogue ones because they

- are easier to store
- can be manipulated by a computer
- don't pick up as much noise in transit.

Compact discs (CDs) store sound in digital form, as a series of **pits** arranged in a spiral on a circular plastic mirror. The equipment used to convert the analogue sound signal into a digital signal for recording on a CD must have a high **sample rate** to avoid distorting the sound.

Now do this

8 Give an example of a an analogue signal b a digital signal.

9 What are the advantages of having a digital signal rather than an analogue one?

Sound and ultrasound

The highest frequency sound that humans can hear is about 20 000 Hz (or 20 kHz). Sound with higher frequency than 20 kHz is called **ultrasound**. It is very useful.

Now do this

1 Here are the frequencies of five different sound waves. List them in order of increasing frequency. Which of them will be ultrasound?

12 000 Hz   24 kHz   47 Hz   50 000 Hz   900 Hz

Ships use pulses of ultrasound to find out what is beneath them. Any solid object in the water reflects these pulses to form **echoes**. A special microphone under the ship listens for these echoes. The time delay between the pulse and its echo is used to calculate the distance to the solid reflector.

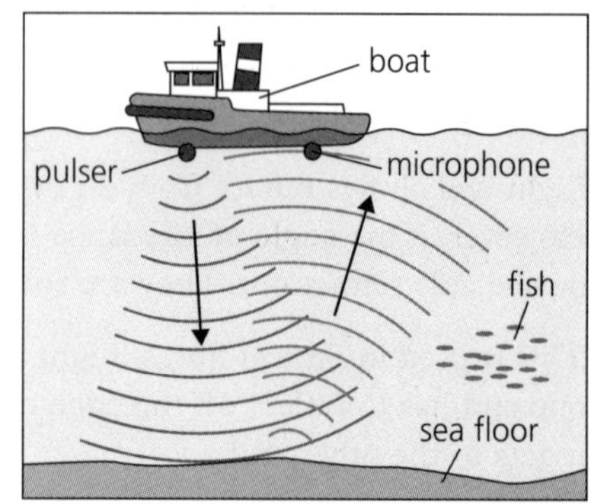

Sound travels at 1 500 m/s in water. So a time delay of 0.1 s between pulse and echo means that the pulse travels $1\,500 \times 0.1 = 150$ m. The pulse moves from the ship to the reflector and back to the ship. The reflector must therefore be $\frac{1}{2} \times 150 = 75$ m below the ship.

Examiner's tip

Don't forget that the wave travels there and back.

Now do this

2 A submarine sends out pulses of ultrasound. Echoes arrive back 0.05 s after each pulse. How far away is the source of the echoes?

Ultrasound can also be used to look inside the human body. Pulses of ultrasound go through the skin. Each time a pulse passes from one organ into another, some of it is reflected back to the skin.

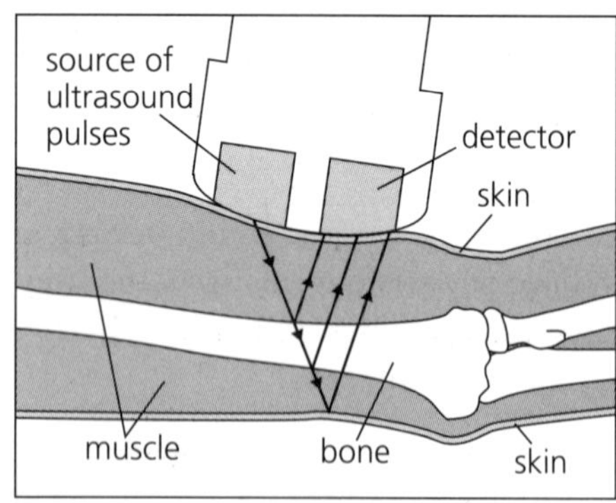

These echoes can be used to form a picture of what lies under the skin without the need for surgery. Ultrasound is often used to scan babies before they are born. Unlike X-rays, ultrasound does not damage the baby. X-rays are dangerous because they ionise tissue. Ultrasound is safe because it doesn't ionise matter.

Now do this

3 Explain how ultrasound can be used to look inside people.

Seismic waves

Earthquakes produce three different low frequency waves which travel around and through the Earth:

- P-waves are longitudinal and can therefore travel through both solids and liquids.
- S-waves are transverse and can therefore only travel through solids.
- L-waves are transverse waves along the surface of the Earth.

Only p-waves can cross directly from one side of the Earth to the other. This is evidence that the Earth has a liquid core which s-waves cannot pass through. The size of this core can be found by finding those places which receive only p-waves from an earthquake. The density of the rocks changes as you move towards the centre of the Earth, refracting the s- and p-waves.

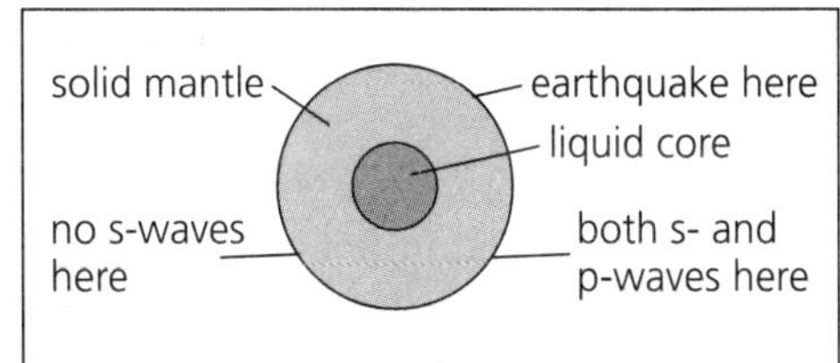

Now do this

4 Describe the differences between s-waves and p-waves. Explain how they can be used to show that the Earth has a liquid core.

Electromagnetic waves

The **electromagnetic spectrum** is a family of waves which can pass through empty space at the speed of 300 000 000 m/s. This is often called the speed of light, but it is the speed of all electromagnetic waves.

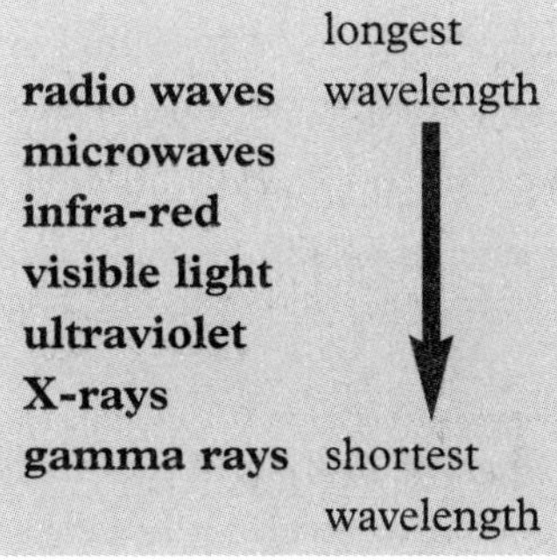

Short wavelength electromagnetic radiation carries more energy than long wavelength radiation.

Radio waves are used to carry information about sound (music and speech) as well as pictures (TV).

Microwaves can be made into beams by curved reflectors. As well as being used to communicate with satellites in space, pulsed microwaves are used to detect aircraft and ships. Microwaves with one particular wavelength are strongly absorbed by water and can be used to heat up food.

Infra-red waves carry heat energy. They are emitted by hot objects, such as the Sun. They can also carry information down optical fibres and allow hand-held remote controls to communicate with TVs and video recorders.

Ultra-violet waves damage living cells. Ultra-violet is present in sunlight and can cause sunburn and skin cancer. Dark skin will absorb ultra-violet waves and protect the living cells underneath.

X-rays pass through flesh but are strongly absorbed by bone. High density materials absorb X-rays better than low density materials. X-rays make images in photographic film, so photographs can be made of the inside of the body. They also kill living cells and can cause cancer. X-rays are produced by firing high speed electrons at lumps of metal.

Gamma rays can pass through steel and concrete, and can make images on photographic film. They are very dangerous because they damage living cells. Gamma rays can be used to destroy cancer cells. They are emitted during the radioactive decay of atoms.

Now do this

5 Write down the **seven** parts of the electromagnetic spectrum. List them in order of increasing wavelength.

6 Which parts of the electromagnetic spectrum are

a used for communication
b dangerous to living cells
c used for heating food
d used to detect aircraft and ships
e used to transmit TV pictures?

The solar system

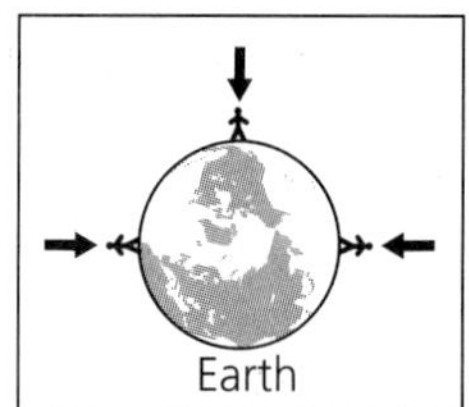

The Earth we live on is a **planet**. It is a sphere of rock, surrounded by a very thin skin of gas and liquid (the atmosphere and oceans). Gravity pulls everything on the Earth towards its centre. It keeps satellites in orbit around the Earth.

The Sun is much larger than the Earth. The Sun is our nearest **star**, a ball of hot gases (mostly hydrogen). It has radiated a lot of light and heat energy for a very long time, and will continue to do so in the future. The energy comes from fusion reactions at the hot centre of the star. These reactions convert hydrogen into helium.

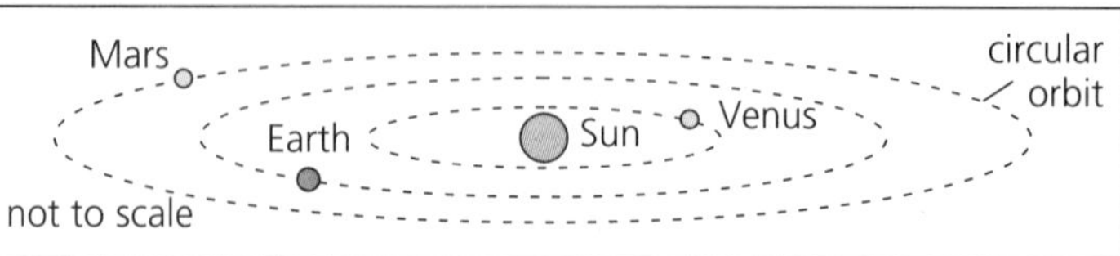

The Earth is only one of several planets which orbit the Sun. The gravity of the Sun tugs each planet towards the Sun. This force keeps each planet moving in either a circle or an ellipse around the Sun. There is no friction in space, so orbits can keep going for billions of years.

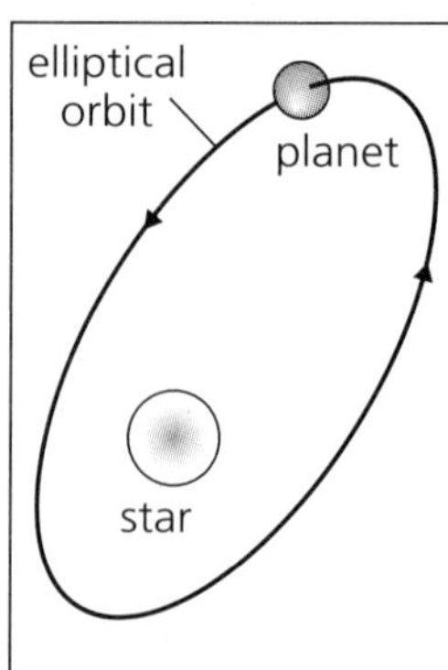

The gravitational pull of the Sun on a planet

- decreases with increasing distance from the Sun
- increases with increasing mass of the planet.

Planets which are close to the Sun get very hot. They catch a lot of the Sun's heat radiation. If a planet has an atmosphere it will trap some of this heat energy (the '**greenhouse effect**'), ending up even hotter. The Earth's atmosphere helps to keep the temperature just right for life. Planets near to the Sun are made of rocky materials. They have a high density. Planets further away from the Sun are cooler and are made from gases with low boiling points such as hydrogen, helium and methane. They have a low density and are sometimes called the 'icy planets'.

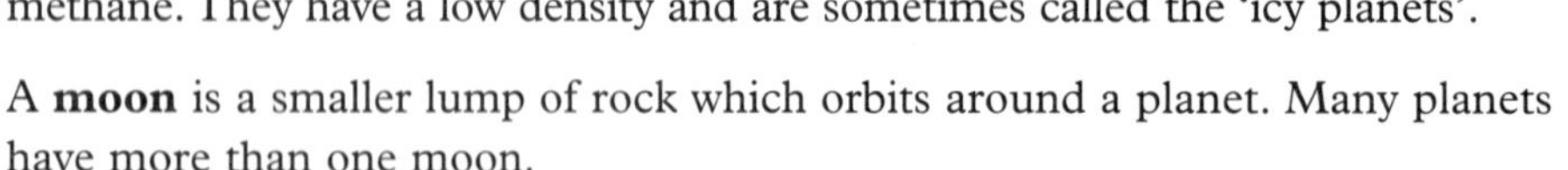

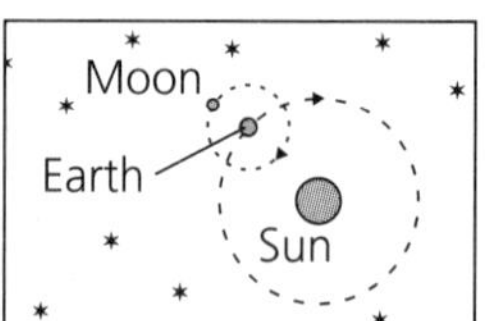

A **moon** is a smaller lump of rock which orbits around a planet. Many planets have more than one moon.

Earth has just one moon. It is held in orbit by the pull of the Earth's gravity. The Moon goes once around the Earth in a month.

Tides

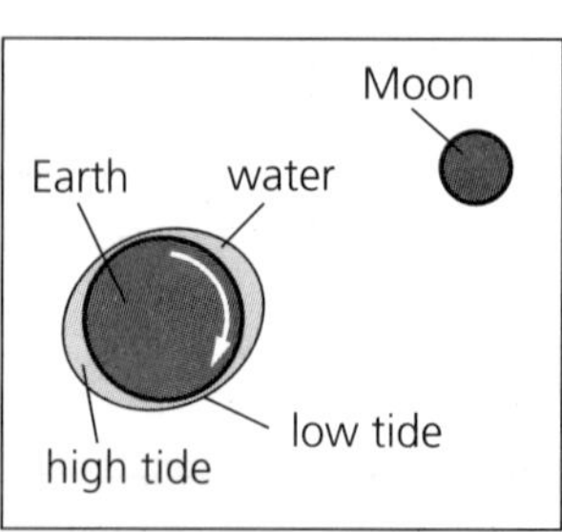

The combined gravity of the Sun and the Moon moves water around on the surface of the Earth. The water level in the oceans is raised at two points along a line going through the centre of the Earth and the Moon.

As the Earth rotates on its axis, these raised areas of water appear to move across the surface of the Earth. Most coastal areas see two high tides in a day. The height of the tide is greatest when the Sun and Moon tug on the water in the same direction.

Communication satellites are often placed in geostationary orbits around the Earth. In this type of orbit, the satellite stays above the same part of the Earth all the time. It appears to stay in the same part of the sky as the Earth spins on its axis. This makes it easy to exchange signals between the surface of the Earth and the satellite.

??? *Now do this*

1 What causes the tides?

2 How many high tides are there in a day?

The Sun, its planets and their moons make up a **solar system**. There are billions of solar systems clumped together in our local **galaxy**, the Milky Way. The Universe contains billions of different galaxies, separated by empty space.

Days, months and years

- The Earth orbits the Sun, taking one year to go round once.
- Day and night are caused by the Earth spinning, taking 24 hours to spin round once.
- The Moon orbits the Earth in 28 days.
- The stars are far away at various distances and only move very slowly.

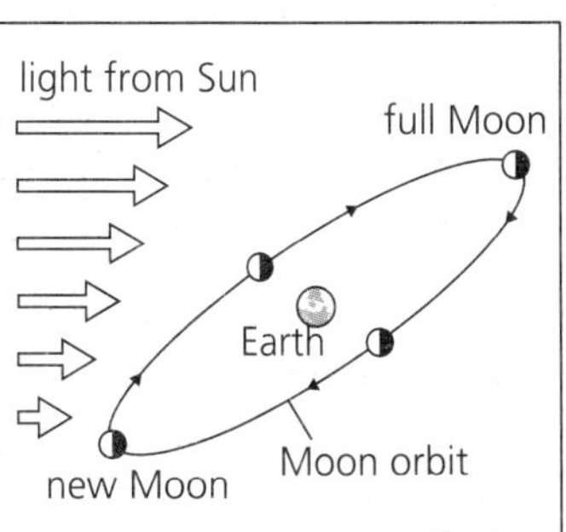

The appearance of the Moon changes as it goes around the Earth. A full moon appears as a white disc. This is because the Moon is reflecting light from the Sun towards the Earth.

Now do this

3 Complete the sentences.

A year is the time it takes for the ________ to orbit the ________. A day is the time it takes for the ________ to spin once on its axis. A month is the time it takes for the ________ to orbit the ________.

4 Explain why the stars appear to move across the sky at night.

The origin of the Universe

The Universe is about 15 billion years old.

At the beginning of the Universe, all the matter and energy was at one point. The Universe expanded rapidly, getting cooler as it did so and forming stable atoms of hydrogen and helium. Gravity made these clouds of gas shrink and heat up. The gas became a star when the temperature of the clouds reached 15 million °C and nuclear fusion converted hydrogen into helium.

After 10 billion years most of the hydrogen in the star's core was used up and it exploded as a supernova. The energy of the explosion created a vast quantity of different atoms as a large cloud of dust and gas. Gravity then pulled the cloud in to form more stars with planets orbiting around them.

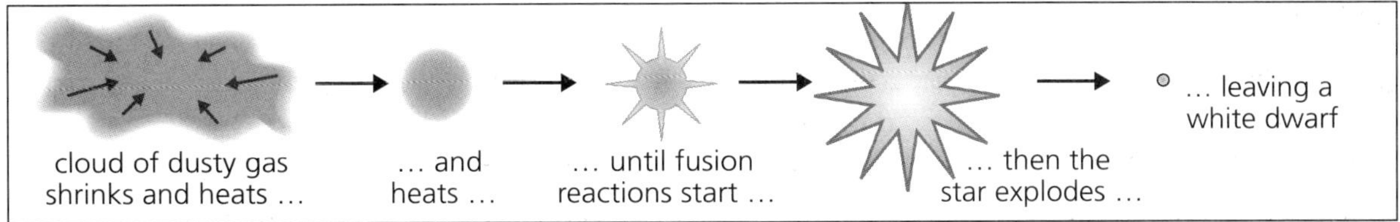

Only very large stars explode. Smaller ones (like our Sun) will just run out of fuel and collapse into a cold lump.

We know that the Universe is expanding because of the **red shift** of the light from other galaxies. When light is emitted by a galaxy moving away from us, its wavelength becomes longer. The increase in wavelength can be used to measure the speed of the galaxy.

Galaxies which are far away from us have a greater red shift than those which are close by.

Red shift and distance measurements provide evidence that all of the galaxies started off in the same place about 15 billion years ago. If there is enough material in the Universe, gravity will stop its expansion and force it to shrink down into a single point - the big crunch! Otherwise, the Universe will carry on expanding for ever.

Radioactivity

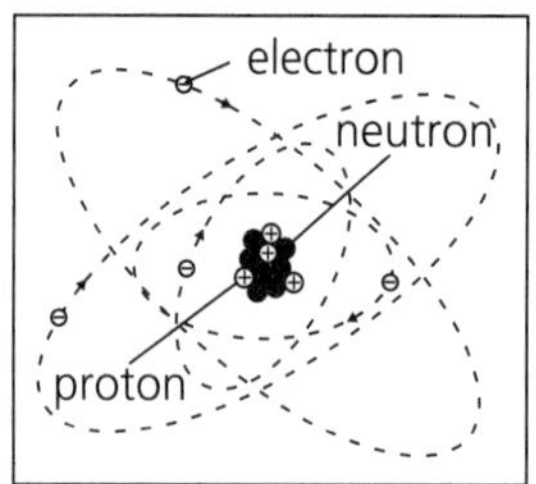

All atoms contain a small nucleus at their centre. The nucleus contains **protons** (positive) and **neutrons** (neutral). Most of the mass and all of the positive charge of an atom are in this nucleus. The rest of the mass and all of the negative charge are in the electrons which move around outside the nucleus.

The **atomic number** of a nucleus tells you how many protons it contains. The **mass number** tells you how many particles (neutrons plus protons) it contains altogether.

Now do this

1 Describe the structure of an atom.
2 What type of charge has a nucleus?
3 What type of charge has an electron?
4 Uranium has a mass number of 234 and an atomic number of 92. What is the number of protons, neutrons and electrons in one atom?

uranium nucleus → thorium nucleus + alpha particle + energy

Some atoms have a nucleus which is unstable. It can break up, spitting out fragments which have a lot of energy. This process is called **radioactivity**.

In the diagram, the atom left behind has lost two protons so it has become a different element.

Some atoms give out α-particles (say 'alpha particles') when they decay. These are made of two protons and two neutrons. A stream of α-particles from a radioactive substance is called α-radiation.

Other atoms give out ß-particles (say 'beta particles') when they decay. These are electrons, so they have a negative charge.

At the same time as either alpha or beta decay, some extra energy can be given out as γ-radiation. γ-rays (say 'gamma rays') are electromagnetic radiation.

Now do this

5 What is radioactivity?
6 Name the particles which make up the nucleus.

Dangers of radiation

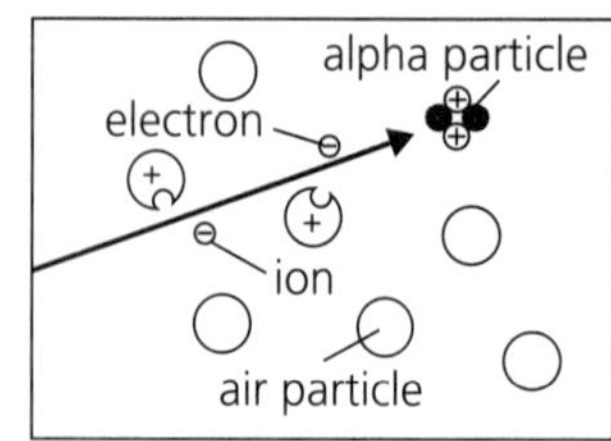

α, β and γ radiation cause **ionisation**. They carry so much energy that as they pass through any substance, they knock electrons off the atoms of the substance. This makes charged particles called **ions**.
In living tissues, ions can cause serious damage.
They can cause cancer or kill cells in the body.

α-particles are the least penetrating of the three radiations. They can be stopped by a thin sheet of paper. β-particles can be stopped by a few millimetres of aluminium. γ-radiation is the most penetrating. It can pass through several centimetres of lead.

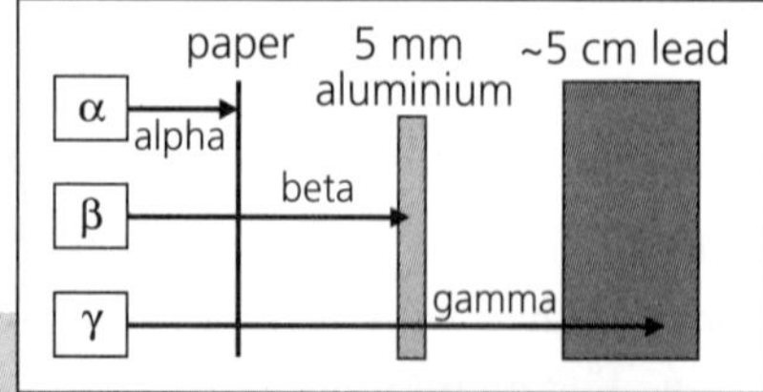

Now do this

7 Name the **three** different nuclear radiations.
8 Which part of an atom does nuclear radiation come from?
9 State the charge of each of the nuclear radiations.
10 Name the radiation which
a has the greatest mass **b** is a wave **c** is a nucleus **d** is an electron.
11 Which radiation is the most penetrating? Which is the least penetrating?

Background radiation

We are surrounded by background nuclear radiation from
- radioactive atoms, such as uranium, in rocks
- radioactive gases, such as radon, from the soil
- fallout from nuclear bomb tests and nuclear power stations
- cosmic rays from space.

Radioactive decay

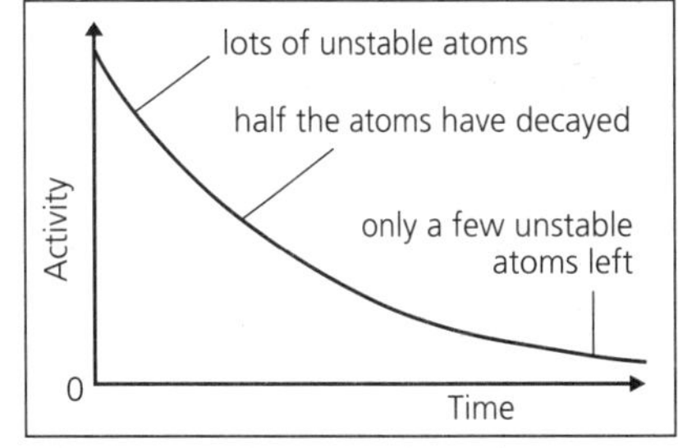

The activity of a radioactive material goes down as time goes on. When the last unstable nucleus has split, the material is no longer radioactive. Some materials take a long time to decay, others are only radioactive for a short while.

Activity is measured in **becquerels (Bq)**. It tells you the rate at which atoms are changing. So if the activity is 365 Bq, there are, on average, 365 atoms decaying in one second.

Now do this

12 Name the **four** sources of background radiation.

13 A radioactive source has an activity of 200 Bq. How many atoms in it decay in a minute?

14 How does the activity of a radioactive material change with time? Explain why.

Half-life

The half-life of an element is the amount of time it takes for half of the atoms to decay. Each element has its own half-life.

Worked example

Q A radioactive source has a half-life of 3 hours. If its activity is 400 Bq now, what will it be in 12 hours time?

A

Time (hours)	0	3	6	9	12
Activity (Bq)	400	200	100	50	25

The final activity will be 25 Bq.

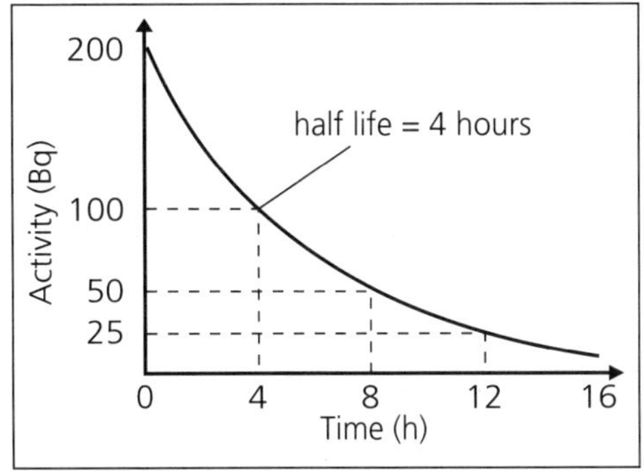

Uses of radioactivity

- Uranium can be used to boil water in a nuclear power station.
- Gamma rays can be used to sterilise surgical instruments.
- Alpha particle sources are used in smoke alarms.
- Beta particle sources can be used to measure the thickness of sheets of material.
- Gamma rays can be used to kill cancer tumours.
- Radioactive materials make good tracers in plants and people.

Now do this

15 A source has a half-life of 12 hours. Its activity is 800 Bq. What will its activity be after 3 days?

16 The activity of a source goes from 100 Bq to 25 Bq in 6 hours. How long is its half-life?

Nuclear equations

Radioactive decay can be represented by equations. The mass and atomic numbers of the particles are shown above and below their symbols. Here are some examples.

Alpha decay: $^{234}_{92}\text{U} \rightarrow {}^{230}_{90}\text{Th} + {}^{4}_{2}\text{He}$

Beta decay: $^{90}_{38}\text{Sr} \rightarrow {}^{90}_{39}\text{Xe} + {}^{0}_{-1}\text{e}$

The mass numbers and atomic numbers have to add up to the same value on both sides of the equation.

Now do this

1 Write out balanced equations for these radioactive decays.

a $^{239}_{93}$Np becomes Pu by emitting an alpha particle.

b $^{239}_{92}$U becomes Np by emitting a beta particle.

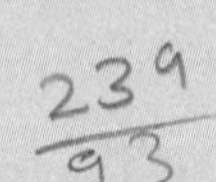

Nuclear fission

Nuclear power stations use a particular isotope of uranium instead of coal or oil to make electricity. A uranium–235 nucleus can undergo fission. It breaks up into smaller nuclei, releasing a lot of energy. In this example, the energy is carried away by six neutrons.

$^{235}_{92}\text{U} \rightarrow {}^{133}_{52}\text{Te} + {}^{96}_{40}\text{Zr} + 6{}^{1}_{0}\text{n}$

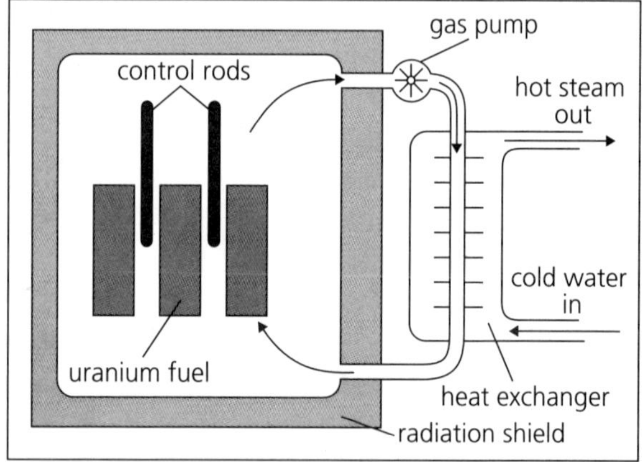

The neutrons emitted by the fission of one nucleus can trigger the fission of other nuclei. This can lead to a chain reaction, where each fission results in other fissions until there are no uranium-235 nuclei left. To keep the chain reaction stable, control rods of substances which absorb neutrons are lowered into the uranium fuel.

The waste produced by fission contains radioactive atoms. Much of them must be stored safely until their radioactivity falls to a safe level.

Now do this

2 Describe the process of nuclear fission.

3 Explain why neutron absorbers are placed in the uranium fuel.

Dating rocks

Many radioactive elements decay to form lead. The age of some igneous rocks can be found by comparing the amount of different isotopes of lead in them.

An isotope of potassium decays to form argon. By comparing the amounts of potassium and argon in igneous rocks, it is possible to measure their age.

Now do this

4 Describe how igneous rocks can be dated.

Exam questions

1 Tom sends a wave to Jill along a rope. Look at the diagram.

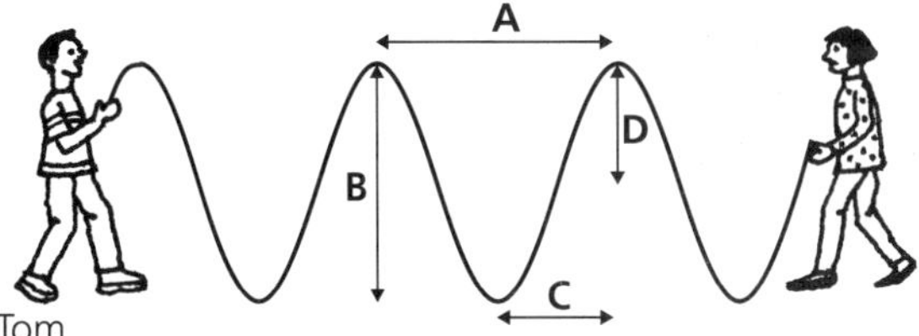

a i State the type of wave. Explain how you can tell. [3]

ii Which letter shows the wavelength of the wave? [1]

iii Tom moves his hand up and down six times in two seconds. Calculate the frequency of the wave. [2]

iv The wavelength is 0.5 m. Calculate the speed of the wave. [3]

b Jill uses two paper cups to send a different wave along the rope. Look at the diagram.

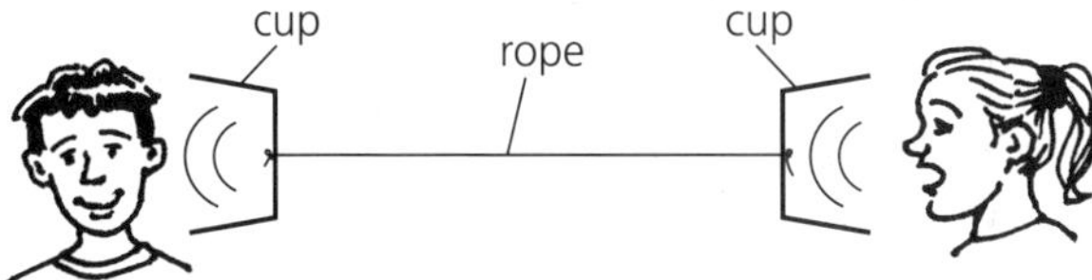

Jill speaks into her cup. Explain why Tom hears a sound from his cup. [3]

[12 marks]

2 Sanjay shines his torch on a mirror. The light reflects off the mirror.

Look at the diagram.

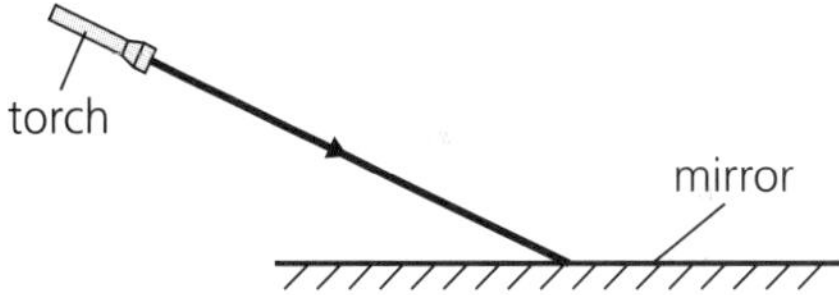

a Draw the path taken by the ray on the diagram. [1]

b Some reflected light reaches Susan. Susan sees an image of Sanjay's torch behind the mirror. Explain why she sees the image there. [2]

[3 marks]

3 Here are some frequencies for sound waves.

200 Hz 5 000 Hz 120 000 Hz

a Which frequency can you not hear? [1]

b Which sound wave has the longest wavelength? [1]

c Ultrasound is used to find cracks in a bar of steel.

Look at the diagram.

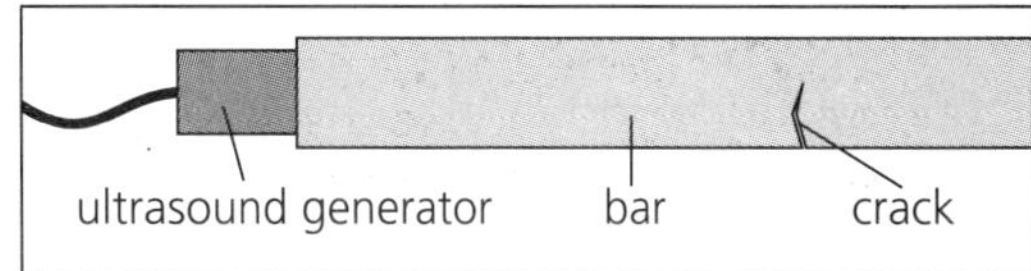

Ultrasound goes through the bar.

It goes from left to right.

How do the particles in the bar move? [2]

d The ultrasound passes through the bar in 0.001 s.

The bar is 5 m long. Calculate the speed of the ultrasound. [3]

[7 marks]

4 Sue uses a lens to form an image of the window on a piece of paper.

a State the type of lens Sue is using. Give a reason. [2]

b Sue wants to make a larger image on the paper. What must she do to the lens? [1]

[3 marks]

5 The diagram shows the Solar System. The planets orbit the star. (The diagram is not drawn to scale.)

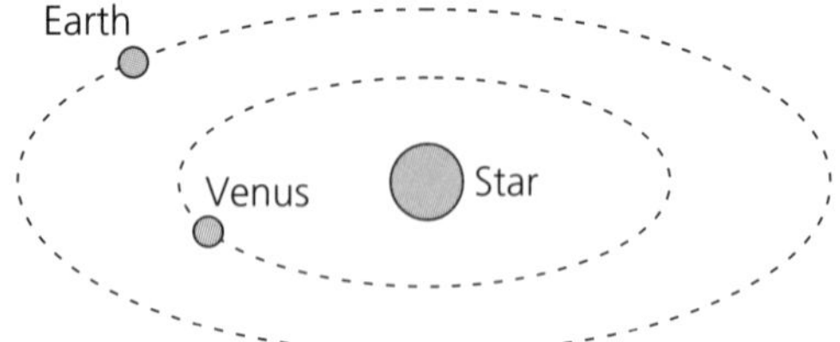

a What is the difference between a planet and star? [2]

b Stars are kept hot by fusion. Describe the fusion reaction. [1]

c Stars start off as a large cloud of dust and gas. Explain how this can become a star. [4]

d Suggest what will happen to a star when its fusion rections stop. Give an explanation. [2]

[9 marks]

6 There are satellites in orbit around the Earth.

a Name the force which keeps a satellite in orbit around the Earth. In what direction does it act on the satellite? [2]

b Explain why there are satellites around the Earth. [2]

[4 marks]

7 Radioactivity is dangerous.

a Explain why radioactivity is dangerous. [2]

b Explain why a piece of radioactive material becomes less dangerous as time goes on. [3]

c A radioactive source has an activity of 500 Bq now. Its half-life is 10 days. Calculate the activity of the source in 30 days time. [3]

[8 marks]

8 **a** Name the **three** different types of nuclear radiation. [3]

b Describe what each of the radiations is made from. [3]

c State what is needed to absorb each of the radiations. [3]

[9 marks]

9 **a** Here are the names of some waves.

infra-red microwaves radio
ultrasound X-rays

Answer the following questions.

Choose your answers from the list.

i Which wave is longitudinal? [1]

ii Which wave has the longest wavelength? [1]

iii Which wave can cause cancer? [1]

iv Which wave can detect airplanes? [1]

v Two of the waves can be used to find broken bones. Which two? [2]

b Infra-red can pass down optical fibres.

i Describe what happens to a ray of infra-red as it passes from air into glass. [2]

ii Describe what happens to a ray of infra-red when it hits the side of the fibre. [1]

[9 marks]

Energy

You will have met the ideas in this section when you worked on the units *Energy matters*, *Energy today and tomorrow*, *Atmosphere* and *Making use of oil*. This section is divided into three spreads.

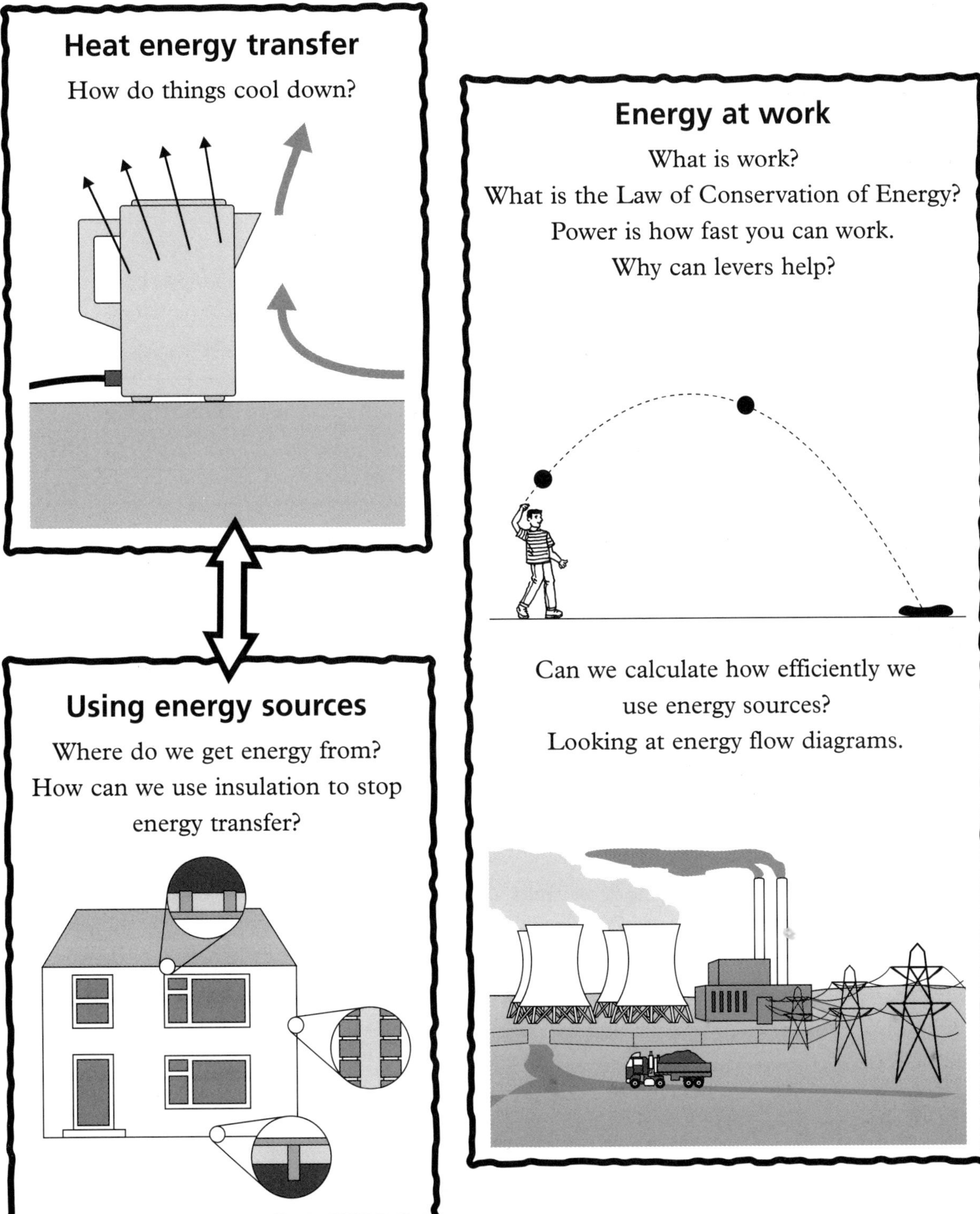

Heat energy transfer

Sam boils a kettle of water. Then he switches it off. Heat energy flows from the hot kettle to the cold room until they are both at the same temperature.

There are three ways in which the kettle loses its heat energy:

- by **conduction** through the base into the table
- by **convection** as hot air rises from the sides
- by **radiation** as infra-red waves carry energy away.

infra-red waves from hot kettle
hot air rises
air heated by kettle
heat energy is conducted into the table
cold air moves in to replace heated air

Now do this

1 A mug of coffee at 40 °C is placed in a freezer at –20 °C. State the final temperature of the mug. State the **three** ways in which the heat energy leaves the mug.

Conduction

The heat energy of the kettle is the kinetic energy of the particles vibrating in the solid kettle walls. The particles vibrate more when they are hot.

When one end of a solid is hotter than the other, the motion of the particles passes kinetic energy from the hot end to the cold end. The heat energy is **conducted** through the material.

energetic particles
heat energy flow
heat energy goes in
hot end
cold end

Convection

Air particles which hit the hot surface of the kettle gain extra kinetic energy. So the air around the kettle heats up. This makes it expand and rise up, carrying the extra heat energy with it. The heat energy is **convected** upwards.

There is a flow of cool air towards the kettle to replace the warm air moving upwards. These are **convection currents** around the kettle.

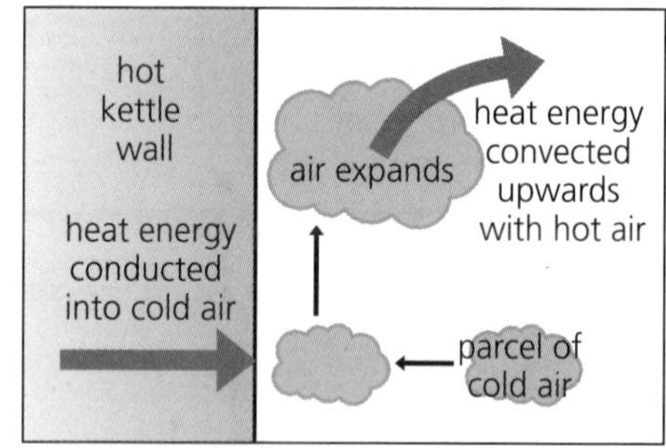

Radiation

Like all hot objects, the surface of the kettle emits infra-red **radiation**. Black surfaces are much better at radiating heat than shiny ones. So a shiny kettle will lose heat energy less rapidly than a dull one.

Radiation does not travel by moving particles. This means that it can travel through a vacuum (empty space). This is how light and heat from the Sun get to the Earth.

Examiner's tip

Shiny objects reflect infra-red rays, so they heat up slowly. Black objects absorb infra-red rays, so they heat up quickly.

Now do this

2 Copy and complete the sentences. Particles in a solid have ______ energy which makes them ______. Particles in a hot solid have more ______ than particles in a cold solid. The process of heat transfer through a solid is called ______.

Warm buildings

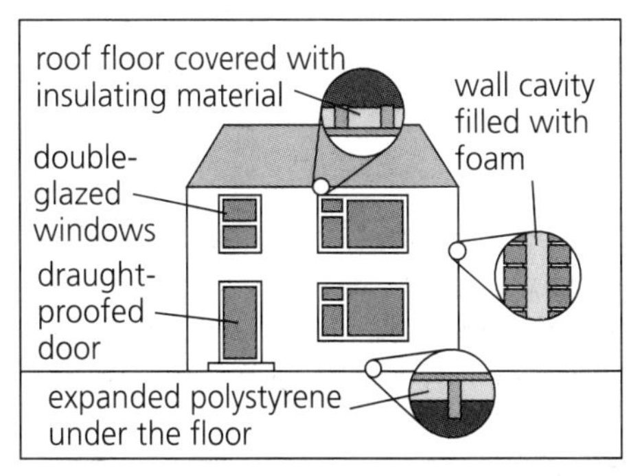

Heat energy lost by conduction from a house can be reduced by trapping air in:

- layers of fluffy material in the roof
- cavities in the outside walls
- double glazing in the windows.

Heat energy lost by radiation from a house can be reduced by:

- painting roofs and walls shiny white
- using window glass which does not transmit infra-red radiation.

Heat energy lost by convection from a house can be reduced by:

- sheltering it from the wind
- keeping the surface area small.

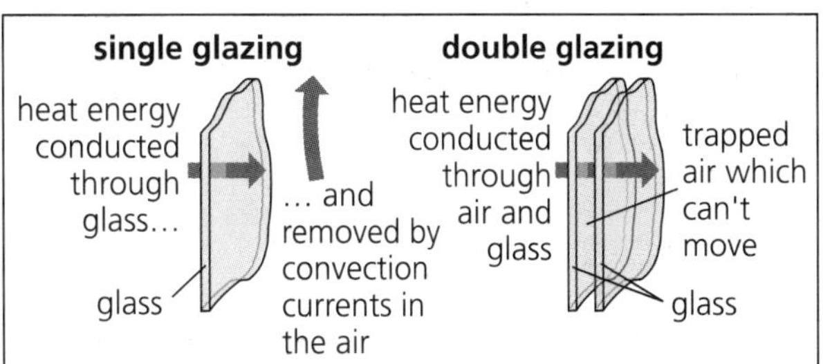

A material which is used to cut down the flow of heat energy is called an **insulator**. Most insulators contain a lot of air. Air is a poor conductor, so it makes a good insulator when it is trapped. Clothes, curtains and double glazing all use trapped air to cut down heat energy loss.

Metals are good conductors. Heat energy flows quickly through them. They feel cold to the touch. Insulators feel warm.

U-values

The rate at which heat energy passes through a material depends on its **U-value**.

rate of energy transfer (W) = U-value (W/m^{2}K) × area (m^2) × temperature difference (K)

Worked example

Q The window of a house has a U-value of 3 W/m^{2}K. The window measures 3 m by 2 m. At what rate does energy pass through if one side is at 20 °C and the other is at –5 °C?

A temperature difference = 20 – (–5) = 25 K
area = 2 × 3 = 6 m^2
rate of energy transfer = 3 × 6 × 25 = 450 W

Now do this

3 Brick walls have a U-value of 2 W/m^{2}K. One side of a wall is at 15 °C, the other is at 5 °C, and it measures 3 m by 5 m. Calculate the rate at which heat energy passes through the wall.

Heat energy calculations

The energy transferred from an object can be calculated from its temperature change.

energy transferred (J) = mass (kg) × specific heat (J/kg/K) × temperature change (K)

Worked example

Q Water has a specific heat of 4200 J/kgK. How much heat energy must you add to 3 kg of water to raise its temperature from 10 °C to 80 °C?

A temperature change = 80 – 10 = 70 K heat energy = 3 × 4200 × 70 = 882 000 J or 882 kJ

Energy at work

Jo lifts up a brick from the floor. She puts it on the table.

This increases the **potential energy** (or **PE**) of the brick. This extra energy comes from Jo.

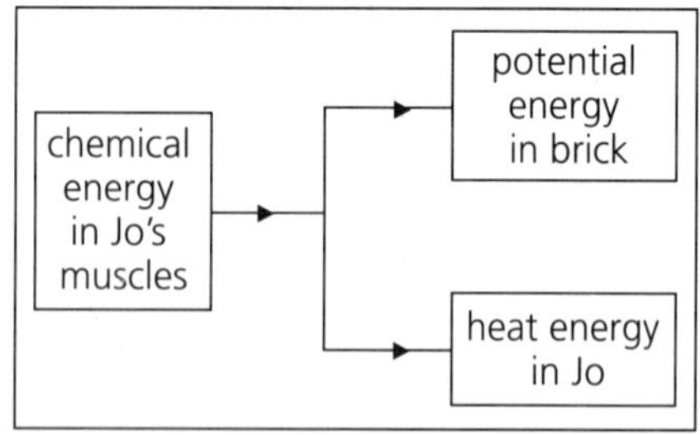

Calculating work

The work done by Jo equals the PE gained by the brick. Work is done whenever a force moves. It can be calculated with this formula.

work = force × distance or $W = Fs$

Symbol	Meaning	Units of measurement
W	work	joules or J
F	force	newtons or N
s	distance	metres or m

Worked example

Q Sam moves a table across the floor, pushing with a force of 20 N. How much work does he do if the table moves 4 m?

A $W = ?$ $F = 20\,\text{N}$ $s = 4\,\text{m}$
$W = F \times s$ $? = 20 \times 4 = 80\,\text{J}$

Now do this

1 Write down the formula for work. Explain the symbols and their units.

2 A brick weighs 25 N. Calculate the work needed to raise a brick by 3 m. How much PE does the brick gain in the process?

3 If 1 000 J of work is done lifting a block of weight 50 N, through what height is it raised?

4 50 000 J of work must be done to stop a car going at 10 m/s. If the car stops in a distance of 20 m, how big a force is required?

Changing energy

All moving objects have **kinetic energy** (or **KE**). The faster they move, the more KE they have. Like all forms of energy, both PE and KE are measured in joules.

Sam throws a ball of clay into the air. As it rises, it transforms its KE into PE. The clay has maximum PE at the top of its flight. On the way down again, the PE is transformed back into KE. When the clay lands on the ground, all of the KE that Sam gave it becomes heat energy. At all stages, the total energy (PE + KE + heat energy) remains the same.

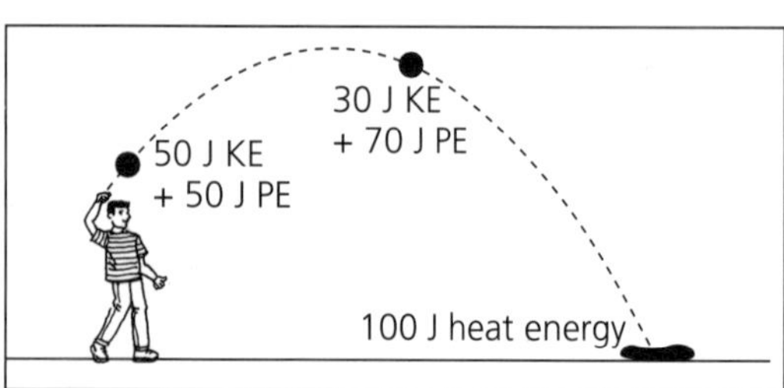

Now do this

5 Jo applies a force of 50 N to her bike. It moves forwards on level ground. How much KE has it gained after moving 10 m?

6 Which of these situations involve doing work?
- **a** lifting up a weight from the floor
- **b** stretching an elastic band
- **c** holding a weight still above your head
- **d** thinking out these answers.

7 Copy and complete the sentences.
Sally climbs up the ladder of a slide, transforming __________ energy into __________ energy. As she moves down the slide, she transforms __________ energy into __________ energy. As she slides to a halt at the end, all of KE has become __________ energy.

Calculating KE and PE

KE and PE can be calculated with the help of these formulae.

$$KE = \frac{1}{2}mv^2 \qquad PE = mgh$$

Symbol	Meaning	Unit
KE	kinetic energy	J
PE	potential energy	J
m	mass	kg
v	speed	m/s
g	acceleration of free fall	m/s^2
h	height raised	m

Worked examples

Q Calculate the KE of a 500 kg car at 15 m/s.

A KE = ? $m = 500$ kg $v = 15$ m/s
$KE = \frac{1}{2}mv^2$ $? = 0.5 \times 500 \times (15^2) = 56\,250$ J

Q A ball has a mass of 0.5 kg. Calculate the increase in PE when it is thrown 20 m into the air. Assume that the acceleration of free fall is 10 m/s^2.

A PE = ? $PE = mgh$ $m = 0.5$ kg $g = 10\ m/s^2$ $h = 20$ m
$? = 0.5 \times 10 \times 20 = 100$ J

Now do this

8 Calculate the KE of a 70 kg man running at 10 m/s.

9 Calculate the increase in PE of a 50 kg girl who climbs a vertical distance of 5 m up a ladder.

Power

Machines (such as motors) are often labelled with their **power**. This tells you how much work they can do in a second.

$$\text{power} = \frac{\text{work}}{\text{time}} \qquad P = \frac{W}{t}$$

A motor with a high power can deliver energy more quickly than one with a low power. So cars with high power engines can accelerate and climb up hills faster than cars with low power engines.

Symbol	Meaning	Units
P	power	watts or W
W	work	joules or J
t	time	seconds or s

Worked example

Q Joe does 2000 J of work lifting bricks up a building. This takes him 50 s. Calculate his power.

A $P = ?$
$W = 2000$ J $P = \frac{W}{t}$ $P = \frac{2000}{50} = 40$ W
$t = 50$ s

Levers

Jo needs to lift a large mass (Sam, 70 kg). She decides to use a lever, a bar of length 4.0 m.

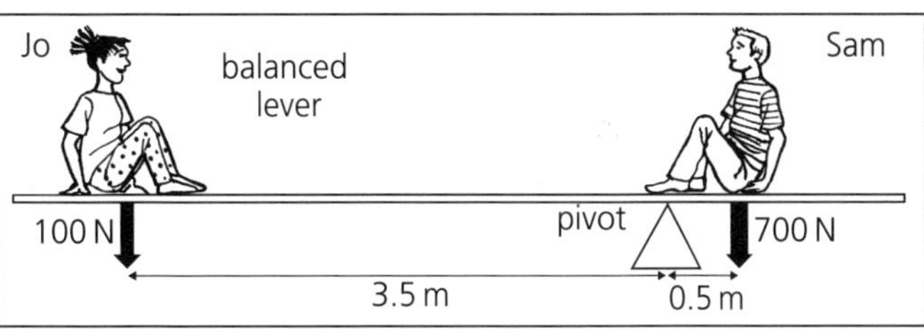

The lever applies a **moment** to Sam. The size of the moment is given by the formula

moment = force × distance to pivot

moment = 700 N × 0.5 m = 350 Nm

Jo needs to apply a moment as well. It has the same size as the moment on Sam.

moment = force × distance to pivot = 100 N × 3.5 m = 350 Nm

Jo is using the lever as a force multiplier. It increases her 100 N downward push to a 700 N upwards push on Sam.

Using energy sources

Coal, oil and gas are **fossil fuels**. They are **non-renewable** sources of energy. Once they have been used up, we will have to use renewable sources of energy, which use energy from the Sun. Energy is continually arriving from the Sun in the form of heat and light radiation.

Renewable sources of energy include:

- **solar** energy, using solar cells to make electricity directly or solar panels to heat water
- **wind** energy, caused by the heating of air by the Sun. Winds are convection currents, carrying cool air towards hot places
- **wave** energy, transferred to the oceans from the wind
- plants which use photosynthesis to convert light energy into chemical energy in wood and other **biomass**
- **hydroelectric** energy, using rainwater which has fallen on mountains. The Sun evaporates the water from the sea and the wind carries the damp air above the mountains. As the air rises, it cools and the water turns to rain.

As fossil fuels are convenient and reliable, it is important to make them last as long as possible. Using energy from fossil fuels efficiently reduces demand and can extend their lifetime. The use of renewable resources helps to conserve non-renewable ones.

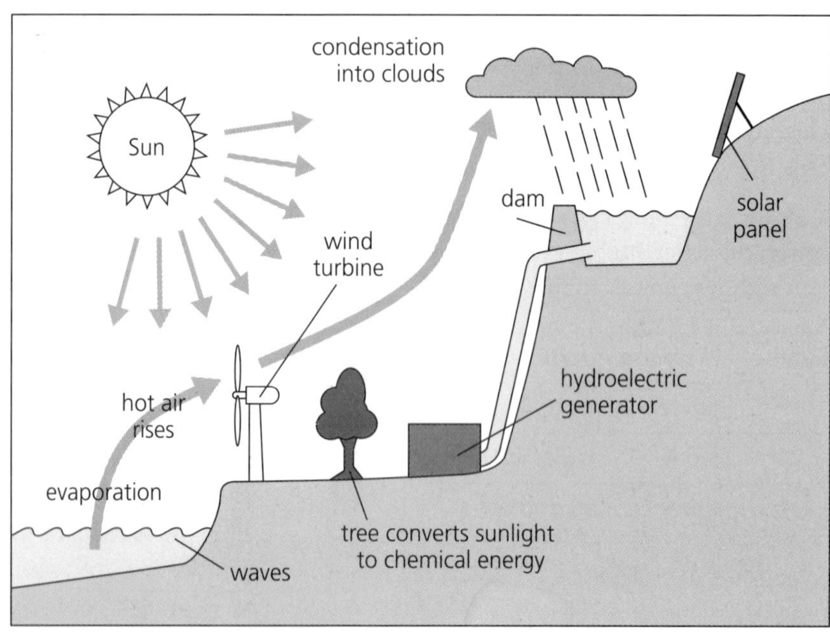

Now do this

1. Name **three** non-renewable fuels.
2. What does non-renewable mean?
3. Describe **five** renewable sources of electricity.
4. Why is it important to use renewable resources as much as possible?

Exam questions

1 Freddie spends £100 a month to keep her house warm.

Look at the table.

How the heat escapes	Value
through the windows	£10
through the floor	£15
through the roof	£25
through the walls	£35
by draughts	£15

a The most heat escapes through the walls. Use your idea of particles to describe how the heat travels through a wall. [2]

b Freddie decides to save money by reducing heat lost through the roof.

i Suggest a good insulating material to put in the loft. [1]

ii Explain why it is a good insulator. [2]

c Freddie draughtproofs her house.

i What could Freddie do to stop the draughts? [1]

ii The cost of heat wasted through draughts is now only £5 a month. The draughtproofing costs £80.

How long does it take for the money saved to pay for the draughtproofing? [2]

d Freddie wants to save even more money on her heating bills.

Explain **two** ways in which she could do this. [4]

[12 marks]

2 a Jane is driving a car. She puts on the brakes.

i Describe the energy transfers which take place as the car stops. [2]

The brakes exert a force of 500 N on the car. It stops in a distance of 20 m.

ii Calculate the work done on the car by the brakes. [3]

iii The car can stop in less than 20 m when it goes uphill. Use the idea of energy to explain why. [2]

b Jane pushes hard on the accelerator for 10 s.

The engine transfers 50 000 J of kinetic energy to the car.

i Calculate the power of the engine. [3]

ii 200 000 J of chemical energy was transferred into the engine during the 10 s.

Calculate the efficiency of the engine. [3]

[13 marks]

3 Pete takes some ice cream out of the freezer. He puts it on the table.

a What will happen to the temperature of the ice cream? [2]

b Energy is transferred by conduction to the ice cream. Use the idea of particles to explain how. [2]

c Pete wraps the ice cream in shiny foil. This keeps it cold for a long time. Explain how. [2]

d The cooling unit of Pete's freezer is at the top. Suggest a reason why it is at the top. Give a reason. [3]

[9 marks]

4 Julie throws a ball high into the air. The ball has a mass of 0.3 kg. The ball leaves Julie's hand with 60 J of kinetic energy and 30 J of potential energy.

a Show that the ball leaves Julie's hand with a speed of 20 m/s. [2]

b At the top of its flight, the ball has 80 J of potential energy.

i How much kinetic energy does it have? [1]

ii How high above the ground does the ball rise? [3]

c If the ball stays on the ground when it hits it, what happens to its energy? [1]

[7 marks]

Pages 2 and 3

1 Movement, reproduction, sensitivity, growth, respiration, excretion, feeding.

2 **a** Chloroplast; **b** cell membrane; **c** cell wall.

3 So more room for haemoglobin to carry more oxygen.

4 Only some things can pass through.

5 Active transport using energy to move the minerals from an area of low concentration to an area of higher concentration.

6 Diffusion.

Page 7

1 Breakdown of large insoluble molecules into small soluble ones.

2 Fatty acids and glycerol; amino acids.

3 They speed up the chemical breakdown of food (catalyse the reactions).

4 Bile emulsifies fats to give a larger surface area for the enzymes to work on.

5 Any two of salivary glands; stomach; pancreas; small intestine.

6 Provides the right conditions for pepsin to digest protein; kills germs on the food.

7 Large intestine or colon.

8 Finger like projections of the small intestine which help absorption by: large surface area; good transport system; thin walls.

9 Physically broken up in the mouth; enzymes in saliva start to break down starch to simple sugars; protein in cheese starts to be digested by pepsin in the stomach; fats emulsified by bile; remaining carbohydrates, fats and proteins digested by pancreatic enzymes; absorbed into the blood through the walls of the villi.

Pages 8 and 9

1

Component	What it looks like	What it does
plasma	straw coloured fluid	transports materials
platelets	tiny fragments	help with clotting
white blood cells	large cells with distinctive nuclei	defend body against infection
red blood cell	biconcave disc with no nucleus	carries oxygen

2 Prevents excessive blood loss; prevents microbes getting into the body.

3 Becomes insoluble forming strands which trap platelets and red blood cells to form a plug.

4 To withstand high pressure of blood inside them.

5 Ventricles have to pump blood around the body whereas atria only receive incoming blood and allow it to pass into the ventricles.

6 Muscle.

7 To prevent blood flowing backwards, either from the ventricles to the atria, or from the arteries back into the ventricles.

Pages 10 and 11

1 Inhale – diaphragm flattens, ribs move up and out, volume of chest cavity increases. Exhale – diaphragm relaxes into domed position, ribs drop back down, chest cavity decreases.

2 The cartilage supports the tubes so that they do not collapse when the internal pressure changes.

3 To use for respiration for the release of energy from food.

4 Oxygen is at a high concentration in the lungs and at a lower concentration in the blood, therefore it moves from a high to a low concentration by diffusion.

5 Any three of large surface area; thin walls; moist surface; good supply of blood.

6 By diffusion.

7 To ensure maximum amount of gas exchange possible.

Pages 12 and 13

1 $C_6H_{12}O_6 + 6O_2 \rightarrow 6CO_2 + 6H_2O$ + Energy
Glucose + Oxygen → Carbon dioxide + Water + Energy

2

Aerobic respiration	Anaerobic respiration
uses oxygen	does not use oxygen
releases a lot of energy	releases less energy
produces carbon dioxide and water	produces lactic acid

3 Mitochondria.

4 It is the amount of oxygen you need to take into your body after vigorous exercise to replenish oxygen levels of the blood and tissues.

5 Heart beat will increase to pump more blood to muscles to supply oxygen and glucose; breathing rate will increase to get more oxygen into the body – as respiration also generates heat, if they are steep flights of steps you could also feel a lot hotter!

Pages 14 and 15

1 Stimulus is the ball coming towards your eye; receptor is the retina; sensory neurone is the optic nerve; motor neurone goes to eye lid muscle which is the effector; response is the eye closing.
2 Suckling; sneezing; swallowing.
3 The iris controls the amount of light entering the eye; the lens changes shape to bend the light; the optic nerve carries messages to the brain.
4 Concave lens to spread the light out so that it will focus on the retina rather than in front of the retina.

Pages 16 and 17

1 A chemical messenger produced by an endocrine gland and carried around the body in the blood.
2 A nervous response is limited to the connections one neuron has to another whereas because hormones travel in the blood they visit every part of the body.
3 High levels of progesterone prevent the uterus lining coming away and also prevent an egg developing and ovulation occurring.
4 It contains hormones which mimic the levels found in a pregnant woman therefore the body thinks that it is pregnant and ovulation does not occur.
5 It repairs the uterine wall ready for an embryo to implant.
6 Pancreas.
7 A meal.
8 High blood glucose levels are needed for insulin to be released – during a long race the glucose is used to release energy and therefore the blood glucose level is too low to stimulate release of insulin.
9 Adrenaline diverts blood away from the surface of the skin so that it can be used to supply muscles with more oxygen and glucose – in this case, to run away from the bull.

Pages 18 and 19

1 Keeping the conditions in the body at the optimum levels for cellular activity.
2 Pancreas; liver.
3 Urine.
4 Water levels still have to be maintained and on a cold day there is less water lost through sweat so more has to be lost as urine.
5 Glucose.
6 Large surface area; permeable to small molecules.
7 Brain (hypothalamus).
8 Heat from the body is used to evaporate the sweat from the skin thereby leaving the skin feeling cooler.
9 Reactions in the body are controlled by enzymes which are destroyed if the temperature gets too high – if the temperature is too low then the reactions will not happen quickly enough.

Page 21

1 Inherited – haemophilia; ageing – dementia; poor environmental conditions – food poisoning; infections – measles.
2 Viruses; bacteria; some fungi; protozoa.
3 Protozoa.
4 Tears contain a substance which kills bacteria.

Pages 22 and 23

1 White blood cells eat invaders or produce antibodies to attack them.
2 A chemical which attacks and destroys microbes.
3 Your body now recognises tetanus and will rapidly produce antibodies to prevent tetanus causing a problem if you meet it on your holiday.
4 Organs are very closely matched before being transplanted; patient treated with drugs to suppress defence system.
5 Smoking prevents the beating of the cilia in the trachea therefore mucus and bacteria are not removed and are more likely to end up clogging up the lungs. This encourages the bacteria to grow and cause infections.
6 All three slow down brain activity and therefore reaction times are likely to be slowed down as well.

Pages 28 and 29

1 The animals that lions eat are either primary consumers or animals which feed on primary consumers; primary consumers feed on plants, and plants need sunlight to make their food and survive.
2 Glucose is converted into insoluble starch which is stored in the leaf.
3 No because they need light to photosynthesise and it is dark at night time.
4 Water; phosphates; nitrates; potassium salts; magnesium salts – or any named trace element taken up by plants.

5 Growing wheat plants remove a lot of minerals/nutrients from the soil and these are not returned to the soil because the plants are harvested and removed from the field. The nutrients need to be returned to the soil and fertiliser does this.

Page 31

1 In distilled water there is a higher concentration of water around the potato than there is inside the cells, therefore water moves by osmosis from an area of high concentration to an area of low concentration. The salt solution contains less water than inside the cells therefore water moves out of the cells into the salt solution and the potato shrinks.

2 Increased evaporation due to higher temperature; increased photosynthesis due to sunlight.

3 Control growth of shoots and roots; control flowering; control ripening of fruit.

4 Light – to ensure they have plenty of light for photosynthesis; gravity – to ensure roots grow down into the soil to anchor the plant and to find water.

5 The shoots grow up towards the light and away from gravity; the roots grow away from the light and towards gravity.

Page 35

1 A group of organisms which can interbreed to produce fertile offspring.

2 Hereditary – blood group; environmental – pierced ears.

3 It is made of DNA which is a polymer made of two chains of sugar and phosphate molecules joined together by pairs of bases.

Pages 36 and 37

1 19.

2 bb × Bb possible offspring bb; Bb which would be 50% brown eyes; 50% blue eyes.

3

Gametes	T	t
t	Tt	tt
t	Tt	tt

Pages 38 and 39

1 Sex linked means the allele is on the X chromosome.

2 If the mother is a carrier she can put her faulty X chromosome into her son and the father will put his Y chromosome into the son this will give X^hY which is a son with haemophilia.

3 They could not produce a daughter with the condition because the father will put his X chromosome into the daughter and for him to be normal in the first place, he cannot have a faulty X – as haemophilia is recessive a daughter would need to inherit two faulty X chromosomes.

4 Genetic engineering and cloning the modified plant is an alternative for plants but both of these techniques meet with ethical and biological problems when applied to animals, therefore selective breeding is still the mainstay for animals.

5 The transfer of DNA from one organism to another, so that the DNA will work in the new organism.

Page 41

1 A change in the genetic code.

2 Mutation causing the genetic disorder cystic fibrosis; mutation causing black peppered moths.

3 Gradual development of organisms over a long period of time to become well adapted to their environment.

4 Remains of dead organisms which have been preserved in stone.

5 Natural selection is the survival of the fittest and when the tree bark was blackened by soot, the fittest moths were the black ones which were hidden against the dark background. The black moths therefore gradually became more numerous than the white ones because more of them survived to breed. The darkening of the bark was the environmental change and the increasing numbers of black moths was the survival response to the change.

Page 45

1 Body lifted high off hot sand; allows effective air circulation and heat removal from body.

2 Low temperature – polar bear; low water availability – cactus; low oxygen – blood worm.

3 Food; mates; space; water.

4 When the prey numbers start to increase, they can support more predators; more predators however will eat more prey and will therefore reach a point where they are eating so many prey that numbers of prey start to drop; predators either move away or die of starvation therefore there is a drop in the number of predators; this allows the number of prey to start to increase again, etc.

5 At freezing temperatures it is too cold for most metabolic reactions to operate successfully therefore although it does not necessarily kill the bacteria, it does stop them growing and increasing in number.

Pages 46 and 47

1 Apply herbicides to reduce competition by weeds; pesticides to reduce damage by pests; fertilisers to provide extra nutrients for growth.

2 Phosphates and nitrates in fertilisers are soluble and get leached into local waterways where they encourage algal growth; this blocks the light getting to underlying plants which die and decompose; decomposing bacteria use up all the oxygen and all living things suffocate and die.

3 Burning – advantage that energy released may be used – but may release toxic fumes; recycling – saves on raw materials but some of the special reprocessing plants are expensive.

4 Clean because it contains a variety of species which can only survive in clean water.

5 Because the phosphates and nitrates promote eutrophication which lowers oxygen levels (see answer to question 2 above).

6 Carbon dioxide; sulphur dioxide; nitrogen dioxide.

Pages 48 and 49

1 **a** Heather – producer; rabbits, grouse, bees, deer – primary consumers; fox or eagle as a predator.

b Any two as long as they both start with heather, move on to a primary consumer and end with a predator.

c Either it would increase because there would be more heather for the grouse to eat due to a lack of rabbits; or it would decrease because the rabbit eating predators would have no rabbits to hunt and would therefore eat more grouse.

2 Restrict movements, no energy wasted moving; constant temperature, therefore energy not wasted in keeping warm.

Pages 50 and 51

1 Bacteria and fungi.

2 They enable nutrients to be recycled rather than remaining locked away in waste or dead things.

3 Photosynthesis; dissolves in sea water.

4 Nitrogen fixing bacteria – convert atmospheric nitrogen into nitrates; denitrifying bacteria – convert nitrates back into atmospheric nitrogen; nitrifying bacteria – convert ammonium compounds in the soil into nitrates.

5 Beans are leguminous plants therefore their roots fix a lot of nitrogen – by ploughing the whole plant into the soil the nitrates are returned to the soil enriching it for the next year.

6 Methane.

7 Compost heaps are not normally anaerobic whereas landfill sites are.

Pages 54 and 55

1 Particles can move through the container, particles are randomly arranged.

2 Particles are held in position and can't move closer.

3 Particles in 'cold' solid are already vibrating; vibration increases with heating; on melting the particles can move freely in all directions; distance between particles will only change a small amount.

4 The forces have the same strength at each temperature; at 100 °C the particles have enough energy to overcome the forces between the molecules of water.

5 Hydrogen sulphide, sugar, nitric acid.

6 Salt and sand, salty water.

Page 57

1 Evaporate.

Filter.

Filter, evaporate.

Dissolve, filter, evaporate.

2 Temperature change, the change is difficult to reverse.

Pages 58 and 59

1

HCl	2	2
H_2O	3	2
CH_4	5	2
CO_2	3	2
$AlCl_3$	4	2
H_2SO_4	7	3
$C_6H_{12}O_6$	24	3

2 H_2S

3 NH_3

4 $MgCl_2$, Fe_2O_3

5 CH_4; C_2H_6; C_3H_8; C_4H_{10}

6 $H_2 + Cl_2 \rightarrow 2HCl$
$Mg + 2HCl \rightarrow Mg\,Cl_2 + H_2$
$C_3H_8 + 5O_2 \rightarrow 3CO_2 + 4H_2O$
$C_2H_4 + 3O_2 \rightarrow 2CO_2 + 2H_2O$

Pages 60 and 61

1 26
2 30
3 $^{18}_{8}O$ has two more neutrons.
4 a 7
b 7
c 2,5
5 2,8,1
6 2,8,8,1

Pages 62 and 63

1

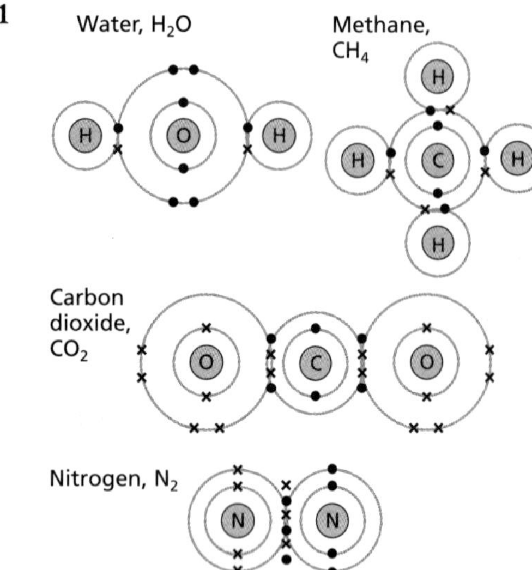

2 Covalent.
3 Giant.
4 Covalent bonds.
5 Weak forces.

Pages 66 and 67

1 8 to 14
2 7
3 3
4 Baking soda.
5 Ammonium sulphate.
6 Carbon dioxide.
7 Bubbles.
8 In the liquid.
In the gas.
9 A salt and hydrogen.
A salt and carbon dioxide and water.
10 Copper, silver.

Pages 68 and 69

1 300°C, 100°C, 200°C.
2 Because it has a lower boiling point.
3

```
                                                        H
                                                        |
                                                      H—C—H
   H H H H H            H H H H                       H | H
   | | | | |            | | | |                       | | |
H—C-C-C-C-C—H        H—C-C-C-C—H                   H—C-C-C—H
   | | | | |            | | | |                       | | |
   H H H H H            H H | H                       H | H
                           H—C—H                      H—C—H
                             |                          |
                             H                          H
```

Pages 70 and 71

1 Methane + oxygen → carbon dioxide + water
2 Produces carbon monoxide, which is poisonous.
3 $C_3H_8 + 5O_2 \rightarrow 3CO_2 + 4H_2O$
4 Diesel fuel has weaker forces between molecules, so it is harder to vaporise.
5 Ultra-violet radiation from the Sun heats the Earth; the Earth emits infra-red radiation; greenhouse gases absorb some infra-red, warming up the atmosphere.
6 Fossil fuels contain small amounts of sulphur; the sulphur creates sulphur oxides when it burns; sulphur oxides dissolve in rain water to make acid rain.
7 Attacks limestone buildings; makes lakes too acidic for fish to survive; releases metals from the soil which are toxic to animals and plants.

Page 73

1 C_2H_4
2 Ethene has a double bond between the two carbons.
3
4

```
  H   Cl  H   Cl  H   Cl
  |   |   |   |   |   |
—C — C — C — C — C — C—
  |   |   |   |   |   |
  H   H   H   H   H   H

  H   CN
  |   |
  C = C
  |   |
  H   H
```

5 It goes soft.
6 Less oil is needed to make new plastic.
7 Poisonous fumes are given off as the plastics are burnt.
8 Hydrogen.

Pages 74 and 75

1 **a** Underneath, into the mantle.
b The rocks melt.

2 Earthquakes and volcanoes.

3 Interlocking crystals.

4 Layers; fossils; rounded grains.

5 The high temperature of the igneous rock changes any surrounding rocks.

Pages 76 and 77

1 Cooled slowly; it must have been well insulated so it was underground.

2 Shallow sea in a very hot area.

3 Sea; for a very long time (hence the thick layer of chalk).

4 To break the ore and the surrounding rock into different pieces.

5 Stone for roads, stone for buildings, to make cement, to make other chemicals.

6 Calcium carbonate → calcium oxide + carbon dioxide *or* limestone → calcium oxide + carbon dioxide.

Pages 78 and 79

1 Aluminium + iron oxide → aluminium oxide + iron.

2 Aluminium + copper oxide → aluminium oxide + copper.

3 **a** Copper oxide,
b Forms copper and water.

4 Carbon + iron oxide → carbon dioxide + iron.

5 Carbon + copper oxide → carbon dioxide + copper.

6 $C + 2CuO \rightarrow CO_2 + 2Cu$

Page 80

1 $2H^+ + 2e^- \rightarrow H_2$

2 $O^{--} \rightarrow \frac{1}{2}O_2 + 2e^-$

Page 81

1 Oxygen, water.

2 Oxidation.

3 Iron oxide.

Pages 82 and 83

1 0.04%

2 20%

3 Respiration, combustion.

4 Photosynthesis, solution in the seas.

5 Volcanoes.

6 Water vapour, carbon dioxide.

7 Photosynthesis by the first green organisms.

8 The rate of removal of oxygen is the same as the rate of production.

Pages 84 and 85

1 12 g

2 48 g

3 17

4 16

5 40

6 5 g

7 44 tonnes

8 1 g

9 11.7 g

10 H_2S

11 SO_2

Page 90

1 **a** Li has one outer electron.
b Li forms a single positive ion, Li^+.

2 **a** S has six outer electrons.
b S forms a double negative ion, $S^=$.

3 BCl_3

Page 91

1 Sodium + water → sodium hydroxide + hydrogen.

2 Sodium chloride + water.

3 Sodium sulphate + water + carbon dioxide.

4 **a** Chlorine.
b Oxygen.
c Sodium ions (Na^+), hydroxide ions (OH^-).

Page 92

1 Silver bromide.

2 Silver nitrate + sodium bromide → silver bromide + sodium nitrate.

3 $Ag^+ + Br^- \rightarrow AgBr$

4 Silver chloride, silver bromide, silver iodide (and also silver nitrate).

5 To kill microbes.

6 Electrolysis of sodium chloride solution.

Page 93

1 Conducts electricity, reacts with acids.

2 Forms coloured compounds, acts as a catalyst.

3 Speeds up a reaction.

Page 95

1 Increase the temperature; increase the concentration *of the acid*; break the solid carbonate into smaller pieces.

2 Increase the temperature; increase the acid concentration.

3 It has a larger surface area.

4 a Platinum

b It is not used up, so it appears on both sides of the equation.

5 a A; the slope is steepest.

b C.

Page 97

1 Alcohol and carbon dioxide.

2 a Oxygen from the air.

b Acid from the lemon juice damages the enzyme.

c The cooking denatures the enzyme.

d Oxygen cannot get to them.

3 a Each chemical fits onto a particular site on the enzyme; the chemicals are held the right way round for them to react and then leave the surface of the enzyme. The enzyme is then ready to react again. Each enzyme will only work for one type of reaction.

b The site on the enzyme matches the shape of the chemical. If the chemical is the wrong shape it will no longer fit.

Pages 98 and 99

1 A reaction that will go in either direction.

2 Nitrogen and hydrogen.

3 Bacteria in some plant roots and in the soil.

4 From plants.

5 Denitrifying bacteria in the soil.

6 Sulphur, oxygen, water.

Page 100

1 a Energy is taken in to break bonds; energy is given out when bonds are made; in exothermic reactions more energy is given out than is taken in.

b To break the first few bonds – to provide the activation energy for the first few molecules.

Page 101

1 Use fog; use full protective clothing; contain the spilt chemical; consider evacuation.

2 The chemical reacts violently.

Pages 106 and 107

1 15 C

2 20 A

3 OFF, OFF; OFF, ON; ON, OFF; ON, ON.

4

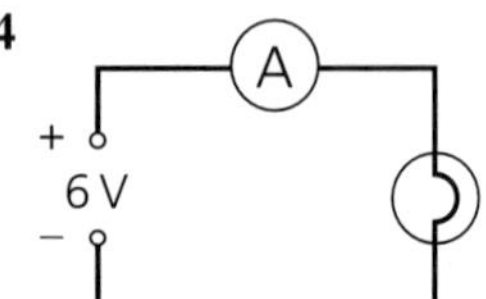

5 Both 2 A

6 2 A

7 **a** dc; **b** ac; **c** ac; **d** dc

Pages 108 and 109

1 **a** Parallel; **b** series; **c** bulbs in series, heater in parallel.

2 96 J

3

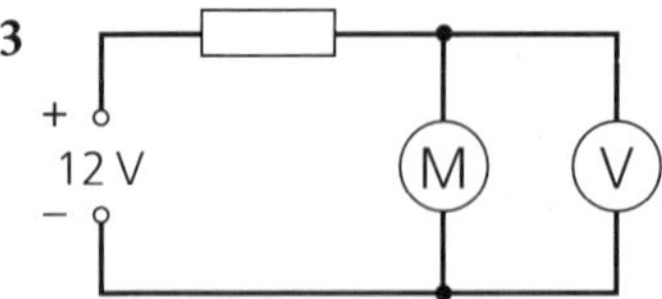

4 b

5 $R = V/I$. R is resistance (ohms), V is voltage (volts) and I is current (amps).

6 48 Ω

7 See page 108.

8 4 A

9 100 V

10 LDR's resistance decreases with increasing light intensity. Thermistor resistance decreases with increasing temperature. In both cases, the extra energy frees electrons from atoms to increase the current.

11 See page 109 for diagram. Wire resistor does not heat up. Filament in lamp heats up, so resistance increases with increasing current.

12

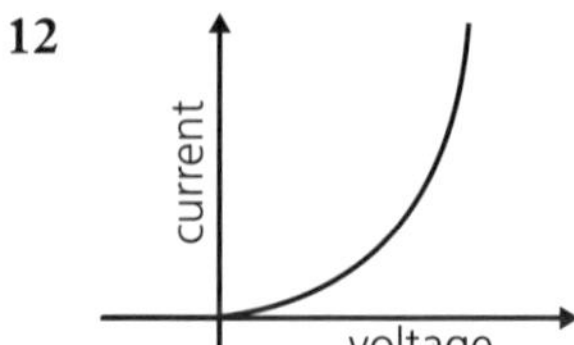

Pages 110 and 111

1 Power P (watts), current I (amps), voltage V (volts). $P = VI$.

2 60 W

3

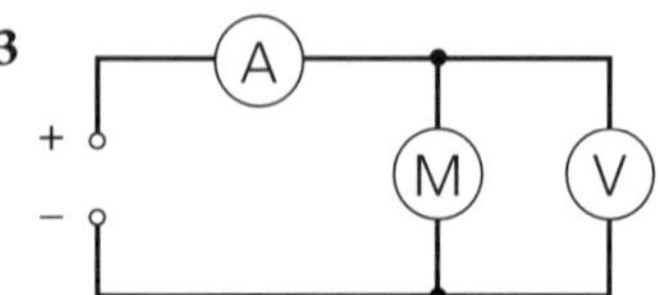

4 0.4 A

5 40 W

6 6.75 p

7 60 p

8 0.13 p

9 37.5 p

Pages 112 and 113

1 Live, neutral and earth.

2 Brown, blue and yellow/green. To tell them apart, stop short-circuits, fires and electrocution.

3 Thin wires get hotter than thick ones, for the same current.

4 Live carries energy from the supply, neutral provides return path for the current, earth provides for safety if the live wire becomes loose.

5 The fuse blows when the current gets high enough to raise the temperature of the wires high enough to damage the insulation.

6 13 A because current is 8.7 A.

7 The fuse blows if a large current flows from the live to the earth wires, isolating the appliance from the mains supply.

8 In the live line.

9 Double insulated

10 Metal outside. So that it cannot rise to a high voltage when touched by the live wire.

Pages 114 and 115

1 Electrons.

2 Copper, aluminium, etc.

3 Wood, nylon, etc.

4 Fur, glass, negative, positive.

5 Glass is positive, silk is negative.

6 Electron current flows from negative to positive, conventional current flows the other way.

7 Negative. Positive.

8 Plane gets charged by friction as it flies. Sparks could ignite fuel as the plane is refuelled. Metal strap to earth removes charge from plane.

9 The car becomes charged by friction, so transfers its charge to people when they touch it. The car should be connected to earth by a conductor.

Pages 116 and 117

1 Attract; attract; repel; ignore.

2 Iron, steel, cobalt, nickel.

3 North.

4 Left.

5 Copper for the coils, steel for the magnets.

6 See page 117.

7 It allows current to enter and leave the spinning coil.

8 Increase the current, stronger magnets, more coils of wire.

9 Electrical energy in coil becomes mechanical energy in the cone which becomes sound energy in the air.

10 Coil, magnet, alternating, vibrate, sound.

Pages 118 and 119

1 See page 118.

2 More current; more coils, an iron core.

3 **a** 0 V **b** –0.1 V

4 Steel for the magnets, copper for the spinning coil.

5 Twice as many cycles, twice the maximum value.

6 Sound; electrical; coil; magnet; alternating.

7 ac in the electromagnet creates patterns of changing magnetism on tape passed steadily by its poles. When the tape is moved past a coil, it induces an alternating voltage which can be amplified.

Pages 120 and 121

1 Oil is burnt to heat water and create steam. A turbine uses the steam to rotate the generator, making electricity.

2 See page 120.

3 efficiency = (useful output energy/input energy) × 100.

4 25 %

5 A set of wires which carry electricity all over the country.

6 To save energy. High voltage means low current and less heat energy in the wires.

7 One transformer steps up the voltage from the power station, the other steps it down for domestic use.

8 See page 121.

9 They use alternating magnetism of the core to induce a voltage across the secondary coil.

10 12 V.

Pages 126 and 127

1 v is speed (m/s), s is distance (m), t is time (s).

2 $v = s/t$

3 20 m/s

4 350 m/s

5 1.7 m/s

6 30.6 m/s

7 3 km

8 5 s

9 1 = **b**, 2 = **c**, 3 = **a**.

10 Acceleration = velocity change/time taken.

11 m/s, s, m/s^2.

Pages 128 and 129

1 Steady speed; speeding up; slowing down.

2 **a** 30 m/s **b** 15 m/s **c** 45 m.

3 Air resistance upwards, weight downwards.

4 Gravity; speed; counter; upwards; increases; balanced; doesn't change.

5 Hot gases are pushed down out of the rocket with a force greater than its own weight.

6 6000 N

7 65 000 N

8 2 m/s^2

Pages 130 and 131

1 The distance moved before the brakes begin to slow the car down. Increased by tiredness, lack of concentration, drinking alcohol.

2 The distance moved while the brakes are on. Increased by wet road, brakes not adjusted, wrong tyre pressure.

3 Airbags provide a soft cushion; seatbelts slow people down securely; crumple zones absorb kinetic energy.

4 Elastic materials return to their original shape when the force on them is removed.

5 **a** 10 cm; **b** 60 N.

6 B is most stable; A least stable.

Pages 132 and 133

1 $P = F/A$

2 N, m^2, Pa.

3 50 000 Pa

4 0.025 m^2

5 Weight; area; pressure; pressure.

6 2 500 N

7 The weight of the air above.

8 Its particles collide with the solid object and put pressure on the object.

9 Doubles.

10 500 kPa

Pages 136 and 137

1 2000 Hz

2 4 m

3 Vibrations; frequency; Hz; longitudinal; energy flow.

4 Pitch; increases; amplitude; decibels.

5 3, 4 m, 25 cm

6 The energy flows from left to right, but the rope wiggles up and down.

7 Speed = wavelength × frequency.

8 24 m/s

9 50 m, 600 000 Hz

Pages 138 and 139

1 A: 60°, 60°; B: 40°, 40°

2 See page 138.

3 60°, 30°

4 See page 139.

5 See page 139.

6 See page 139.

Pages 140 and 141

1 See page 140.

2 Convex lenses focus rays to a point, concave lenses diverge rays. Only convex will form an image on the screen.

3 See page 140.

4 Image gets smaller and closer to the lens.

5 See pages 140 and 141.

6 See page 141.

7 If the angle of incidence is greater than 42°, light will not be able to refract out of the glass.

8 **a** sound; **b** CD recording.

9 Avoids noise in the recording.

Pages 142 and 143

1 47 Hz, 900 Hz, 12 000 Hz, 24 kHz, 50 000 Hz. The last two.

2 37.5 m

3 Probe sends pulses of ultrasound into the body. As the pulse moves between flesh and bone, some of it is echoed back to the probe. The time delay between pulse and echo allows the position of the bone to be calculated.

4 S-waves are transverse, p-waves are longitudinal. Only p-waves can travel through the Earth's liquid core.

5 Gamma rays, X-rays, ultra-violet, visible, infra-red, microwaves, radio.

6 **a** Radio, microwaves, infra-red

b ultra-violet, X-rays, gamma rays

c microwaves, infra-red

d microwaves

e radio, microwaves.

Pages 144 and 145

1 The Moon (and the Sun).

2 Normally two.

3 Earth; Sun; Earth; Moon; Earth.

4 The Earth spins on its axis.

Pages 146 and 147

1 A central nucleus (protons and neutrons), surrounded by electrons.

2 Positive.

3 Negative

4 92, 142, 92.

5 The emission of matter or energy from a nucleus.

6 Proton, neutron.

7 Alpha, beta, gamma.

8 Nucleus.

9 Alpha is positive, beta is negative, gamma is neutral.

10 **a** alpha; **b** gamma; **c** alpha; **d** beta

11 Gamma, alpha.

12 Rocks, soil gases, nuclear power, cosmic rays.

13 12 000

14 Decreases, because there are fewer undecayed atoms left.

15 12.5 Bq

16 3 hours.

Page 148

1 **a** ${}^{239}_{93}\text{Np} \rightarrow {}^{235}_{91}\text{Pu} + {}^{4}_{2}\text{He}$

b ${}^{239}_{92}\text{U} \rightarrow {}^{239}_{93}\text{Np} + {}^{0}_{-1}\text{e}$

2 A neutron added to a uranium nucleus makes it break up into smaller nucleii, emitting other neutrons at the same time.

3 To control the chain reaction. They ensure that each fission produces enough neutrons to create just one fission.

4 By looking at the ratio of different isotopes.

Pages 152 and 153

1 –20°C; Conduction, convection, radiation.

2 Kinetic; vibrate; energy; conduction

3 300 W

Pages 154 and 155

1 $W = Fs$. W is work (J), F is force (N), s is distance (m).

2 75 J

3 20 m

4 2.5 kN

5 500 J

6 **a** and **b**.

7 Chemical; potential; potential; kinetic; heat.

8 3500 J

9 2500 J

Page 156

1 Coal, oil, gas.

2 Once you have used it, it will not be replaced for a very long time.

3 Hydroelectric, solar, wind, tidal, biomass.

4 They extend the lifetime of non-renewable resources.

Life processes and cell activity

Question	Answer	Marks	Total
1 a	Eye spot; flagellum for movement; no cell wall. *any two*	2	
b	Chloroplast for photosynthesis which only plants do.	1	**3 marks**
2 a	Nucleus.	1	
b	Controls cell activities; contains the genetic material of the cell.	1	
c	Contains haemoglobin; no nucleus so more room for haemoglobin; large surface area to aid take up of oxygen. *(any two)*	2	
d	Mitochondria release energy; sperm cells need a lot of energy to enable them to swim.	2	**6 marks**
3 a	Only allows certain things to move through.	1	
b	Diffusion; osmosis; active transport.	3	
c	Diffusion; from a high concentration of glucose inside the intestine to a low concentration in the blood capillaries.	2	
d	Active transport; if all the glucose is to be reabsorbed it must be going against the concentration gradient.	3	**9 marks**
4 a	Plant because it has a cell wall.	1	
b	On the roots of a plant.	1	
c	Long and thin for a large surface area; thin wall.	2	**4 marks**

Humans as organisms

Question	Answer	Marks	Total
1 ab	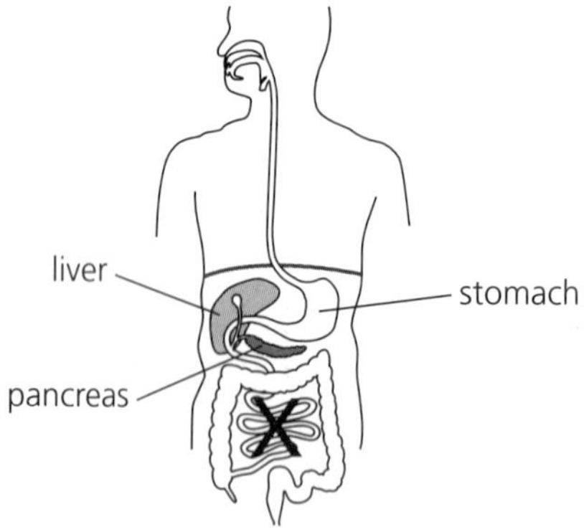	4	
c	Provide a large surface area; thin walls; good transport system. *(any two)*	2	
d	Simple sugars; glycerol and fatty acids.	3	
e	Emulsifies; fats; providing larger surface area for enzyme attack.	3	
f	Enzymes.	1	**13 marks**
2 a	Oxygen; carbon dioxide; glucose; amino acids; water; salts; hormones; heat. *(any three)*	3	
b	Fibrin strands are formed; platelets try to plug the hole; fibrin catches platelets/red blood cells to form a plug; plug dries and hardens to form a scab.	4	
c	White blood cell/phagocyte.	1	
d	It engulfs the bacteria; breaks it down inside the cell.	2	
e	Chemical produced to attack a foreign invader/microbe.	1	
f	Her white blood cells have recognised the flu as an antigen; and have produced antibodies to attack and get rid of it.	2	**13 marks**

Question	Answer	Marks	Total
3 a	(Graph)	3	
b	Slows down reaction time/impairs judgement.	1	
c	Alcohol is broken down in the liver; over use results in liver failure; or other effect explained.	2	**6 marks**
4 a	A hormone.	1	
b	It would be digested in the stomach if taken orally.	1	
c	Pancreas.	1	
d	Homeostasis is keeping conditions stable; for example the glucose concentration in the blood; if it goes too high, insulin is released; insulin lowers blood glucose; if it goes too low, glucagon is released; glucagon raises blood glucose.	5	**8 marks**
5 a	position of contact lens (diagram)	1	
b	Retina.	1	
c	Light comes in through the cornea which starts to bend it; the lens bends the light just the right amount; so it will focus on the retina; light receptors in the retina send messages along the optic nerve to the brain.	4	
d	Lee is short sighted therefore has a concave lens; Joe has convex lenses.	2	
e	Light is focused before the retina; due to long eyeball/lens which bends the light too efficiently.	2	**10 marks**
6 a	A **b** E	1 1	
c	A receptor detected the hot stimulus; message sent along sensory neurone; to motor neurone; to effector (muscle) making arm move.	3	
d	Swallowing, blinking, suckling, coughing. *(any two)*	2	**7 marks**
7 a	Oxygen **b** Nitrogen	1 1	
c	Diaphragm contracts and flattens; rib-cage lifts up and out; volume of chest cavity increases; pressure decreases causing air to rush in; diaphragm returns to domed position; rib-cage drops down; air squeezed out of the lungs.	5	**7 marks**
8 a	Pasta; sausages. **b** 3745 kJ **c** Respiration	2 2 1	
d	Water; carbon dioxide.	2	**7 marks**
9 a	Heart beating faster; breathing faster; feeling hotter.	3	
b	Heart beats faster to get blood to exercising muscles more quickly; breathing rate increases to supply blood with more oxygen; feel hotter because more respiration is going on to release the energy needed for running and heat is also released during respiration.	3	
c	Build up of lactic acid.	1	
d	The amount of oxygen which has to be taken back into the body; to repay the oxygen used up during heavy exercise; when body has to respire anaerobically.	3	**10 marks**
10 a	Right ventricle. **b** A	1 1	
c	E towards the heart; F away from the heart.	2	
d	Prevents backflow of blood into the atrium.	2	**6 marks**

Question	Answer	Marks	Total
11 a	normal body temperature → temperature too high → normal body temperature; normal body temperature → temperature too low → normal body temperature	2	
b	Brain/hypothalamus.	1	
c	He feels colder because he is wet and the water is evaporating off his skin; using body heat for the evaporation.	2	**5 marks**

Green plants as organisms

Question	Answer	Marks	Total
1 a	–3.9mm	1	
b	(Graph)	4	
c	Read the point on the graph where the line passes through 0 mm.	1	
d	In 0 sugar solution and 0.2 there is more water outside the rhubarb cells than inside therefore water moves into the cells and this makes the rhubarb appear longer; in stronger concentrations of sugar there is more water inside the cells therefore it moves out of the cells, making the cells shrink, movement is by osmosis; which is the movement of water from a higher to a lower concentration through a semi-permeable membrane.	4	**10 marks**
2 a	$6CO_2$; $6O_2$	2	
b	Light; chlorophyll.	2	
c	Phloem.	1	
d	Water plant in beaker; inverted funnel over it; graduated tube full of water inverted over funnel; illuminate set up with one coloured light; count bubbles of gas produced per minute; change to different coloured light; same distance from set up; allow to acclimatise; repeat bubble counting.	5	
e	It is the factor which is controlling the rate of the reaction therefore it is likely to be in short supply.	1	
f	Temperature.	1	**12 marks**
3 a	Respond by growth movements; either towards or away from the stimulus; controlled by auxins/plant hormones.	3	
b	Shoot will grow towards the light; because it is positively phototropic; root will grow down towards gravity.	2	
c	Auxin produced at the tip of the shoot; diffuses back down shoot; causes shaded side to grow more rapidly than the illuminated side, therefore shoot bends towards the light.	3	
d	Constant rotation has fooled roots into growing straight; as fast as the auxin is released the root has changed orientation and therefore it grows straight.	2	
e	Used as a rooting powder; in the commercial growing of plant cuttings/or any other use explained.	2	**12 marks**

Variation, inheritance and evolution

Question	Answer	Marks	Total
1 a	Smooth, regular.	1	
b	Allele which is only expressed if it is homozygous.	1	
c	S = smooth, s = jagged SS × ss = all Ss	4	
d	Ss × Ss = SS and ss 50% smooth: 50% jagged	4	
e	Jagged are homozygous; breeder takes jagged and only breeds the best jagged together; hand pollinates/covers flowers to prevent other pollen getting in.	3	**13 marks**
2 a	N = normal, n = cystic fibrosis Nn × Nn = NN; Nn; nN; nn the nn is the baby.	4	
b	25 %	1	
c	It is sex linked therefore it is on the X chromosome; males only have one X chromosome; therefore if they inherit a faulty one then it will show; reverse argument for females.	3	
d	The sequence of bases on the DNA of the chromosomes.	2	
e	Ionising radiation; mutagenic chemicals.	2	**12 marks**
3 a	Transfer of DNA from one organism into another.	1	
b	1 Isolate desired piece of DNA. 2 Cut DNA and plasmid with same enzyme. 3 Mix plasmid and DNA to allow them to join up. 4 Get a bacterium to take up the recombinant plasmid.	6	
c	Human insulin DNA isolated; taken up by a plasmid; plasmid taken up by a bacterium; bacterium grows and makes the insulin; it has no use for the insulin and releases it into its surroundings.	3	
d	Three advantages of genetic engineering and three disadvantages obtain from table in text page 39.	6	**16 marks**
4 a	Allele is on the X chromosome.	1	
b	Allele which only shows in the phenotype, if homozygous.	2	
c	From his mother; she must be a carrier because she provides him with his X chromosome.	2	
d	No; he passes his Y chromosome to his son and this is not affected.	2	
e	50%	1	**8 marks**

Living things in their environment

Question	Answer	Marks	Total
1	Nitrates encourage growth of surface algae; this cuts off light reaching underlying plants; they die because they do not have light for photosynthesis; bacteria decompose dead material; bacteria respire and use up oxygen; all other living things die as result of no oxygen; result dead, smelly, rotting waterway.	6	**6 marks**
2 a	2–3 **b** Divide into two/binary fission.	1 1	
c	A is the lag phase where there are relatively small numbers of bacteria; they are getting used to their environment.	2	
	B is the log phase where they are increasing exponentially; conditions are ideal with no limiting factors yet.	2	

Question	Answer	Marks	Total
d	Food; warmth; moisture.	3	
e	Accumulation of waste products; death rate exceeds birth rate; defence system of body.	1	**10 marks**
3 a	Nitrogen fixing. **b** Nitrifying.	1 1	
c	Plants need nitrates to grow; wheat removes nitrates from the soil therefore needs a supply of nitrates in the soil; beans are legumes; they can fix nitrogen in their root nodules to make their own supply of nitrates.	4	
d	Normal shaped pyramid; wheat or bean on the bottom; rabbit in the middle; fox on top	3	**9 marks**
4 a	X – photosynthesis; Y – consumption/eating; Z – respiration.	3	
b	Bacteria/fungi.	1	
c	Increased combustion of fossil fuels; as population/industrialisation increases.	2	
d	Carbon dioxide allows short wavelength radiation from the Sun into the atmosphere; but it will not let it out when it comes back from the Earth as longer wavelength radiation; it remains trapped, like heat in a greenhouse.	3	
e	Global warming; melting ice caps; increased sea levels; loss of coastal habitats; more severe weather conditions.	3	**12 marks**

Classifying materials

Question	Answer	Marks	Total
1 a	Sodium chloride + grit; sodium chloride in water.	2	
b	Sodium chloride, water. **c** Iron	2 1	**5 marks**
2 a	B	1	
b i	It will go in.	1	
ii	Particles are far apart, so can be pushed closer together.	1 1	
c i	Plunger will not go in.	1	
ii	Particles close together, so cannot be pushed any closer.	1 1	**7 marks**
3 a i	X and Y **ii** They have high melting points.	2 1	
b i	Y **ii** It conducts electricity when melted.	1 1	**5 marks**
4 a	$FeCl_3$ **b** 2 **c** 2 **d** 6	1 1 1 1	
e	Sea of electrons, attract the positively charged iron ions.	2	**6 marks**
5 a	Calcium oxide + water → calcium hydroxide	1	
b	$CaO + H_2O \rightarrow Ca(OH)_2$ left hand side correct, right hand side correct	2	**3 marks**
6 a	Methane + oxygen → carbon dioxide + water	1	
b	$CH_4 + 2O_2 \rightarrow CO_2 + 2H_2O$ correct formulae on left hand side, correct formulae on right hand side, balanced correctly.	3	**4 marks**
7 a	Protons and neutrons.	2	
b	33 **c** 60	1 1	**4 marks**
8	Se^{--}. The atom takes two electrons to make up eight its outer shell.	2	**2 marks**

Changing materials

Question	Answer	Marks	Total
1 a i	A **ii** F	1 1	
iii	Forces between gas molecules are few/weak so are easily overcome; there are more forces between liquid molecules; more energy is needed to break them.	4	
b i	Hexane → propane + propene + hydrogen	1	
ii	Use bromine water. No change/stays orange with propane; goes colourless with propene.	3	
c i	If only small quantities are needed *or* to cope with sudden changes in demand.	1	
ii	Possibility of accidents; cost (of employing drivers).	2	
d i	PVC **ii** Acrylic **iii** Polythene **iv** Polycarbonate	1 1 1 1	
e	Thermosetting polymers have cross-links which hold the molecules together/prevent them sliding past each other. For example:	3	
	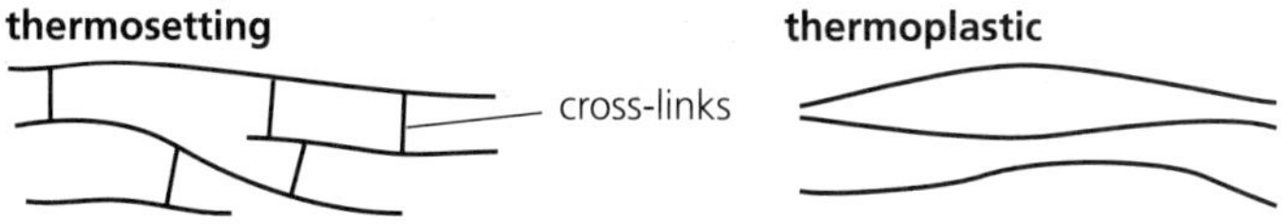		**20 marks**
2 a	Exothermic. **b** Paraffin + oxygen → carbon dioxide + water	1 2	
c	Carbon monoxide is produced; carbon monoxide is poisonous.	2	**5 marks**
3 a	Igneous.	1	
b	Rock A cooled at the surface, it cooled quickly, it has small crystals. Rock B is the opposite; it has large crystals.	4	
c	Plate split, and the two halves moved apart.	2	
d	First rock eroded/was broken into small particles; particles were rounded by the action of streams (or allow wind); particles were cemented/stuck together.	3	**10 marks**
4	Any **four** points from: tree/fern swamp makes the coal coal formed before the limestone because the coal is beneath the limestone area was under the sea when the limestone formed from the bodies of sea creatures.	4	**4 marks**
5 a	Decreases; oxygen has been removed.	2	
b i	48 g (1 mark if answer wrong but working shows 112/56)	2	
ii	6 g (1 mark if the answer is given as 3g)	2	
c	$Fe_3O_4 + 4H_2 \rightarrow 3Fe + 4H_2O$ correct formulae on the left hand side correct formulae on the right hand side correct numbers *in front of* the formulae.	3	
d	Hydrogen is more reactive than iron; hydrogen is less reactive than calcium.	2	**11 marks**
6 a	CaO **b** $Ca(OH)_2$ **c** 74 g	1 1 1	
d	Some water will evaporate or boil.	1	**4 marks**
7 a	Ultra-violet radiation from the Sun hits the Earth; the Earth gives out infra-red radiation; the infra-red radiation is absorbed by gases in the atmosphere; which warms up the atmosphere.	4	

Question	Answer	Marks	Total
b i	Respiration; is greater than photosynthesis.	2	
ii	C; photosynthesis has been taking place all day; so most of the carbon dioxide has been used up.	3	
iii	A; highest levels of carbon dioxide.	2	
c i	Any **two** of oxides of nitrogen; and unburned hydrocarbons; react with the air.	2	
ii	Causes breathing difficulties; makes the eyes water.	1	
d	(Microscopic) sea creatures die; covered by layers of sediment (which turns into rock); the pressure and temperature of the layers of rock forms oil from the dead bodies.	3	**17 marks**
8 a i	Copper. **ii** Oxide. **iii** Copper.	1 1 1	
b	Oxygen.	1	
c	Iron oxide + carbon monoxide → iron + carbon dioxide *or* Iron oxide + carbon → iron + carbon dioxide	2	
d	Sodium	1	**7 marks**
9 a	Increased.	1	
b	Any **two** of copper ions attracted to the electrode the copper ions are neutralised at the electrode copper atoms are deposited on the electrode.	2	
c	Decreased.	1	
d	Copper atoms from the electrode turn into copper ions which dissolve into the solution.	2	**6 marks**
10	Availability of raw materials, energy, skilled work force, ease of distribution of the chemicals to the buyers.	4	**4 marks**
11 a i	Sulphur dioxide. **ii** $S + O_2 \rightarrow SO_2$. **iii** Sulphuric acid.	1 1 1	
b	Damages leaves; removes essential minerals from the soil; releases poisonous minerals from inside the soil.	3	**6 marks**
12 a	Acidity. **b** Slightly acidic. **c** Neutralises (the bee sting).	1 2 1	
d	Suitable named indicator e.g. Universal Indicator (*not* 'indicator' – it isn't a named type) (*not* 'litmus' – it doesn't test pH, only if things are acid or alkali) suitable result.	2	**6 marks**

Patterns of behaviour

Question	Answer	Marks	Total
1 a i	Group II.	1	
ii	It is on the left hand side of the Periodic Table.	1	
iii	Two electrons.	1	
iv	Sr^{++}.	1	
b	Strontium is in the same group as calcium so its properties are very similar.	2	
c i	Strontium is very reactive. **ii** On the left, near the bottom	1 1	
iii	Strontium hydroxide and hydrogen.	2	
iv	Between 7.1 and 8.9 = 1 mark higher than 9 = 2 marks	2	**12 marks**

Question	Answer	Marks	Total
2 a i	Sugar, moisture, warmth. **ii** Alcohol (ethanol).	3 1	
b	Enzymes are denatured (NOT 'killed'). **c** Carbon dioxide gas.	2 1	
d	Speeds up; maximum rate at 37°C; then slows down and stops; as the yeast enzyme is denatured.	4	**11 marks**
3 a	Collisions; greater surface area/more places for collision.	2	
b	Collisions; particles move faster/have more energy/collide more often.	2	
c	Increase the concentration, use a catalyst.	2	**6 marks**
4 a	Ammonia. **b** It has not caught fire. **c** Wash it down the drains.	1 1 1	
d	Full protective clothing. **e** The letter 'E'.	1 1	**5 marks**
5 a	White, solid (precipitate). **b** Sodium nitrate.	2 1	
c	$AgNO_3 + NaCl \rightarrow AgCl + NaNO_3$	2	
d i	Silver bromide or silver iodide.	1	
ii	Bromine/iodine are in the same group as chlorine.	1	**7 marks**
6 a	The reaction can go in either direction.	1	
b	From the atmosphere. **c** Nitrogen is unreactive.	1 1	
d i	It is alkaline.	1	
ii	Rainwater runs off from the fields into the rivers; ammonia dissolves in the water.	2	
e	Acid = 1 mark, nitric acid = 2 marks	2	
f i	Bacteria; in the plant roots *or* in the soil.	2	
ii	Protein (or amino acids).	1	**11 marks**
7 a	Oxygen. **b** Musket balls have a larger surface area.	1 1	
c	New cannon ball conducts better; metals conduct electricity, metal compounds don't.	2	
d	Aluminium is in group III/is not a transition metal; transition metals form coloured compounds.	2	**6 marks**
8 a	It will decompose rapidly (to inflate the bag before the occupant hits the steering wheel or dashboard).	1	
b i	Bonds between sodium and nitrogen.	1	
ii	Bonds between nitrogen atoms.	1	
iii	Energy is taken in to break bonds; energy is given out when bonds are made; more energy is given out than taken in.	3	
c	Activation energy; small amount of energy needed for the reaction to get going.	2	
d	Diagram shows products at a lower energy level than reactants. Diagram shows activation energy hump.	1 1	
	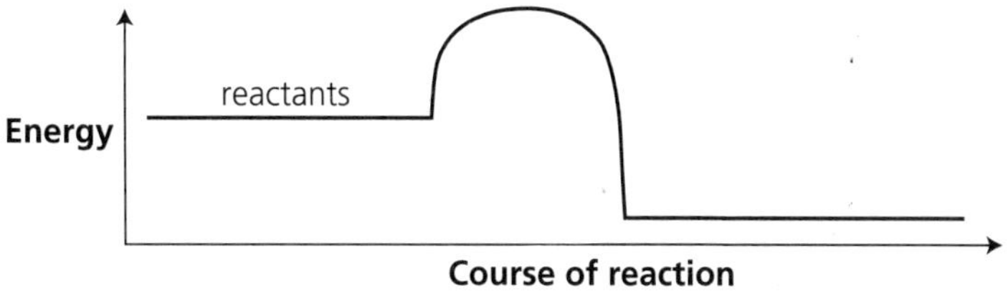		**10 marks**
9 a	Positive or anode.	1	
b	Any three of Cl^- ions attracted to anode		

Question	Answer	Marks	Total
	because of opposite charge each Cl^- ion gives electron to the anode *one* electron per ion.	3	
c	$H_2O \rightarrow H^+ + OH^-$	2	
d	Sodium hydroxide.	1	**7 marks**

Electricity and magnestism

Question	Answer	Marks	Total
1 a	The heater, because it will take the most electrical energy from the supply.	1	
b i	1.2 kWh **ii** 9.6 p	2 1	
c i	Live; neutral; earth.	3	
ii	The fuse is in the live wire to disconnect the circuit from the mains if the current becomes too great for safety.	2	
iii	Heater current = 8.7 A. So a 5 A fuse will blow immediately.	1 1	**11 marks**
2 a	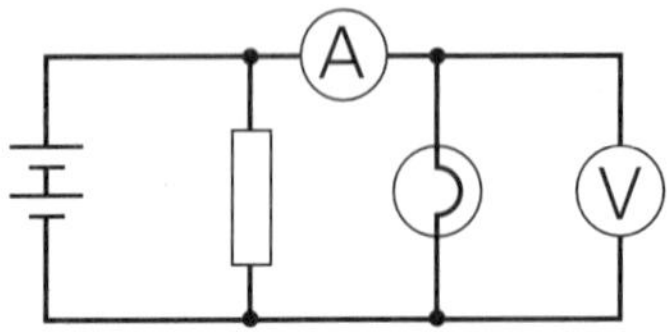 A V	2	
b	Electrical energy from the cell is transferred to light and heat energy in the lamp, just heat energy in the resistor.	5	
c i	5.0 Ω **ii** 1.25 W	3 3	
d i	0.25 A **ii** 0.75 A	3 1	**17 marks**
3 a	Place the lamp and motor in parallel, remove the motor, add another cell.	2	
b i	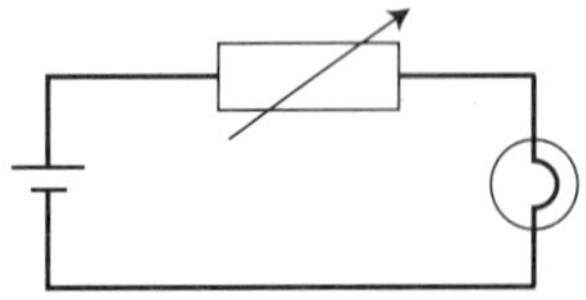	1	
ii	As the resistance increases, the current decreases and the lamp becomes dimmer.	2	**5 marks**
4 a	D because it has the lowest resistance and greatest voltage.	2	
b	D because it has the greatest current.	2	**4 marks**
5 a	Rub it against a different insulator. Negative electrons from one insulator are transferred to the other, leaving them with opposite charges.	1 2	
b	Negative, because like charges repel each other.	2	**5 marks**
6 a	Friction with the air removes electrons from the surface of the airplane, leaving it positively charged.	2	
b	Sparks from the airplane to the nozzle could ignite the fuel-air mixture.	2	
c	The strap allows electrons from the earth to move into the airplane and neutralise it.	2	**6 marks**

Question	Answer	Marks	Total
7 a	Iron, so that it can be magnetised and demagnetised easily.	2	
b	Change the number of coils, or the current in the coils.	2	
c i	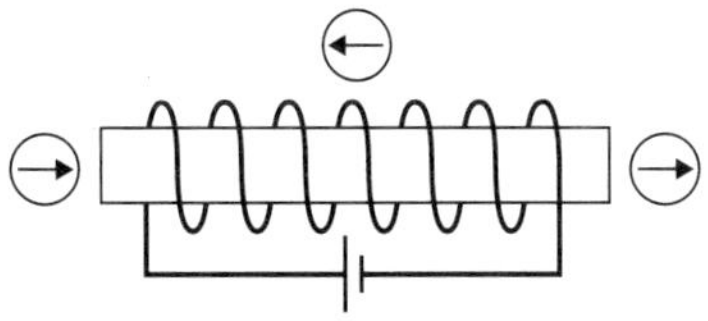	2	
ii	Reverse the current in the coils.	1	**7 marks**
8 a	See page 121.	3	
	Coils made out of copper, to have low resistance.	2	
	Core out of iron for easy magnetisation and demagnetisation.	2	
b	Electrical energy in primary coil becomes magnetic energy in the core which becomes electrical energy in the secondary coil.	3	
c i	23 V **ii** 2 A	3 3	
iii	No transfer of energy to heat in the transformer. **iv** 0.2 A	1 2	
v	Less current in the primary, so can afford to have a greater resistance.	1	**20 marks**
9	See page 119 for diagram.	3	
	Sound wave vibrates the coil	1	
	which moves in a magnetic field	1	
	generating an alternating voltage across the coil.	1	**6 marks**
10 a	Chemical energy in the coal → heat energy in the steam → kinetic energy in the turbine → electrical energy in the generator.	4	
b	30% **c** At the boiler, from the turbine and in the generator.	2 3	
d i	A set of wires transporting electricity over the whole country.	1	
ii	To raise the voltage, thus reducing the currents in the grid and reducing the energy wasted as heat.	3	**13 marks**
11 a i	Reverse the cell. **ii** Put a resistor in series.	2	
b	The copper is for the coil which carries the current between the poles of a steel magnet.	4	
c	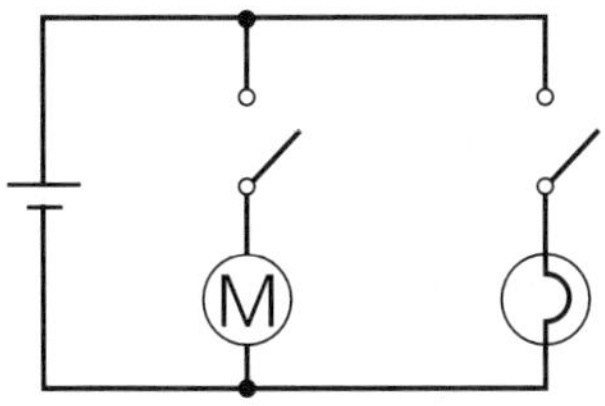	3	**9 marks**
12 a	Current in the coil creates a magnetic field which attracts the iron armature. The plastic core moves down and the copper contacts are brought into contact with each other.	4	
b	The contacts spring apart. The coil is no longer magnetic, so the core is pushed up by the spring.	2	**6 marks**

Forces and motion

Question	Answer	Marks	Total
1 a i	$3\ m/s^2$ **ii** 60 kg	3 3	
b	15 m/s; 300 m	4	
c	The only force acting is the counterforce of friction. So she slows down until she stops.	2	
d	The force of the impact is spread over a large area, resulting in a low pressure on her head.	3	**15 marks**
2 a i	The distance travelled before the driver applies the brakes.	1	
ii	0.7 s **iii** Inebriation, tiredness	1 2	
b i	6.3 s	1	
ii	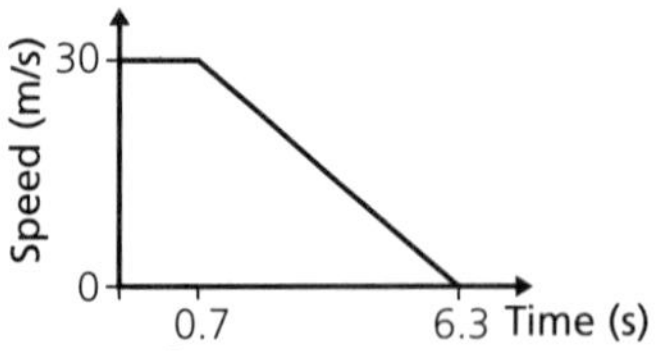 Speed (m/s) 30 0 0.7 6.3 Time (s)	3	
iii	$5.4\ m/s^2$ **iv** 5400 N	3 3	**14 marks**
3 a	12 500 Pa	3	
b	Have the 0.1 m side vertical, 6 250 Pa	2	**5 marks**
4 a i	40 m/s **ii** 20 m/s **iii** 80 m	2 1 2	
b i ,ii	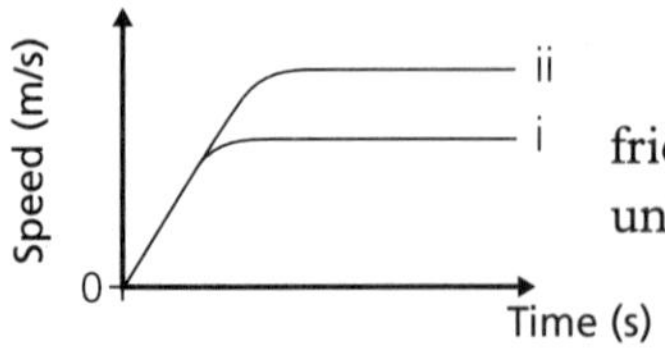 Speed (m/s) 0 Time (s) ii i friction increases with increasing speed until fraction and weight are balanced.	2, 1	**8 marks**

Waves, space and radiation

Question	Answer	Marks	Total
1 a i	Transverse;	1	
	the energy flows left to right, but the rope wiggles up and down.	2	
ii	A **iii** 3 Hz **iv** 1.5 m/s	1 2 3	
b	Jill's voice vibrates her cup. This sends a longitudinal wave along the string. This vibrates Tom's cup, creating a sound wave.	3	**12 marks**
2 a	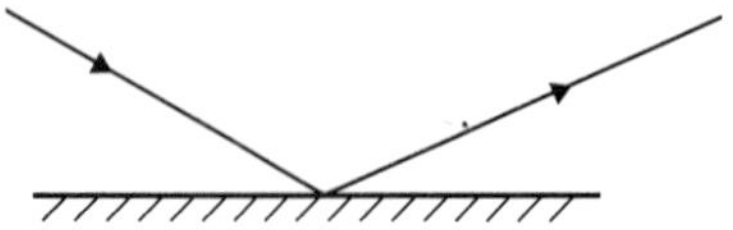 **b** The rays of reflected light appear to come from a point behind the mirror.	1 2	**3 marks**
3 a	120 000 Hz **b** 200 Hz	1 1	
c	They vibrate left and right.	1 1	
d	5000 m/s	3	**7 marks**
4 a	Convex lens because concave lenses cannot put an image on a screen.	2	
b	Move it closer to the object (window).	1	**3 marks**
5 a	Stars generate heat energy by fusion.	2	
b	Hydrogen fuses to form helium.	1	

Question	Answer	Marks	Total
c	Gravity pulls all of the particles towards each other, giving them kinetic energy. So the cloud collapses and heats up. Eventually the pressure and temperature are high enough for fusion to start.	4	
d	The heat of the star will radiate into space, so it will cool down.	2	**9 marks**
6 a	Gravity, from the satellite towards the centre of the Earth.	2	
b	To allow communication between different parts of the Earth, to monitor the climate and the weather.	2	**4 marks**
7 a	The emissions can break up molecules in living cells, killing them or damaging their DNA.	2	
b	Each nucleus can only decay once. As time goes on, there are fewer and fewer nuclei left to decay.	3	
c	63 Bq	3	**8 marks**
8 a	Alpha, beta and gamma radiation.	3	
b	Alpha is two neutrons and two protons. Beta is an electron. Gamma is an electromagnetic wave.	1 1 1	
c	A sheet of paper absorbs alpha, a few millimetres of aluminium absorbs beta and several centimetres of lead absorbs gamma.	3	**9 marks**
9 a i	ultrasound **ii** radio **iii** X-ray **iv** microwave	1 1 1 1	
v	X-ray, ultrasound	2	
b i	It changes direction as it slows down.	2	
ii	It is totally internally reflected.	1	**9 marks**

Energy

Question	Answer	Marks	Total
1 a	Heat energy increases vibration of particles in the wall. Particles in solids touch each other, so the energy of vibration is passed from one particle to another.	2	
b i	Fibre wool **ii** It contains air, which is a good insulator.	1 2	
c i	Block up gaps in doors and windows. **ii** 8 months.	1 2	
d	Double glaze windows to reduce heat conduction. Reduce the temperature of the house to reduce the heat flow to the cold outside.	4	**12 marks**
2 a i	Kinetic energy in the car becomes heat energy in the brakes. **ii** 10 000 J	2 3	
iii	Some of the kinetic energy becomes potential energy, so less has to become heat energy.	2	
b i	5000 W **ii** 25%	3 3	**13 marks**
3 a	Increase to room temperature.	1 1	
b	Heat energy increases vibration of particles. Particles in solids touch each other, so the energy of vibration is passed from one particle to another.	2	
c	The foil reflects heat radiation from the room, reducing the rate at which heat energy enters the ice cream.	2	
d	So that it cools the entire contents of the freezer via convection currents. Cooled air sinks to the bottom of the freezer, so the cooling unit is always surrounded by the warmest air.	3	**9 marks**
4 a	$0.5 \times 0.3 \times 20 \times 20 = 60$	2	
b i	10 J **ii** 26.7 m **c** Becomes heat energy in the ground.	1 3 1	**7 marks**

Exam technique

This book can do a lot to help you prepare for your exams. Make sure you have read about how to revise in the introduction *How to use this book*. Here are some tips to help you answering exam questions.

What's special about Salters' exams?

The real-life situations in the exam questions may be different from the ones you studied in the Salters course. But the science ideas will be the same and the way this book is divided up will help you see the science ideas. The important thing is to think about what *ideas* you can use to explain the situations in the exam questions. You may need to bring ideas together from two or three ATs for one question.

Understanding the exam questions

Read all of the question carefully!
You can lose marks by not reading the question carefully enough. Too many people read it too quickly and miss the main point of the question.
As you read through the question you will find command words which tell you what to do ('explain', 'describe' etc). Underline each of these words to make sure you know what sort of answer is needed. Check carefully to see that you have followed the instructions.

Giving the examiners what they've asked for

Look out for these command words when you answer exam questions and think about what they mean and how much detail to give in your answer.

Give/state/name ... A brief answer, maybe only one word, is all that is needed. You don't have to explain.

What is meant by ... Give a definition, showing how the word or phrase is important in the context of the question.

Describe ... You should mention all the important points – often a diagram helps.

Explain ... Use science ideas to explain why or how something happens (questions often ask 'describe and explain' – for each point that you describe, you should also explain why).

Compare ... When you are asked to compare two things, give the properties of both, e.g. if the question is 'Compare the colour of litmus added to acids and alkalis', it is not enough to say 'Acids turn litmus to red', you also need to give the alkali colours. You lose marks by only giving one half of the answer.

List ... Give a series of short answers. If you are asked to give a certain number of points, e.g. 'list three metals' only write down the number you are asked for. If you write extra answers and some are wrong, you will lose marks.

Suggest ... This is used where more than one answer is possible. You must show clearly how and why you have given your answer.

Predict ... The answer can be brief, but must be based on the information given in the question.

Use the information/graph/table ... Many other questions involve 'data interpretation'. Some information is given, usually at the beginning of the question, and you have to make sense of it. Look carefully at each part of each question to see whether it is asking you to use only the information in the questions in your answer, or whether you also have to bring in other science ideas that you have learned.

Calculate/work out ... Use information in the question, or available on the paper (e.g. from the Periodic Table on the back cover of exam papers) to work out a numerical answer. Write down each step in your working. If you make a mistake somewhere and get the wrong answer, you may still get marks if you were using the right method. Make sure you give the right units as part of your answer.

Concept map: AT2

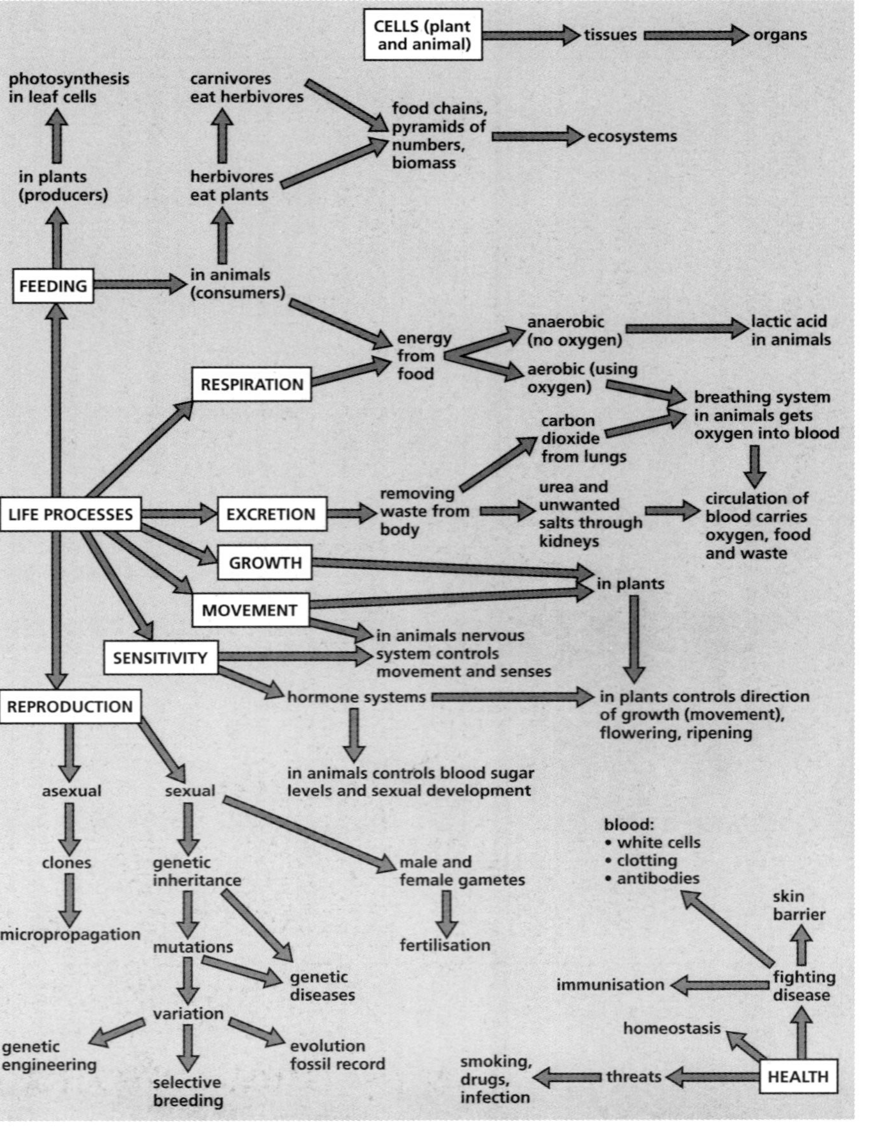

Concept map: AT3

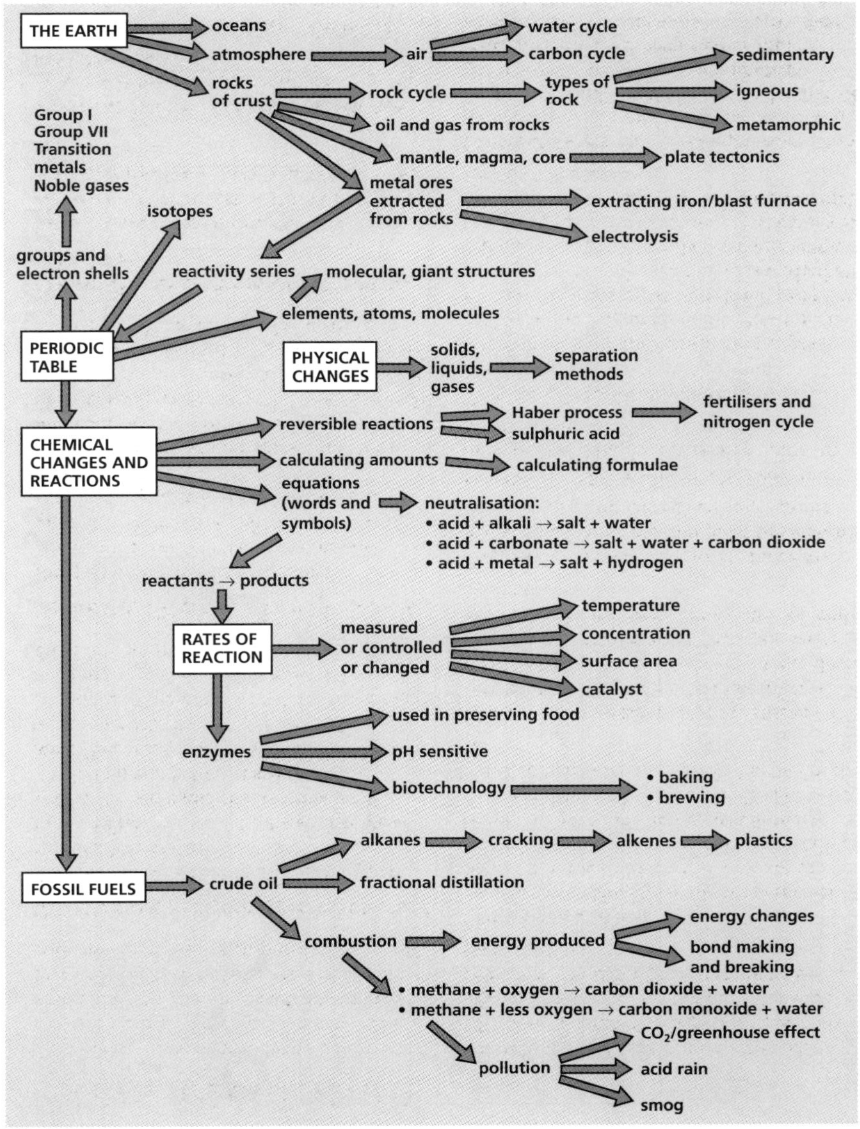

THE EARTH
oceans
atmosphere
air
water cycle
carbon cycle
rocks of crust
rock cycle
types of rock
sedimentary
igneous
metamorphic
oil and gas from rocks
mantle, magma, core
plate tectonics
metal ores extracted from rocks
extracting iron/blast furnace
electrolysis
Group I
Group VII
Transition metals
Noble gases
groups and electron shells
isotopes
reactivity series
molecular, giant structures
elements, atoms, molecules
PERIODIC TABLE
PHYSICAL CHANGES
solids, liquids, gases
separation methods
CHEMICAL CHANGES AND REACTIONS
reversible reactions
Haber process
sulphuric acid
fertilisers and nitrogen cycle
calculating amounts
calculating formulae
equations (words and symbols)
neutralisation:
- acid + alkali → salt + water
- acid + carbonate → salt + water + carbon dioxide
- acid + metal → salt + hydrogen

reactants → products
RATES OF REACTION
measured or controlled or changed
temperature
concentration
surface area
catalyst
enzymes
used in preserving food
pH sensitive
biotechnology
- baking
- brewing

FOSSIL FUELS
crude oil
alkanes
cracking
alkenes
plastics
fractional distillation
combustion
energy produced
energy changes
bond making and breaking
- methane + oxygen → carbon dioxide + water
- methane + less oxygen → carbon monoxide + water

pollution
CO_2/greenhouse effect
acid rain
smog

Concept map: AT 4

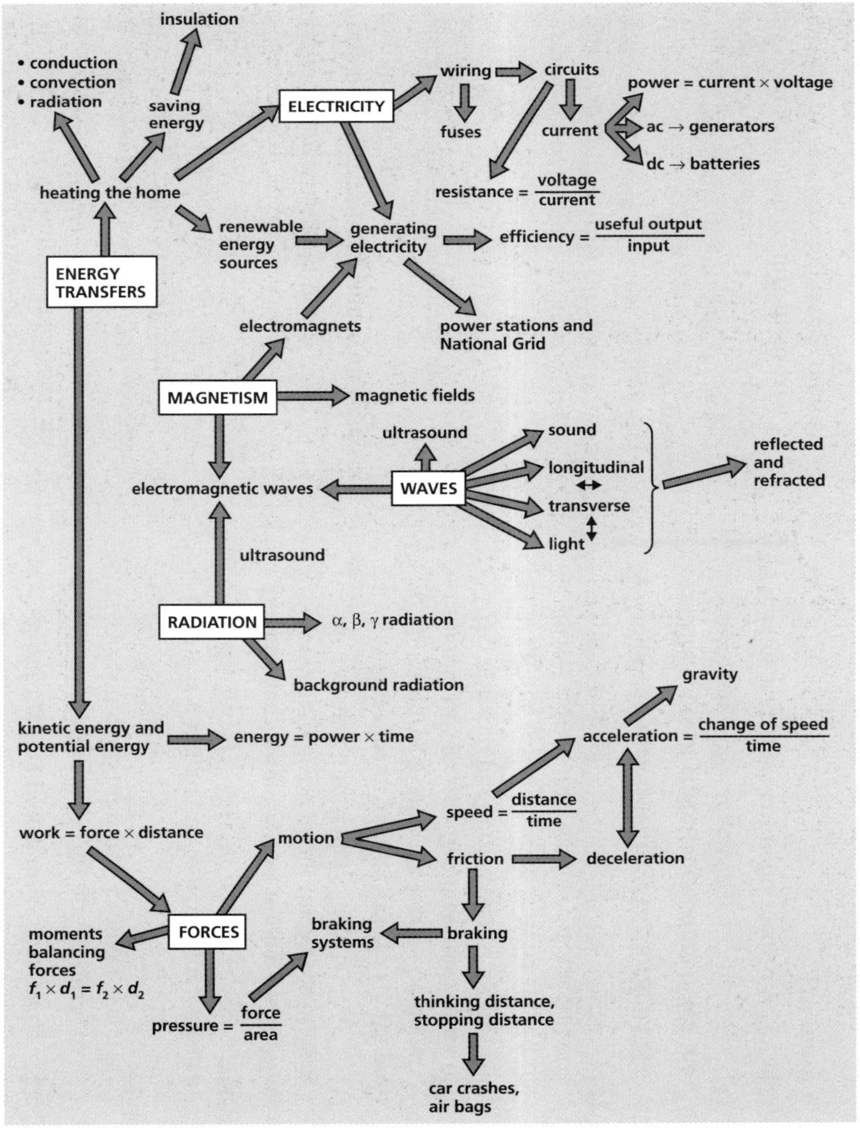

insulation
- conduction
- convection
- radiation

saving energy
heating the home
ENERGY TRANSFERS
ELECTRICITY
wiring
fuses
circuits
current
power = current × voltage
ac → generators
dc → batteries
resistance = $\frac{\text{voltage}}{\text{current}}$
renewable energy sources
generating electricity
efficiency = $\frac{\text{useful output}}{\text{input}}$
power stations and National Grid
electromagnets
MAGNETISM
magnetic fields
electromagnetic waves
ultrasound
WAVES
sound
longitudinal
transverse
light
reflected and refracted
ultrasound
RADIATION
α, β, γ radiation
background radiation
kinetic energy and potential energy
energy = power × time
work = force × distance
FORCES
moments balancing forces
$f_1 \times d_1 = f_2 \times d_2$
pressure = $\frac{\text{force}}{\text{area}}$
braking systems
motion
speed = $\frac{\text{distance}}{\text{time}}$
acceleration = $\frac{\text{change of speed}}{\text{time}}$
gravity
friction
deceleration
braking
thinking distance, stopping distance
car crashes, air bags

Exam questions across ATs

1 Anita grows flowering plants on her window-sill.

a The plants use photosynthesis to capture light energy.

i Write down a word equation for photosynthesis. [3]

ii Fusion reactions in the Sun are the source of light energy for photosynthesis. Describe the fusion reaction in the Sun. [4]

iii Most of the photosynthesis takes place in the leaves. Describe and explain **two** ways in which leaves are adapted for this. [4]

b Plants remove carbon dioxide from the atmosphere.

i Describe one other large-scale process which removes carbon dioxide from the atmosphere. [2]

ii Describe two large-scale processes which add carbon dioxide to the atmosphere. [2]

iii The average temperature of the Earth is rising as the amount of carbon dioxide in its atmosphere increases. Use the idea of heat radiation to explain this. [4]

c Anita has to water her plants with fertiliser from time to time.

i Name **two** important elements in a fertiliser. [2]

ii Explain why the fertiliser is necessary. [2]

iii Farmers routinely add fertiliser to their crops. Explain why this can sometimes be a source of pollution. [3]

[26 marks]

2 This lorry is delivering frozen chickens to different supermarkets. The lorry needs a fast cooling system so that the frozen chickens do not warm up every time the door is opened.

One type of cooling system uses liquid air. The liquid air is sprayed through narrow tubes into the lorry.

The table shows some substances in the air.

Substance in air	Melting point in °C	Boiling point in °C
water	0	100
carbon dioxide	–78	–78
oxygen	–218	–183
nitrogen	–210	–196

a Is nitrogen a solid, a liquid or a gas at –200°C? [1]

b To avoid problems, water and carbon dioxide are removed from liquid air. Suggest one problem that could be caused if they were left in. Use the information about melting points in your answer. [2]

c When liquid air warms up the nitrogen leaves the mixture first. Liquid oxygen is left behind.

i Why is it dangerous to have liquid oxygen in the lorry? [1]

ii Nitrogen has a very low boiling point. What does this tell you about the forces *between* the nitrogen molecules? [1]

Another type of cooling system sprays pure liquid nitrogen into the lorry. The driver should not go into the lorry until some of the nitrogen has been replaced by fresh air.

d Nitrogen is not poisonous. Why should the driver not go into the lorry if it is full of nitrogen gas? [2]

e Nitrogen molecules have the formula N_2.

i What sort of chemical bonding holds the nitrogen atoms together? [1]

ii How is this type of bond formed? [2]

[10 marks]

3 The powerful spotlights at the back of theatres once used 'carbon arcs' instead of light bulbs to produce their light.

In a carbon arc an electric current makes a spark between two carbon rods.

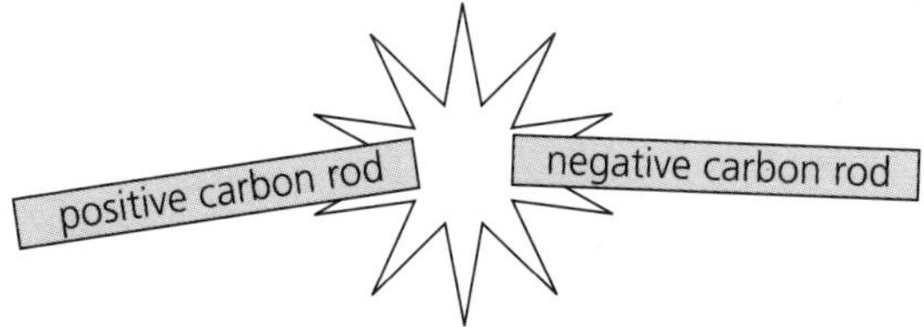

The electric current is carried across the air gap by charged carbon particles. The carbon particles in the air gap glow white hot, and so give out light. The particles are quickly oxidised by the air. Some carbon monoxide may be formed.

a Write a balanced chemical equation for the oxidation of the carbon particles to carbon monoxide (CO). [2]

b The arc operates at such a high temperature that carbon ions are produced. These carbon ions carry the current across the air gap. Find carbon in the Periodic Table.

i Write down the number of electrons in each shell of a carbon **atom**, starting with the shell nearest the nucleus. [2]

ii The carbon **ion** has a charge of 4^+. Write down the number of electrons in each shell of the carbon **ion**. [1]

iii Designers increased the current through the arc. Suggest **two** differences to the flow of charged particles which would produce a greater current. [2]

c The carbon electrodes are made of graphite. Graphite is a good conductor of electricity. Use your knowledge of the structure of graphite to explain **why** it conducts electricity. [2]

d The brightness of the arc depends on the voltage. Use your understanding of voltage to explain why a higher voltage gives a brighter light. [2]

e The arc lamp needs a 30 V dc electrical supply. You could use a transformer to convert the mains at 240 V ac to 30 V ac.

i The primary coil of a transformer has 1 000 turns. How many turns should there be on the secondary coil? [2]

ii In practice the number of turns on the secondary coil needs to be larger than this. Explain why. [2]

iii The ac is then converted to dc. Why do we convert the voltage **before** changing to dc? [1]

iv The arc uses a 30 V 60 A dc electrical supply. How much charge is transferred every second by the arc? [2]

[18 marks]

4 Joy installs electric lighting in her greenhouse. This will help her plants to grow more in the winter. Each light tube has these words written on it.
230 V, 115 W

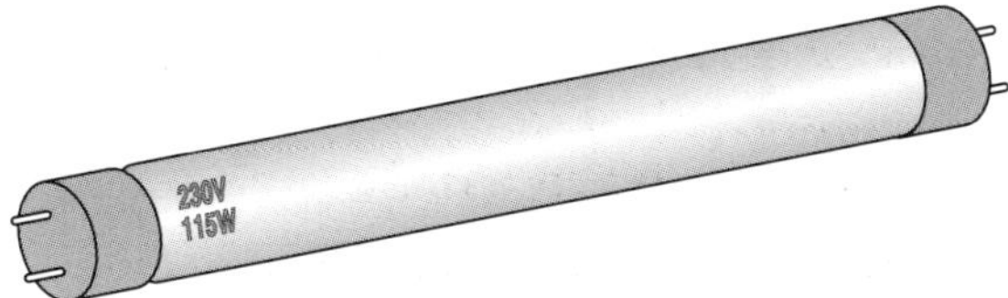

a i Calculate the current in each light tube. [3]

ii The mains cable leading to her greenhouse is rated at 230 V, 5 A. Explain why she should only install up to ten light tubes in her greenhouse. [2]

b The mains cable contains a 5 A fuse.

i Explain how the fuse protects the insulation of the cable. [3]

ii Should the fuse be in the live, neutral or earth lines of the mains cable? Explain your answer. [2]

c Anita pays 7 p for each kilowatt-hour of electricity she uses. How much does it cost her to run ten light tubes continuously for a week? [3]

d Joy thinks it would be cheaper to use a propane burner to light the greenhouse.

i The chemical symbol for propane is C_3H_8. Write down a balanced chemical equation for the complete combustion of propane. [3]

ii One mole of propane creates 2.2 MJ of heat energy when it is burnt in air. Calculate the heat energy created by the combustion of 1 kg of propane. (relative atomic masses: C = 12, H = 1.) [3]

e Neil thinks that the propane burner has other advantages for the greenhouse. Suggest and explain **two** reasons why the propane burners should make the plants grow better than the light tubes. [3]

[22 marks]

5 The world's forests contain a balance of living trees and dead trees. Scientists are studying these trees to get a better idea of how carbon and nitrogen are recycled. Here is part of the carbon cycle for a forest.

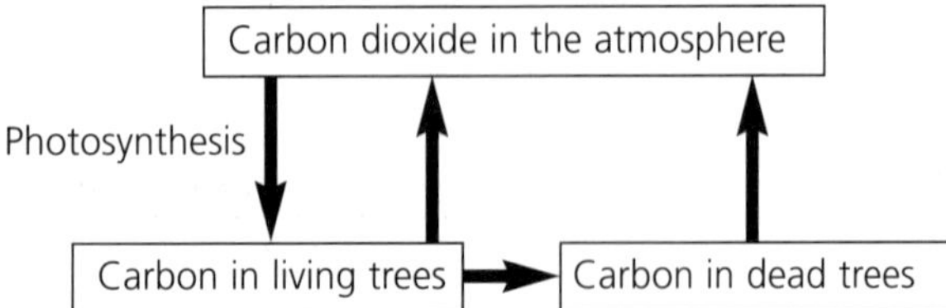

a Photosynthesis produces sugar. Plants convert sugar into larger molecules for storage. Suggest what chemical the sugar is converted into. [1]

b When trees die they rot. Decomposers on the tree surface slowly convert the carbon chemicals back to carbon dioxide. If the trees become buried under the ground, most decomposers stop working. Suggest why they stop working. [2]

c If fewer trees rot, the amounts of carbon dioxide in the atmosphere will drop. Global temperatures will then fall. Suggest and explain how this might affect photosynthesis. [4]

d Scientists are also studying the mass of nitrogen compounds locked up in the forests. A shortage of nitrogen compounds will harm a fully grown tree. Suggest why. [3]

e When trees die, decomposers change the nitrogen compounds back into nitrogen gas.

i What type of decomposer does this? [1]

ii Balance the chemical equation below which shows part of this change.

$4\ HNO_2 \rightarrow$ ____ H_2O + ____ N_2
= ____ O_2 [2]

iii The equation for another part of this process is

$2\ NO \rightarrow N_2 + O_2$

What mass of N_2 would be produced by 120 g of NO? Show your working.
(N = 14, 0 = 16) [3]

iv What is the total mass of $N_2 + O_2$ which is produced by the 120 g of NO? [1]

[17 marks]

6 People have been carving rocks for thousands of years. Microscopic insects and pollen grains stick to the newly carved surface. We can use carbon-dating on these pollen grains to see how old the carvings are.

Carbon-dating measures the amount of the radioactive carbon-14 isotope in the sample. As the sample gets older the carbon-14 decays into nitrogen-14.

a The rock itself can just as easily be dated by another technique. Why do we date the pollen grains and not the rock itself? [1]

b The most common isotope of carbon is carbon-12. What is the difference between a nucleus of carbon -14 and a nucleus of carbon-12? [1]

c Complete this equation to show the decay of carbon-14 to nitrogen-14.

$^{14}_{6}C \rightarrow\ ^{\_}_{\_}N + \beta$ [2]

d What must always change when the nucleus of one element turns into another element? [1]

e An old sample of pollen has a radioactivity of 2 counts per minute [cpm]. A sample of present day pollen has a radioactivity of 64 cpm. The half life of carbon-14 is approximately 5 000 years. How old is the pollen sample? Show your working. [2]

[7 marks]

Question	Answer	Marks	Total
1 a i	Water + carbon dioxide → glucose + oxygen.	1 1 1	
ii	Hydrogen nuclei collide at speed and join to become helium nuclei with a loss of mass which becomes energy.	1 1 1 1	
iii	Large surface area to catch a lot of light held up by stems away from shading from other leaves.	1 1 1 1	
b i	Creation of limestone/chalk rocks under the sea.	2	
ii	Respiration; burning of biomass.	1 1	
iii	Light from the Sun is absorbed by the ground which emits infra-red radiation which is trapped by carbon dioxide.	1 1 1 1	
c i	Nitrogen; phosphorus.	1 1	
ii	Provides the plants with nutrients which it needs to build its tissues.	1 1	
iii	Fertiliser can run off the land into streams and lakes where it encourages algal growth and kills fish.	1 1 1	**26 marks**
2 a	Liquid.	1	
b	Carbon dioxide and water are solids at that temperature and would block the nozzle.	2	
c i	Fire/explosion in the lorry. (NOT 'inflammable')	1	
ii	Weak.	1	
d	Asphyxiation/respiration/to stay alive = 1; further detail which must involve the need for oxygen = 1. (NOT 'too cold')	2	
e i	Covalent.	1	
ii	Electrons are involved (they must get this to go on the second mark) (electrons) shared. (if 'ionic' for **ei**, then ecf for part **eii**)	2	**10 marks**
3 a	$2C + O_2 \rightarrow 2CO$ correct reactants and products [1] balanced [1]	2	
b i	2,4 (any total = 6 gets one mark)	2	
ii	2 [0]	1	
iii	Faster, more per second. (allow higher charge)	2	
c	Electrons can move delocalised (electrons)/free (electrons)/sheets of atoms.	2	
d	(more) energy, per (unit) charge ('bigger current' = 1)	2	
e i	$1\,000 \times 30/240 = 125$	2	
ii	Any two from; energy losses, heat, efficiency, need to compensate.	2	
iii	Transformers don't work on dc.	1	
iv	60 [1] coulombs [1]	2	**18 marks**
4 a i	power = current × voltage current = 115/230 0.5 amps	1 1 1	

Question	Answer	Marks	Total
ii	5 A is 10 times 0.5 A More than ten tubes would exceed safe current.	1 1	
b i	Wire in the fuse melts/blows if current exceeds 5 A preventing excessive heating of the wires.	1 1 1	
ii	Live to cut off the supply before the electricity reaches the light.	1 1	
c	power = 10 × 115 = 1150 W or 1.15 kW cost = 1.15 × (7 × 24) × 7 = 1 352 p or £13.52	1 1 1	
d i	$C_3H_8 + 50_2 = 3C0_2 + 4H_2O$ Correct symbols, correct reactants and products, correctly balanced.	 1 1 1	
i	1 mole of propane is 3 × 12 + 8 × 1 = 44 g 1 g produces 2.2/44 = 0.05 MJ of energy 1 000 g = 1 kg produces 50 MJ of energy	1 1 1	
e	Increased carbon dioxide levels, and temperature, should increase the rate of photosynthesis.	1 1 1	**22 marks**
5 a	Starch. (allow glycogen, not carbohydrate)	1	
b	Idea of lack of oxygen, specific mention of oxygen (e.g can't breathe, NOT light or heat arguments).	2	
c	Less CO_2 reduces photosynthesis, less reactant, lower temperature reduces photosynthesis, slower rate of reaction.	4	
d	Suitable nitrogen compound (e.g. enzyme, amino acid, protein). Use of compound – growth/repair ties, repair to the health of the tree.	3	
e i	(Denitrifying) bacterium.	1	
ii	$4HNO_2 \rightarrow 2H_2O + 2N_2 + 3O_2$; all three correct = 2, any two correct = 1.	2	
iii	RAM of NO = 30, RAM of N_2 = 28, realises that two moles of NO produce one mole of N_2, Answer 56. Term 'mole' not needed. (do not penalise a lack of units)	3	
iv	120 g (do not penalise units unless incorrect)	1	**17 marks**
6 a	Carving is later than rock formation.	1	
b	Number of neutrons.	1	
c	${}^{14}_{6}C \rightarrow {}^{14}_{7}N + \beta$	2	
d	Number of protons/atomic number.	1	
e	Clearly uses five half lives, answer 25 000 (years).	2	**7 marks**

Index